Performance Tuning in Theory and Practice

Two Strokes

A. Graham Bell

ISBN 0 85429 329 9

© A. Graham Bell

First Published June 1983

A FOULIS book

Printed in England by the publishers
Haynes Publishing Group
Sparkford, Yeovil, Somerset BA22 7JJ, England

Distributed in North America by
Haynes Publications Inc
861 Lawrence Drive, Newbury Park, California 91320, USA

Editor: **Jeff Clew**
Cover Design: **Phill Jennings**
Layout Design: **John Martin**

Contents

Preface

FROM A very humble beginning, the two-stroke internal combustion engine has now been developed to a degree that was not thought possible just a few years ago. I am sure even the engineers who have stood by the two-stroke principle for so long find it staggering that this mechanically simple device can produce as much power as it does today, with relative reliability.

Originally, I looked upon two-stroke engines with contempt. They made a horrible ring-ding noise, nothing like the beautiful note of four-stroke racing engines. They emitted a blue haze from their tailpipes too, which appeared unsightly, long before any of us heard of the word pollution. On hot days these engines seized with monotonous regularity. Difficult starting, flooding and plug fouling seemed the order of the day.

Consequently I wrote off two-strokes, convinced I would never lower myself to develop one of these unreliable little beasts in my workshop. But that all changed when two of my friends bought themselves 250cc Bultaco Pursang motocross bikes and insisted I prepared them. I took up the challenge and was rewarded with the knowledge that a ring-ding I had developed came home 3rd in the National Motocross Championship with a B grade rider on board.

From then on the challenge has not abated as I have strived to unravel the mystery of what makes a two-stroke tick. Instead of looking on the two-stroke with contempt, I now view this little marvel with fascination. Four-stroke engine development has just about reached its peak, but there is much yet to be learned about the two-stroke power unit.

It is my hope that this book will assist the enthusiast involved in motocross, enduro, desert, road or go-kart racing to develop and tune his two-stroke engine for horsepower and reliability.

A. Graham Bell

Maitland
New South Wales

7

Chapter 1
Introduction

MECHANICALLY, the two-stroke engine is very simple, and unfortunately on too many occasions this apparent simplicity has fooled would-be tuners into believing that this type of power unit is easy to modify. Just a few hours work with a file in the exhaust and inlet ports can change the entire character of the engine for the better, but if you go just 0.5mm too far, you could end up with a device slower than its stock counterpart.

Therefore modifications must be planned carefully, keeping in mind that seldom, if ever, is the biggest (or most expensive) the best. As you plan your modifications always tend to be conservative. If necessary, you can go bigger later.

Possibly the worst viewpoint you can start out with is that the manufacturer didn't know what he was doing. I started out thinking that way too; but then I began to realise why the engineers did it that way. Pretty soon I was learning more about what makes a two-stroke fire — and making fewer mistakes.

You must keep in mind that all production engines are a compromise, even highly developed racing engines like the Yamaha TZ250. You can make the TZ churn out more power, but will you be able to ride it with the power band narrowed right down, and do you have the experience to handle a sudden rush of power at the top end on an oily or wet track? Also, think about the added wear caused by more rpm and horsepower; do you have the finances to replace the crankshaft, pistons and cylinder more frequently now that you are running at 12,500rpm instead of 11,500rpm? When you begin to think about things like this, you start to understand a few of the reasons why manufacturers make compromise engines and machines. Remember the TZ250 started out as a road racer, so you can imagine some of the problems you could come up against if you were to modify a single cylinder 125 motocross engine for use in a road racer.

Obviously the first work you should do is bring the engine up to the manufacturer's specifications. This is termed blueprinting, and involves accurately measuring everything and then correcting any errors made in production. You will be 9 amazed at the gains to be made, particularly in reliability, and to a lesser extent in performance, by correcting manufacturing deficiencies. I am convinced manufacturers bolt their road racers together merely to make shipping all the pieces easier, such are their tolerances.

I have seen engines that have never been started with piston clearances larger than the manufacturer's serviceable limit. Conrods that vary 0.4mm in centre to centre length and 20 grams in weight, on the same crank. Crankwheels which are 0.1mm outside true centre. Cylinder heads with a squish band clearance of 1.7mm, instead of 0.7-1.0mm. Cylinders with port edges so sharp that the side of the piston and rings would have been shaved away in a few minutes' running. New pistons with cracks. New cylinder heads that are porous.

Included in blueprinting is cleaning the rough cast out of the ports, and matching all gaskets so they don't overlap the ports. The transfer ports must be matched to the crankcase. The carburettor should coincide with the mounting flange and inlet port. Anything the manufacturer has not done (presumably to cut costs), you should do.

Blueprinting is slow, tedious work, and it can be expensive when crankshafts have to be separated and then machined and trued, or when cylinder heads have to be machined to close up the squish band without raising the compression ratio. It is not very exciting work because when you have finished the engine is stock standard, and telling your mates all the work you have done won't impress them. But don't let this put you off, the basis for any serious tuning must begin with bringing the engine up to the manufacturer's specifications.

Most people won't believe how close to standard are the motors used by the factory racing teams. Other riders are convinced that, because the factory boys are quicker, they must have more power and lots of trick parts. In truth, the differences are in frame geometry and the ability of the factory rider to ride faster and make the right choice of tyres, suspension settings, gearing, jetting etc. Plus, of course, they use blueprinted engines.

So that there is no misunderstanding of the two-stroke operating cycle I will describe what goes on in each cylinder, every revolution of the crankshaft.

The first example is the piston-ported Bultaco Matador Mk4 which, like most modern two-strokes, operates on the loop scavenge principle. As the piston goes up, the inlet port is opened by the piston skirt at 75° before TDC (Top Dead Centre) and the atmospheric pressure (14.7 psi) forces air/fuel mixture in to fill the crankcase (FIGURE 1.1). The piston continues to rise to TDC, compressing the fuel/air charge admitted on the previous cycle. At 3.2mm before TDC the spark plug fires, sending the piston down on the power cycle. As the piston continues its descent the inlet port is closed and the fuel/air mixture is partially compressed in the crankcase. 85° before BDC (Bottom Dead Centre) the exhaust port is opened by the piston crown and the exhaust gases flow out. After another 22° (63° before BDC) the blow-down period finishes and the piston crown exposes the transfer ports to admit the fresh fuel/air charge. This is forced up the transfer passages due to the descending piston reducing the crankcase volume by the equivalent of the cylinder displacement, in this instance 244cc. As the piston begins rising, the mixture continues to flow into the cylinder and the exhaust gas continues flowing out. The piston continues rising, closing off first the transfer and then exhaust ports. Next the inlet port opens, to start the cycle over again.

Rotary valve engines operate on the same loop scavenge principle, but in this case

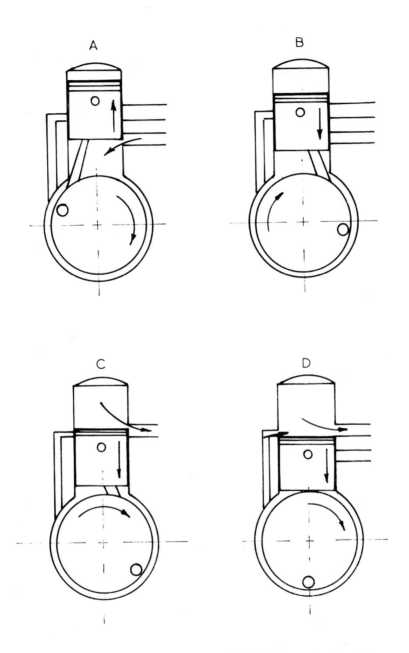

A - mixture in cylinder is compressed & inlet cycle begins.
B - mixture in crankcase is compressed.
C - exhaust cycle begins & primary compression continues.
D - transfer cycle begins & exhaust cycle continues.

Fig. 1.1 Basic two stroke operation.

11

a disc partially cut away and attached to the end of the crankshaft opens and closes an inlet port in the side of the crankcase. The Morbidelli 125 twin road racer is a rotary valve engine. The inlet port opens 30° after BDC and closes 79° after TDC. The piston crown opens and closes the exhaust and transfer ports.

The following pages will provide you with the knowledge necessary to develop a successful two-stroke competition engine, but do keep in mind the principles outlined in this chapter so that you avoid the most basic pitfalls associated with two-stroke tuning.

Chapter 2
The Cylinder Head

THE TWO-STROKE cylinder head certainly doesn't look very exciting but its design has a large bearing on how well your engine will run. Manufacturers use various external shapes and cooling fin patterns but the main requirement here is that the cooling area be large enough to adequately cool the engine. Some people feel that the head must have radial fins to be any good, but I disagree. Conventional finning is entirely adequate. It is the surface area which counts, not the fin pattern.

What is more important is the shape of the combustion chamber and the location of the spark plug. Over the years many combustion chamber designs have been tried, but only a couple are conducive to a reliable, high horsepower engine. The one thing a powerful two-stroke doesn't need is a combustion chamber that promotes detonation, the killer scourge of all racing two-strokes.

To understand the type of combustion chamber you need it is necessary to appreciate just what detonation is and what can be done to be rid of the problem. Detonation occurs when a portion of the fuel/air change begins to burn spontaneously after normal ignition takes place. The flame front created by this condition ultimately collides with the flame initiated by the spark plug. This causes a rapid and violent pressure build-up, and the resulting explosion hammers the engine's internal components.

Detonation leaves many tell-tale signs for which the two-stroke tuner should have an ever-wary eye. The most obvious sign is a piston crown peppered around the edge as though it has been sand blasted. Bikes with plated aluminium cylinders will usually show the same sand blasted effect around the top lip of the bore. A cracked (not molten) spark plug insulator also indicates detonation. If kept running, a detonating engine will eventually seize and/or have a hole punched right through the top of the piston.

The conditions leading to detonation are high fuel/air mixture density, high compression, high charge temperature and excessive spark advance. A high piston crown or combustion chamber temperature can also lead to this condition. In a racing 13 two-stroke all of these detonation triggers are virtually unavoidable, with the exception of excessive spark lead.

Researchers have found that it is the gases at the very outer limits of the combustion chamber, called the 'end gases', that self-ignite to cause detonation. These end gases are heated by the surrounding metal of the piston crown and combustion chamber, and also by the heat radiating from the advancing spark-ignited flame. If the spark flame reaches the outer edges of the combustion chamber quickly enough, these end gases will not have time to heat up sufficiently to self-ignite and precipitate detonation. Herein lies the key to prevent detonation — keep the end gases cool and reduce the time required for the combustion flame to reach the end gases.

The most obvious step that would satisfy the second requirement is to make the combustion chamber as small as possible, and then place the spark plug in the centre of the chamber. Naturally the combustion flame will reach the end gases in a small combustion space more quickly than if the chamber were twice as wide. Additionally, a central spark plug reduces flame travel to a minimum. (FIGURE 2.1)

In meeting the second requirement, the need to keep the end gases cool can also be accommodated. If we move the combustion chamber down as close to the piston crown as possible, no combustion will occur around the edges of the chamber until the piston has travelled well past TDC. This large surface area acts as a heat sink and conducts heat away from the end gases, preventing self-ignition.

The chamber just described is called a squish-type combustion chamber because of the squish band around its edge. Originally, the squish band was designed to squish the fuel/air charge from the edges of the cylinder toward the spark plug which, of course, it still does. The fast moving gases meet the spark plug and quickly carry the combustion flame to the extremity of the combustion chamber, thus preventing detonation.

Since that time, more benefits of the squish chamber have come to light. The mixture being purged across the combustion chamber from the squish band homogenises the fuel/air mixture more thoroughly and also mixes any residual exhaust gas still present with the fuel charge. This serves to speed up combustion by preventing stale gas pockets from forming. Such pockets slow down, and in some instances can prevent, flame propogation.

Turbulence caused by the squish band also serves to enhance heat transfer at the spark-initiated flame front. Without proper heat transfer, jets of flame would tend to shoot out toward the edges of the combustion chamber, prematurely heating the surrounding gases to start off the cycle leading to detonation.

Rapid combustion has other advantages besides controlling detonation. With an increase in combustion speed there is, of necessity, a corresponding decrease in spark advance. The closer to TDC we can ignite the charge, the less negative work we have to do compressing a burning charge that is endeavouring to expand. Also there is less energy loss in the form of heat being transferred to the cylinder head and piston crown.

When less heat is conducted to the head and piston, the engine runs cooler and makes more power. A side benefit resulting from the cooler piston also enhances the power output. A cool piston does not heat the charge trapped in the crankcase as much, therefore a cooler, denser fuel/air charge enters the cylinder each cycle, to make more power.

14   If you think about it, you will see that the compact squish type combustion

Quiescent chamber with offset spark plug.
End gases detonate.

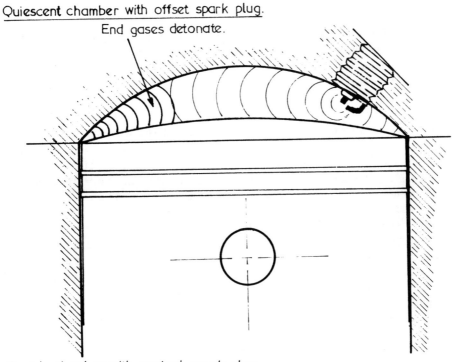

Squish chamber with central spark plug.
Ignition flame advances smoothly.

Squish band.

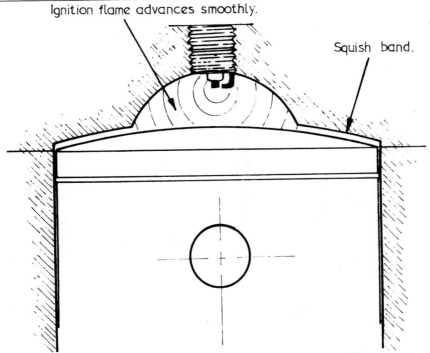

Fig. 2.1   Squish chamber promotes good combustion.

chamber also contributes to a cool piston by confining the very intense combustion flame to about 50% of the piston crown just before and after TDC.

Engine designers have known about these things for a considerable time. This is why you will find the best racing engines follow the squish design. Also you will notice that these engines have a very small bore in relation to their stroke, as this too cuts down the size of the combustion chamber and reduces the area of piston crown exposed to the combustion flame.

In an effort to minimise cylinder and piston distortion, some manufacturers have chosen to use an offset squish type combustion chamber (FIGURE 2.2). The exhaust side of a two-stroke cylinder and piston is always the hottest, even though cooling air flow is much better here than on the back (inlet side) of the engine. There are several reasons for this, all associated with the passage of very hot (630°C) exhaust gas through the exhaust port. The escaping gas heats the exhaust port and cylinder wall as well as the side of the piston. This can cause the piston to expand abnormally and in some circumstances to seize. To take care of this possibility, the manufacturer may choose to increase piston to cylinder clearance, but this may not be desirable as extra clearance can increase leakage past the rings and usually results in high piston wear. A safer step is to move the combustion chamber to the rear of the head. If this is done, the front of the piston crown is shielded from the combustion flame by the squish surface. Then, when the front of the piston is heated during the exhaust stroke, it will not expand so far due to its being initially much cooler.

Several two-stroke engines are produced with squish and offset squish chambers, but unfortunately mass production usually reduces their effectiveness. It is a very difficult task to keep tolerances of closer than about 0.2mm in production. Therefore you find many engines with a squish clearance of 1.3-1.8mm instead of the 0.6-0.8mm clearance that is required.

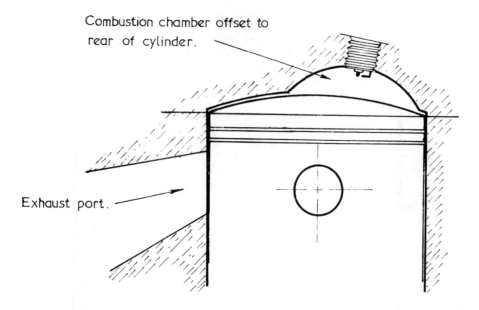

Combustion chamber offset to rear of cylinder.

Exhaust port.

Fig. 2.2 Offset squish type combustion chamber.

If your machine is only for play, and that's the use to which many motocross bikes are put, a wide squish clearance will not matter. You will not get peak power, but you will possibly never know the difference. And you will probably never ride hard enough to experience detonation.

However, if you want top power and no risk of detonation, the squish clearance must be closed up. A squish band that isn't working is worse than no squish band at all as it wastes part of your fuel/air charge. Wasted fuel charge spells less horsepower.

To give you an idea of how much horsepower you could be losing it would be good to consider the example of a TZ250 Yamaha road racer. These engines have a bore 54mm in diameter and an offset squish chamber. The compression ratio uncorrected is about 15:1, meaning that the trapped charge is compressed into a space 8.8cc in volume. If the squish clearance is 1.7mm (lots of motors come from the factory like that) 1.94cc of the trapped charge will not be burned until well past TDC, too late to produce any power. 1.94cc represents 22% of the inlet charge lost. When the squish clearance is reduced to 0.8mm the charge loss is reduced to 0.92cc or 10.5%. On paper it would seem an easy way to pick up 11.5% more power, but losses reduce this increase to about 5-6% on the dyno. Therefore maximum power goes up from 52 to 55 hp. Mid-range power can rise as much as 10%, so the bike is easier to ride and it doesn't detonate.

Reducing the squish clearance is not easy, you can't just machine 1mm, or whatever, off the head as the compression ratio would end up many numbers too high. Also you must be sure not to reduce the clearance so much that the piston will bang into the head at high rpm. The clearance required will vary from engine to engine, and also on how careful you intend to be each time you replace a piston, rod or barrel.

Pistons usually vary in compression height by up to 0.2mm. Conrods are supposed to be within a 0.2mm range but they can be up to 0.5mm out. Cylinder heights are maintained within 0.4mm. In the worst case you could rebuild the motor with a new piston, rod and barrel. The piston could be 0.2mm taller and the rod 0.2mm longer. Together with a cylinder 0.4mm shorter than before, the new parts could reduce your squish clearance by $0.2 + 0.2 + 0.4 = 0.8$mm which would result in a blown motor if the clearance was set at 0.8mm previously. Manufacturers realise this, so they purposely set the clearance wide to make allowance for the worst possible parts size combination.

If you are willing to measure the squish clearance each time you do a rebuild, and then compensate for inadequate clearance by fitting a thicker barrel base gasket or a thicker head gasket, you can reduce the clearance down to the amount shown in TABLE 2.1.

To find accurately what the squish clearance figure is, the barrel must be tensioned down on a standard thickness base gasket. Clean all traces of carbon from the head and piston. Place a strip of modelling clay 20mm wide by 3mm thick across the piston

TABLE 2.1 Minimum squish clearances

Cylinder size (cc)	Clearance (mm)
50- 80	0.6-0.8
100-125	0.7-0.9
175-250	1.0-1.4
300-500	1.1-1.5

crown. Fit the head gasket and head and turn the crank to move the piston just past TDC. Remove the head and then cut the clay down the middle with a sharp, wet knife. Carefully pull one strip of clay off the piston and then measure the thickness of the clay left on the piston. You have to be accurate, so use the end of your vernier calipers. As a cross-check also measure the clay thickness on the other side of the piston. If the thicknesses vary this would indicate that the head gasket surface has been machined on a different plane to that of the combustion chamber. Also at this time measure and record, for future reference, the compressed thickness of the base gasket and head gasket. (FIGURE 2.3).

After the clay thickness is measured you can work out how far the head must be machined to give the desired squish clearance. As mentioned previously, the combustion chamber must also be machined deeper into the head to keep the compression ratio at an acceptable level. If you wish to keep the compression ratio the same as standard, the combustion chamber will have to be machined twice as deep as the amount skimmed off to reduce the squish clearance, assuming a 50% squish band. Therefore if 0.9mm is removed, the combustion chamber will have to be made 1.8mm deeper. A 50% squish band is one having an area equal to half the cylinder bore area ie. an engine with a 54mm bore would have a squish band approximately 8mm wide (FIGURE 2.4).

To check that the machine shop recuts the combustion chamber to the original

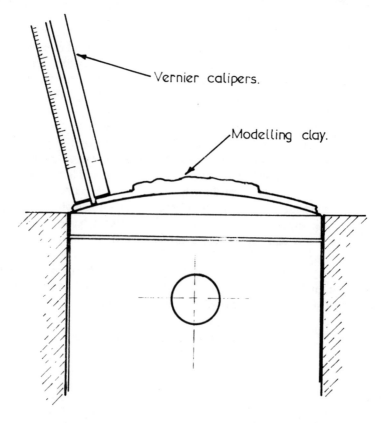

Vernier calipers.

Modelling clay.

Fig. 2.3 Measuring the squish clearance.

contour when it is deepened, you will have to make a template of the chamber shape before you send the head off. The template can be made out of any light gauge metal or even stiff cardboard. (FIGURE 2.5).

Most people like to see the compression ratio pushed up as high as possible. High compression has always been equated with high horsepower. I agree that the compression ratio should be made as high as practicable, but often the manufacturer has already found the limit and built his engines accordingly. All you can do in this instance is check that production tolerances have not lowered the ratio significantly below that which the manufacturer intended.

Something you must always remember when dealing with two-stroke engines is that increasing the compression ratio will not give a power gain equivalent to that which you would pick up with a four-stroke engine.

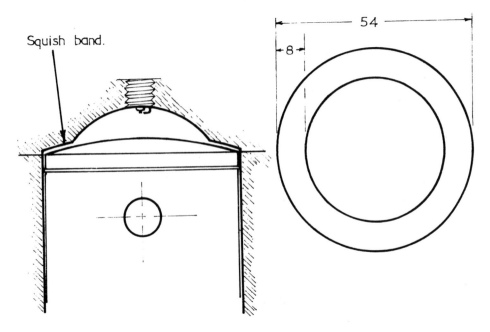

Squish band.

54

8

Fig. 2.4   A 50% squish band.

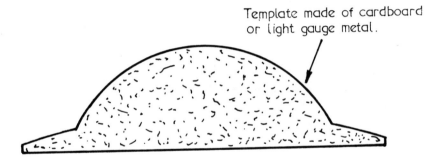

Template made of cardboard
or light gauge metal.

Fig. 2.5   Combustion chamber template.

Heat is the enemy of two-stroke engines and stretching the compression ratio to give a 10% power increase will possibly result in a 3% power rise at the most; the rest will be lost in heat energy and pumping losses. However, at lower engine speeds the cylinder will not be completely filled with fuel/air mixture and the power may jump by 5-6% because there is not such a heat loss. This is, in fact, the real benefit of raising the compression ratio, not to increase maximum power but to pick up mid-range power and possibly widen the power band.

Because so much confusion exists in the motorcycle industry relating to compression ratio we need to define exactly what we are talking about when we use the term. Ever since the first internal combustion engines, regardless of whether the engines were two-stroke, four-stroke, diesel, petrol, etc., compression ratio was taken to mean the ratio of the volume of the cylinder with the piston at BDC to the volume of the cylinder with the piston at TDC (FIGURE 2.6). This relationship is expressed in the formula:

$$CR = \frac{CV + CCV}{CCV}$$

$$\begin{aligned} \text{where } CR &= \text{ compression ratio} \\ CV &= \text{ cylinder volume} \\ CCV &= \text{ combustion chamber volume} \end{aligned}$$

Cylinder volume is found using the formula:

$$CV = \frac{\pi D^2 \times S}{4000}$$

$$\begin{aligned} \text{where } \pi &= \text{ 3.1416} \\ D &= \text{ bore diameter in mm} \\ S &= \text{ stroke in mm} \end{aligned}$$

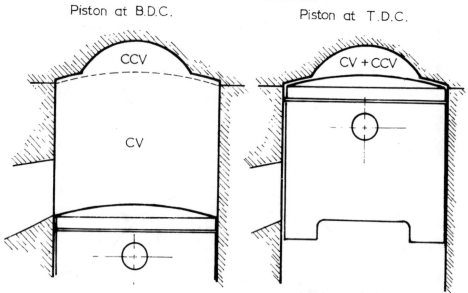

Piston at B.D.C.   Piston at T.D.C.

Fig. 2.6   The uncorrected compression ratio.

CCV, combustion chamber volume, is made up of the volume of the combustion chamber, plus any space existing between the piston crown and the top of the cylinder, plus the head gasket. This volume can be worked out geometrically but it is much simpler to bring the piston up to TDC. Seal around the edge of the piston with a thin layer of grease. Fit the head and head gasket and measure the volume with water or paraffin, using a burette graduated in 0.1cc.

As an example of how these formulas work we will consider the long stroke Bultaco Pursang 125. This engine has a bore of 51.5mm, a stroke of 60mm and, according to the manufacturers, a compression ratio of 14:1.

$$CV = \frac{\pi D^2 \times S}{4000} = 124.98cc$$

Measured with a burette CCV is found to be 9.8cc

$$CR = \frac{CV + CCV}{CCV} = \frac{124.98 + 9.8}{9.8} = 13.75:1$$

Therefore the engine has a compression ratio just a touch lower than specification. As this engine will be running at the speedway using 110 octane fuel (Avgas 100/130) the compression ratio will be increased to 15:1. The standard motor is designed to run on 95 octane fuel.

The formula to find the required combustion chamber volume is:-

$$CCV = \frac{CV}{CR - 1}$$

$$= \frac{124.98}{15 - 1} = \frac{124.98}{14} = 8.93cc$$

Therefore the combustion chamber volume must be reduced by $9.8 - 8.93 = 0.87cc$

To find how much the head must be skimmed to reduce the volume by 0.87cc we use the cylinder displacement formula transposed to read:-

$$S = \frac{CV \times 4000}{\pi D^2}$$

$$= \frac{0.87 \times 4000}{\pi \times 51.5^2} = 0.42mm$$

The above compression ratio is now referred to as the uncorrected compression ratio. The Japanese have introduced a new way of measuring the compression ratio, called in various circles effective, corrected, actual or trapped compression ratio. This can be very confusing because an 8:1 corrected compression ratio is about equivalent to a 15:1 compression ratio calculated by the old method.

The Japanese theory is that compression does not begin until the piston closes the exhaust port. Therefore the corrected compression ratio is taken to mean the ratio of the volume of the cylinder with the piston just closing the exhaust port relative to the 21 volume of the cylinder with the piston at TDC (FIGURE 2.7). This is expressed in the formula:-

$$CCR = \frac{ECV + CCV}{CCV}$$

where CCR = corrected compression ratio
ECV = effective cylinder volume
CCV = combustion chamber volume

To determine the effective cylinder volume, the distance from the top of the exhaust port to the top of the piston stroke (i.e. the TDC point) must be known. The ECV is found using the formula:-

$$ECV = \frac{\pi D^2 \times ES}{4000}$$

where π = 3.1416
D = bore diameter in mm
ES = effective stroke in mm

In this example we will use the Suzuki PE175C enduro bike. It has a bore of 62mm, a stroke of 57mm and a corrected compression ratio of 7.6:1, according to Suzuki. By measurement I have found that the exhaust port is 31.5mm from the top of the barrel, but at TDC the piston is 0.3mm from the top of the barrel, which means the effective stroke is 31.5 − 0.3 = 31.2mm.

$$ECV = \frac{\pi D^2 \times ES}{4000}$$

$$= \frac{\pi \times 62^2 \times 31.2}{4000} = 94.19cc$$

Measured with a burette, the combustion chamber volume was found to be 14.7cc. Therefore the corrected compression ratio is:-

$$CCR = \frac{ECV + CCV}{CCV}$$

$$= \frac{94.19 + 14.7}{14.7} = 7.4:1$$

Instead of working with corrected, actual, true, call them what you like compression ratios, I prefer to convert back to the old uncorrected figures which make sense to me, even if they don't make sense to the Japanese. If there were any basis to the Japanese system we should be able to race a PE175 in the 100cc class as its effective displacement is only 94cc, but try getting any motorcycling or karting organization to swallow that one! What I would really like to know is why isn't the PE175 called a PE100? Also, while we are on the subject, how does Yamaha work out the corrected compression ratio for their YZR500 road racer? This motor has a variable exhaust port that changes height to suit the rpm the motor is operating at, to give more power out of the corners.

As the Japanese motorcycling industry has been working with expansion chambers as long as most, I am sure they are aware of the fact that the return wave actually forces

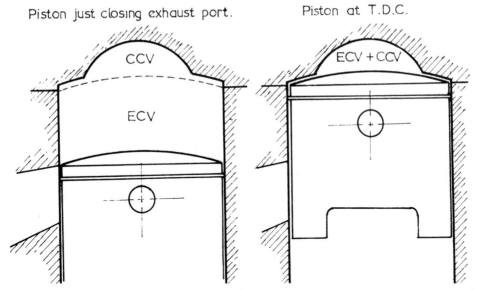

Piston just closing exhaust port.   Piston at T.D.C.

Fig. 2.7   The corrected compression ratio.

any fuel/air charge which has escaped into the exhaust port back up the port and into the cylinder. Therefore the 72cc of fuel/air mixture that appears to be lost out of the PE175's exhaust is not really lost, it is just temporarily misplaced.

Going back to the old system we find the PE175 has a compression ratio of:-

$$CR = \frac{CV + CCV}{CCV}$$

$$= \frac{172 + 14.7}{14.7} = 12.7:1$$

To find how the compression ratio of 12.7:1 compares with what the manufacturer intended it to be, we have to convert the manufacturer's corrected figure of 7.6:1 back to the old system using the formula:-

$$CR = \frac{1 + (CCR - 1) \times S}{ES}$$

where CR = uncorrected compression ratio
CCR = corrected compression ratio
S = stroke in mm
ES = effective stroke in mm

$$CR = \frac{1 + (CCR - 1) \times S}{ES}$$

$$= \frac{1 + (7.6 - 1) \times 57}{31.2} = 13.06:1$$

As this bike is designed to run on 90-95 octane fuel the compression can safely be bumped up to 13.7:1 for competition use on 100 octane racing fuel.

After all this confusion over all sorts of compression ratios you are probably bewildered and wondering what compression ratio your motor will be safe on. If you take a look at TABLE 2.2, you will find the answer. These figures are what I consider to be the maximum safe compression ratio for competition engines with good air

TABLE 2.2   Permissible compression ratio

		Fuel type		
Cylinder size (cc)	*100 Octane*	*100/130 Avgas*	*115/145 Avgas*	*Methanol*
50-80	15.5:1	16:1	17:1	19:1
100-125	14.3:1	15:1	15.7:1	18:1
175	13.5:1	14:1	14.7:1	16.5:1
250	12.5:1	13:1	14:1	15.7:1
350	12.2:1	12.5:1	13:1	15:1
500	11.8:1	12:1	13:1	15:1

cooling and an operative squish band. Water-cooled engines will generally run 0.5 – 1 ratio higher than indicated and motors grossly oversquare for their capacity i.e., Yamaha IT175 usually require a number 0.5-1 lower than shown. Engines running a pump fuel should not have the compression ratio pushed higher than the manufacturer has specified. Most companies set their off-road engines up to run on 90-95 octane petrol (gasoline) but some, like the Rotax engines used in the SWM and Can-Am bikes, are really only happy on 100 octane. Road racing engines require 100 octane fuel on standard compression.

To keep all that tightly compressed fuel/air charge in the engine there must be a perfect seal between the head and barrel. If you are really desperate, you could weld the head to the barrel like they do in the twin turbo Le Mans Porsches, but the the more usual method is to use an annealed copper or aluminium head gasket inserted between the two.

McCulloch go-kart engines have used a thin 0.4mm aluminium head gasket for years without too many problems, providing the engine remains stock, but I can't really recommend aluminium for any other two-stroke as there always seems to be a problem with leakage. McCulloch experienced a reverse problem in that they had used aluminium gaskets for years then, on the MC-92 motor, they switched to copper. The copper gasket always seemed to leak as you couldn't get the head tension high enough to crush the copper gasket without the head distorting. On the new MC-93 they have reverted back to the old aluminium gasket.

When a copper gasket is used, there is always a temptation to reuse the old one. My advice is don't, unless the gasket has exactly the same inside and outside diameter as the top lip of the barrel. Even then the gasket should be heated with a low heat gas flame and allowed to cool and anneal.

Generally, I prefer to run air-cooled motors without a head gasket if the head is recessed to give a spigot fit with the top of the barrel. In this instance I lap the head onto the barrel, using valve grinding paste. When you are finished, be very careful to get all traces of paste out of the cylinder and then clean the head and barrel so that the

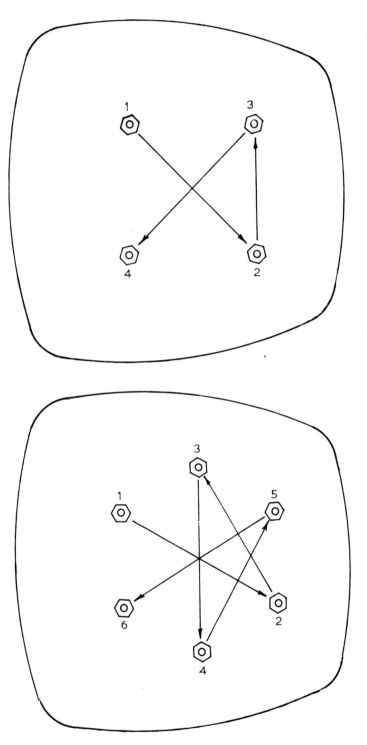

Fig. 2.8 Cylinder head tensioning sequences.

gasket sealant will take. Remember that removing the head gasket will raise the compression ratio significantly.

Regardless of the type of gasket used, or even if you choose not to use a gasket, I recommend the use of either Permatex No.3 or Hylomar SQ-32M gasket sealant. Both sealants will provide a good seal at the elevated temperatures experienced in two-stroke engines.

To ensure the head-barrel joint will not leak, the head bolts must be progressively tensioned in sequence, to the tension recommended by the manufacturer. A typical sequence is shown in FIGURE 2.8. This sequence must be reversed when the head is being removed.

Two-stroke cylinder heads are easily distorted, so you have to be very careful not to tension the studs more than recommended. Overtensioning will always cause the head to warp. You must be careful to tighten the studs in at least three progressive steps. If the head required 20ft/lb tension, you should take all the nuts down finger tight and then to 10, 15 and finally 20ft/lb. After about 15 minutes go over the nuts again and then, after the motor has cooled from a run for a minimum of one hour, tension the nuts again.

Chapter 3
Porting and
Cylinder Scavenging

TODAY, when we take a look down the cylinder of a two-stroke engine, we find its walls literally filled with ports to handle the induction, transfer and exhaust phases of gas flow through the engine. Those of us who have grown up in the Japanese two-stroke era take it for granted that every cylinder has a huge exhaust port flanked by anything from four to six transfer ports. However, it hasn't always been this way. As far back as 1904 Alfred Scott patented his original two-stroke vertical twin. Then in 1906 the French Garard motor appeared with a rotary disc inlet valve. Scott also developed a rotary valve engine in 1912, winning the Senior TT in that year and the following year. However in spite of some very innovative designs being incorporated in two-stroke engines they continued to be embarrassingly unreliable and this single factor stifled development right up until the time of World War II.

In the mid-1930s, the DKW company set out to make two-strokes respectable. They were in the business of manufacturing economical two-stroke motorcycles and stood to profit from changing the two-stroke's image. They engaged the services of an engineer named Zoller to build a 250 racer, which ultimately won the Isle of Man TT in 1938. This led to the development of a 125 single employing a porting arrangement originally invented for two-stroke diesels by German engineer Dr.E.Schneurle. It was this concept which ultimately brought success to the two-stroke, both as an economical power source for transport and as a powerful, light-weight power source for competition. Schneurle's loop-scavenging method, patented in 1925, employed a single exhaust port flanked by two small scavenge or transfer ports, whose air streams were aimed to converge on the cylinder wall opposite the exhaust (FIGURE 3.1). Being aimed away from the exhaust, the transfer streams had a natural resistance to short-circuiting straight out the exhaust. Earlier designs had used deflector-dome pistons to keep the fuel/air charge away from the exhaust port. This increased the piston's heat gathering area and meant that only low power outputs could be aimed for without continually risking piston seizure.

After the war DKW moved to Ingolstadt in West Germany, while their old plant at 27

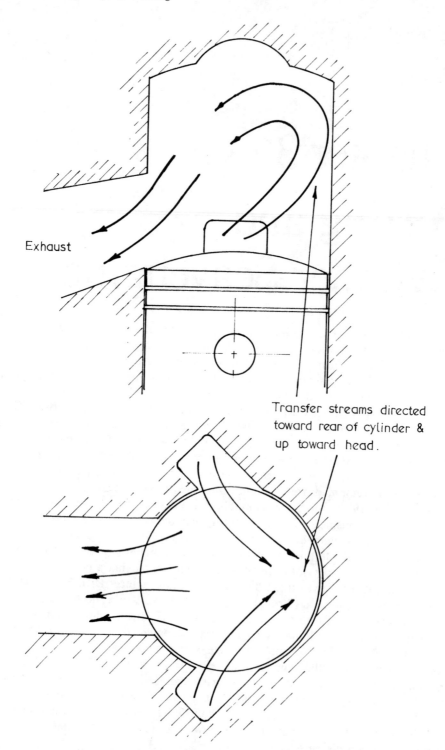

Exhaust

Transfer streams directed toward rear of cylinder & up toward head.

Fig. 3.1 The Schneurle loop scavenge system.

Zschopau in East Germany was rebuilt as Motorradwerke Zschopau, or MZ. In 1952 Walter Kaaden joined MZ to take over development. His early work concentrated on exhaust development and alternate scavenge methods. After much experimentation he proved that the Schneurle loop-scavenge system yielded the best power and reliability. Then in 1957 he added a third transfer port, opposite the exhaust. Its air stream joined with the two main transfer ports, directing flow up toward the head (FIGURE 3.2).

Contemporary two-stroke technology was introduced initially to Suzuki, and later to Yamaha in Japan when Ernst Degner defected from East Germany to join Suzuki. By combining designs which Degner brought from MZ with Japanese technology in the field of metallurgy two-stroke power outputs and reliability took a leap forward. During the '60s Suzuki and Yamaha both won world championships using exotic porting and rotary valve induction systems originally developed by DKW and MZ. The Yamaha engineers, however, went one step further. They added a pair of auxiliary transfer ports alongside the main transfers, which also directed mixture flow toward the rear of the cylinder and up (FIGURE 3.3). The Japanese engineers then realised, as did Walter Kaaden back in 1957, that there was a section of cylinder wall at the rear which could also be filled with another one or two ports. Transfer flow improved and, as the velocity of the fuel/air charge entering the cylinder was reduced, mixture loss out of the exhaust was decreased (FIGURE 3.4).

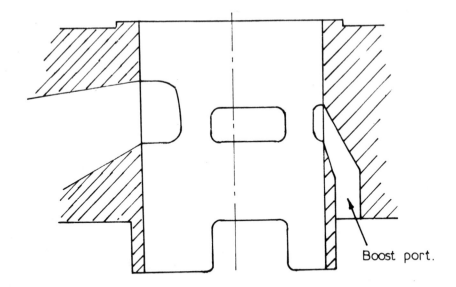

Boost port.

Fig. 3.2   Komet K78 TT porting.

Back in Europe two-stroke engineers were battling excessive ring and cylinder wear, due to the exhaust port width being too great. A narrow port reduced power but improved reliability. A taller port restored lost power but made the power band unacceptably narrow. To get around the problem Rotax engineer Dr.Hans Lippitsch added a pair of small auxiliary exhaust ports alongside the large oval exhaust port and above the main transfers. The two auxiliary ports connect with the main exhaust port before the exhaust flange (FIGURE 3.5).

All dimensions in mm.

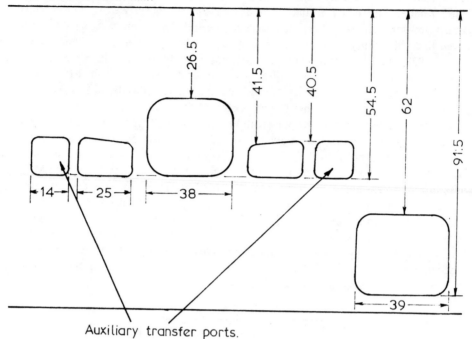

Auxiliary transfer ports.

Fig. 3.3   Yamaha   TZ250 D/E/F porting.

All dimensions in mm.

Boost ports in rear of cylinder.

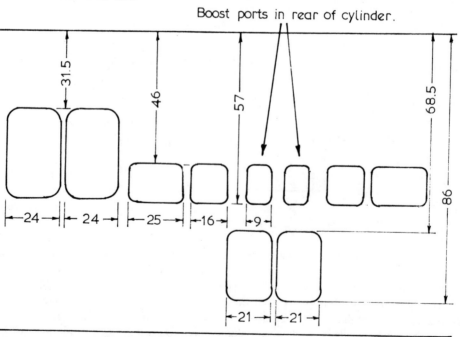

Fig. 3.4   Suzuki   PE 175 C porting.

All dimensions in mm.

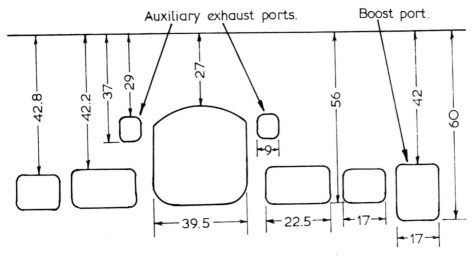

Fig. 3.5 Rotax 124 LC porting.

Yamaha engineers tackled the problem with their power valve system (FIGURE 3.6), which is basically a mechanism to vary the exhaust port height without narrowing the power band. As you can see, there is a drum-like valve up against the cylinder wall. At high rpm the port is raised, increasing hp while permitting a relatively narrow port width for good ring life. At lower speeds the port is lowered, which improves mid-range power and widens the power band. The YZR500 works racer's power valve is controlled electronically by a battery-powered motor, but the TZ500 production machine utilises a much simpler system. Cables run from the tachometer to a centrifugal governor that raises and lowers the port in harmony with engine rpm. Exhaust duration at higher speeds (i.e., above 10,500 rpm) is 202°, which is about average for a road racer. Low rpm duration is about 180°, or similar to that of a 400 motocross engine.

When it comes to modifying a cylinder, the most logical place to start is the

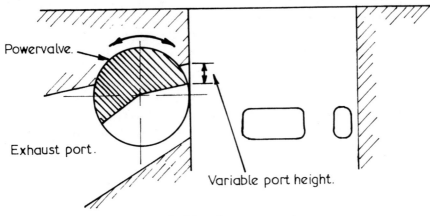

Fig. 3.6 Yamaha powervalve.

exhaust port. A little grinding (or filing) at the sides and top of the port will yield large power increases if approached correctly. Exhaust ports come in all shapes and sizes; each type has its advantages and disadvantages. The port in FIGURE 3.7 is really rectangular but it is usually referred to as a square port. This is the type that you will find in many low performance engines. The size of it has to be small so that the rings won't catch on the top of the port and break. There are two ways this port can be modified: either it can be widened at the top or it can be ovalised. We have to be careful that the exhaust port doesn't get too close to the transfers, otherwise there will be excessive loss of fuel/air mixture out of the exhaust. I like to see 8mm separation between these ports, but at times it is possible to go down to as little as 5mm without ill effect.

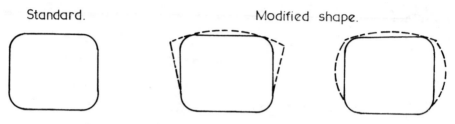

Standard.   Modified shape.

Fig. 3.7   Square exhaust port modifications.

If port spacing is a problem, you will have no alternative other than to widen the exhaust port at the top. This type of port will give the engine good power from the upper mid-range to maximum hp. When you grind this type of port, the centre of the port should be 4° to 5° higher than the ends. The reason for this is that when the engine is on the compression stroke the ring bulges out into the port to its greatest extent just as the port is being closed. However, by raising the centre of the port, the ring has less chance of hanging up on the edge of the port and breaking because the ends of the port actually begin pushing the ring back into the piston groove before the port closes.

The elliptical or oval port is the one which I prefer if the port spacing is suitable. It is the type which you will find in most competition two-strokes. The shape of the port is fairly gentle on rings providing it isn't made excessively wide. What is an excessive width? Well, I'm not sure; but I have found that a port 0.71 of the bore diameter is a good compromise for most road race and motocross engines using ductile iron rings (the maximum safe port size is about 0.65 with brittle cast iron rings). Some tuners take the port size up to 0.75 but ring, piston and port damage is unacceptable. I have been able to take some ports out to 0.73 of the bore size, but this is the exception rather than the rule.

The square bridged port is fairly common in large displacement motocross and enduro engines (FIGURE 3.8). It has a very large port area, but then it has to have a large area as it flows only about 85% as well as an unbridged port of equivalent area. In past years this type of port gave a lot of trouble as the bridge would overheat and bulge, pressing hard against the piston and causing a seize-up. However, the bridge gives little trouble now, providing it is not narrowed down. If heavy bridge-to-piston contact does occur, the piston should be relieved where it scuffs against the bridge. As bridged ports are usually quite close to the transfers, there is only one way to increase the port area, and that is by making the top of the port wider. Modify the port as shown, don't copy the 'eyebrows' type exhaust port discussed next.

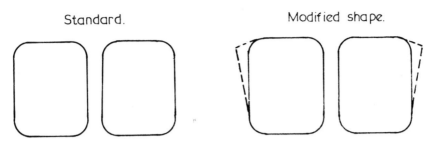

Standard.   Modified shape.

Fig. 3.8   Bridged exhaust port modification.

The 'T' or eyebrows port is seldom seen these days although it was used by Suzuki, Kawasaki and Honda in the past (FIGURE 3.9). This type of port has very little going for it as the sudden change in shape above the main transfers is very harsh on both piston and rings. Usually there is very little that can be done to improve this type of port.

Bridged exhaust ports can be made very wide, but there is a limit to how far you can go. With the Suzuki RM125 engines (all models A to T), the maximum width is 23mm for the left port window (viewed from the front of the bike) and 25.5mm for the right half of the port. If you go any wider than this, the piston will not be able to seal the crankcase from the exhaust port because the skirt is relieved around the pin bosses. There should always be sufficient cylinder wall on the sides of both exhaust and inlet ports for a 2mm width of piston skirt to bear against and effect a seal.

To ensure that you don't go too far in widening the exhaust port, you will have to carefully scribe the outline of the port windows on the piston skirt with the crankshaft

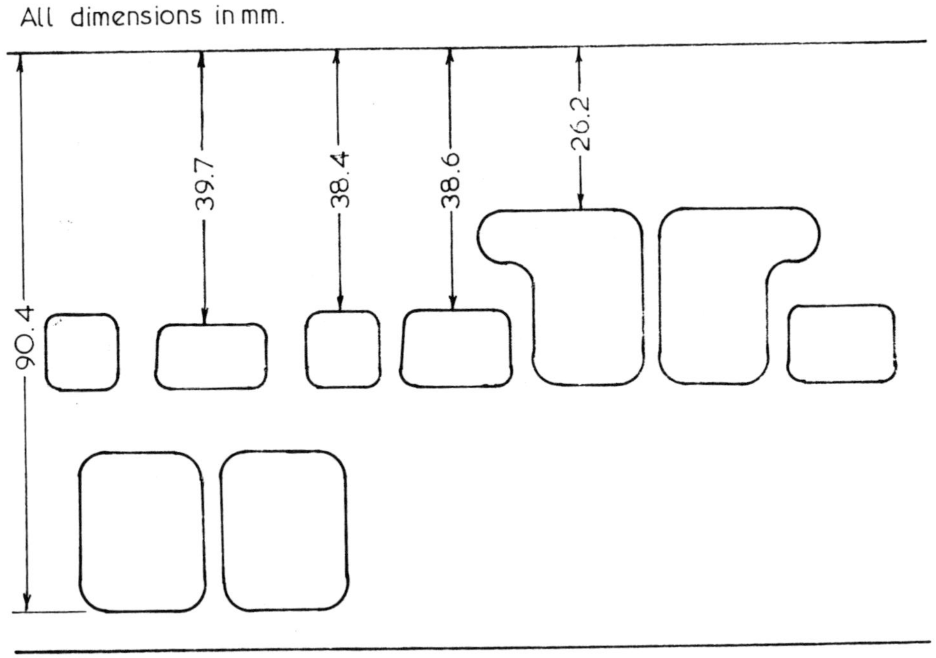

All dimensions in mm.

Fig. 3.9   Honda MT125 RIII porting.

rotated to TDC. Then remove the barrel and measure the distance from the scribed lines to the relieved area around the piston pin bosses. Subtract 2mm from the measurement and this is the amount the port can be increased in width. The amount which can be removed from bridged inlet ports can be ascertained in a similar way, but with the piston at BDC.

Thus far we have talked about changing the shape and width of the exhaust port but not the height. Increasing the width of an exhaust port will always result in a power increase from the upper mid-range to peak rpm. Usually there will be little or no loss in mid-range power. Raising the port, on the other hand, will always knock bottom end power. Increasing the duration, the port open period, by just a couple of degrees can make a bike unrideable in some instances. Just how far you can raise the exhaust port is the million dollar question everyone would like to know. Some tuners work to a time-area/angle-area formula devised some time back. Frankly, I have found this method of calculating port timing completely useless. The geometry and mathematics involved is very tedious and, when you have finished the entire routine, you find that the answer bears little relationship with present-day two-stroke technology.

I have certain ideas on exhaust port timing, but blindly following my suggestions could get you into a lot of trouble. My theory is that an engine requires a certain exhaust duration to attain a specific engine speed. Therefore, if an engine is required to make maximum hp at, say, 12,000rpm, the exhaust duration required will be the same (±1°) regardless of whether the engine is an 80cc motocross engine or a twin cylinder 250 road racer. From experience I have a fair idea of just how much duration specific engines need (see TABLE 3.1). However, if the cylinder has a shorter transfer open period than I like, the exhaust duration will have to be reduced, otherwise the bike will

TABLE 3.1   Exhaust port duration

Engine size (cc)	Application	Engine speed (rpm)	Exhaust duration (°)
2 × 62	Road race	13500	206-208
1 × 80	Moto X	11000	196-198
1 × 80	Moto X	12000	202-204
1 × 80	Road race	13000	205-207
1 × 100	Moto X	11200	198-200
1 × 100	Go-kart	10800	176-178
1 × 125	Moto X	10000	190-192
1 × 125	Moto X	11000	196-198
1 × 125	Road race	12000	202-204
1 × 125	Road race	12500	203-205
2 × 125	Road race	12000	202-204
4 × 125	Road race	11500	200-202
1 × 175	Enduro	9000	184-186
1 × 175	Enduro	9500	186-188
2 × 175	Road race	11200	198-200
1 × 250	Enduro	8000	180-182
1 × 250	Moto X	8500	183-185
1 × 250	Road race	10500	194-196
1 × 400	Enduro	7000	175-177
1 × 400	Moto X	7500	176-178

Note: 1 × 100 go-kart refers to a motor with fixed gearing, hence short exhaust open period.

be too 'pipey' to ride. On the other hand, I may choose to raise the transfer ports and use the suggested exhaust timing.

You can easily tie yourself in knots when you tackle cylinder porting. I've known tuners who have moved exhaust ports up and down and all over the place, searching for more power or a better spread of power. After months of hard work they have achieved nothing, basically because the transfer duration was too short and/or the expansion chamber was all wrong. While it may appear rather arbitrary to select an exhaust timing figure and stick to that, I feel that this is currently the best way to go about two-stroke tuning. Then, if the engine does exhibit some undesirable trait, like a narrow power range, I change the expansion chamber design to produce the required power characteristics. What I'm saying is that expansion chamber design is far more critical than exhaust port duration. The exhaust open period determines to some extent what the maximum hp will be and at what engine speed it will be produced. The expansion chamber, on the other hand, 'adjusts' the power characteristics of the engine at speeds above and below maximum hp revs.

The formula which I use to calculate exhaust open duration (and transfer duration) is fairly straight forward, but if you do much work on two-strokes it would be money well spent if you purchased an electronic calculator with a full scientific function to speed up your calculations. The formula is as follows:-

$$D = \left(180 - \text{Cos}\ \frac{T^2 + R^2 - L^2}{2 \times R \times T} \times 2\right)$$

where T = R + L + C - E
      R = stroke divided by 2 in mm
      L = con rod length in mm centre to centre (usually the stroke multiplied by 2)
      C = deck clearance in mm (i.e. the distance the piston is below the top of the barrel at TDC)
      E = distance from the top of exhaust port to top of barrel

For example, the exhaust duration of the Morbidelli 125 twin production racer (FIGURE 3.10) is as follows:-

$$R = 20.5\text{mm}$$
$$L = 87\text{mm}$$
$$C = 0\text{mm}$$
$$T = R + L + C - E$$
$$= 20.5 + 87 + 0 - 18.2$$
$$= 89.3$$

$$D = \left(180 - \text{Cos}\ \frac{T^2 + R^2 - L^2}{2 \times R \times T}\right) \times 2$$

$$= \left(180 - \text{Cos}\ \frac{89.3^2 + 20.5^2 - 87^2}{2 \times 20.5 \times 89.3}\right) \times 2$$

$$= (180 - \text{Cos}\ .22553) \times 2$$
$$= (180 - 77) \times 2$$
$$= 206°$$

All dimensions in mm.

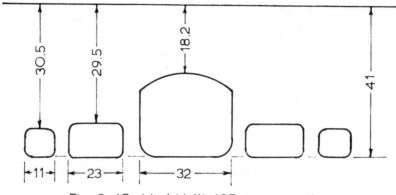

Fig. 3.10 Morbidelli 125 racer porting.

Looking at TABLE 3.1 you can see that the exhaust duration is right where we want it for peak hp at 13,500-13,700rpm. However, if we were going to modify this engine extensively by boring the Mikunis 1mm to 29mm and fabricating a new set of expansion chambers, we would want the power peak at a little over 14,000rpm, which would mean that the duration would have to be increased to 208° to take advantage of the engine's improved breathing. Therefore we would raise the exhaust port 0.35mm. E will now equal 17.85mm and T will equal $20.5 + 87 + 0 - 17.85 = 89.65$.

$$D = \left(180 - \text{Cos } \frac{89.65^2 + 20.5^2 - 87^2}{2 \times 20.5 \times 89.65}\right) \times 2$$

$$= (180 - \text{Cos } .24169) \times 2$$
$$= (180 - 76) \times 2$$
$$= 208°$$

On some engines fitted with Dykes rings, the top piston ring and not the piston crown controls the opening and closing of the exhaust and transfer ports. With these engines, the exhaust duration is calculated using the same formula, however dimension C (the deck clearance in mm) must be very carefully measured using a depth gauge otherwise your calculations will be several degrees out. In engines where the Dykes ring actually determines the port opening and closing, dimension C is the distance the ring is below the top of the barrel at TDC. Referring back to FIGURE 3.5 you will note that the Rotax kart engine appears to have mild porting for a road racer. This engine, in fact, has a single Dykes ring located very close to the top of the piston. Dimension C is 1.8mm, so what looks like motocross porting is truly road race porting. In this case the exhaust duration is 201°.

If you have not had any previous experience tuning two-strokes it is a lot safer to modify the piston crown to increase exhaust duration rather than raise the port. Once you have taken the metal away you can't put it back, but fortunately pistons are a good deal less expensive than barrels so all you have to do is keep accurate notes and then retrogress one step when you have gone too far (FIGURE 3.11). The idea is to progressively file 0.5mm off the exhaust side of the piston crown until you reach a

Piston cutout.

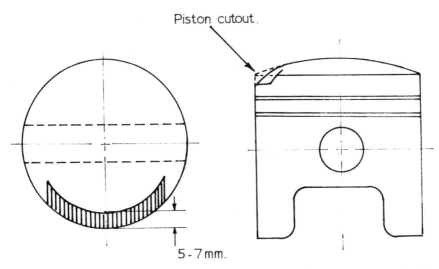

5-7mm.

Fig. 3.11   Piston modification to increase exhaust open period.

point where you are happy with the power output. If you accidentally go one step too far, it is easy to back-track. All you need is a new piston and then, when you modify the exhaust port proper, raise it 0.5mm less than the amount you filed off the piston. This type of tuning is back to front to the way in which I prefer to do things, but if you don't want to get involved in expensive and time-consuming expansion chamber fabrication, it is the safest way out. You will never get the best possible power out of the motor by shifting the exhaust port around to work within the limitations imposed by the expansion chamber fitted to your bike. However, this is one of the safer places to begin modifying two-strokes, and even within the boundary set by the stock expansion chamber you should end up with an engine which works better than the stock item.

When working on the exhaust port, there are two checks which should be made. Firstly, with the piston at BDC, the bottom of the port window should be level with, or lower than, the piston crown, otherwise high speed gas flow will be disrupted (FIGURE 3.12). Secondly, in the case of bridged ports, ensure that both halves of the port open simultaneously. If one side opens a little before the other, gas flow is disrupted to some extent, but worse the pressure waves transmitted to the expansion chamber are of a lower amplitude. This reduces the effectiveness of the exhaust pulses in evacuating and recharging the cylinder with fresh mixture (FIGURE 3.13).

If you own a Power Valve type Yamaha there is an additional inspection which must be made. Regardless of whether the exhaust port is standard or has been raised check that the power valve opens fully to align with the exhaust port roof. Manually push the actuator arm as far as it will go to see if the valve and port align. Usually some adjustment is required. After loosening the adjusting nut and moving the valve to the correct position be sure to Loctite the nut so that it does not vibrate loose. Finally verify that the valve timing is correct with the engine running. This is accomplished by marking the full extent of the actuator arm travel on the cylinder and revving the engine in short bursts to see if the valve actually opens that far. If it does not you will have to adjust the valve to a position slightly higher than the exhaust port roof with the 37

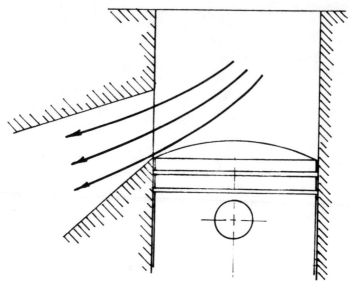

Fig. 3.12 Exhaust port must be lower than piston at B.D.C.

actuator arm pushed to the full open position. Then recheck for full open with the engine running.

The only other Power Valve adjustment which is permissible alters the governor spring preload and changes the mid-range rpm valve timing. When spring preload is increased, lower rpm exhaust duration is increased. As this has the effect of raising top end power and narrowing the power range, it is a modification recommended only for expert riders on fast circuits. Begin testing with an additional 0.020 in shim fitted

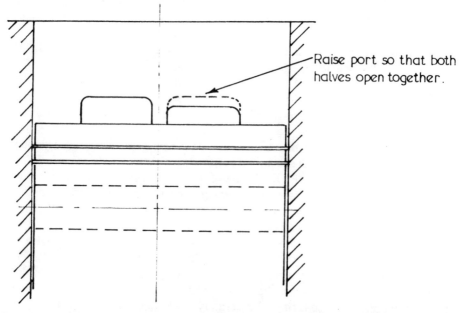

Raise port so that both halves open together.

Fig. 3.13 Both halves of bridged exhaust ports must open simultaneously.

behind the governor spring. If the power comes on too quickly or the power range is too narrow, try a 0.012 in shim.

In recent years, the physical size and shape of the exhaust port between the port window and the flange where the expansion chamber connects, is under close scrutiny. Attempts are now being made to keep the diameter of the port as small as possible, without impeding the flow of gas out of the cylinder. Whereas the port diameter of a typical 125cc cylinder was 40 to 42mm a few years ago, most exhaust ports for a 125 are now about 37 or 38mm diameter. This is being done to keep the exhaust pulse wave at a high amplitude so that the cylinder is scavenged and recharged more completely. It has been found that allowing the exhaust gases to expand and cool too quickly, as occurs when the exhaust port is large, actually diminishes the strength of the exhaust pulse.

Naturally the tuner's desire to keep the exhaust gas confined so that a strong pulse wave is transmitted through the expansion chamber, has to be balanced against the need for a free-flowing exhaust passage, which allows the burnt gases to stream unimpeded out of the cylinder. To this end, the exhaust port must be relatively straight, without abrupt directional changes, to eliminate eddying, and the exhaust flange must match the port perfectly and not change the direction of exhaust flow. When an exhaust port meets these requirements, gas flow out of the cylinder will be good, even though the port diameter is relatively small to keep pulse intensity at a high value.

A quick look through the exhaust flange and port will indicate how straight is the exhaust passage. However, unless you are very experienced in the science of gas flow, you will not know if the exhaust gases are eddying or not. If you are using castor oil or some other oil which produced a fair buildup of carbon, you will be able to see where the exhaust port is 'dead'. Any place where there is a layer of carbon in a port which is basically carbon-free is a place of little flow activity. In such an area you can be fairly certain that the gases are eddying and disrupting flow out of the cylinder.

At times, the low pressure area can be eliminated by grinding metal out of the port, but more often than not the port will require welding up. The exhaust port illustrated in FIGURE 3.14 is a particularly nasty one. The flange changes the direction of flow very abruptly, which produces an eddy current in the top of the flange. Also the floor of the port drops away too quickly, causing eddying in this area.

There are two ways to tackle the problem with the flange. The roof of the port may be ground higher and the flange raised to reduce the kink in the port's roof. On the other hand a new flange can be fabricated with the roof in line with the roof of the exhaust port. Either way, the floor of the port, and perhaps the floor of the flange too, will have to be welded up to improve the profile. The aluminium floor naturally will have to be argon-arc welded. Fill in only a little at a time and allow the cylinder plenty of time to cool between each run, otherwise it will distort.

As shown in FIGURE 3.15 the exhaust flange may be out of line when viewed from above. Again this must be corrected by fabricating a new flange which aligns with the exhaust port.

From the aspect of two-stroke engine design, I feel that the transfer ports are the most important. Unfortunately, from the average tuner's viewpoint, the transfers are the most difficult to modify and the least understood. By definition, the transfer ports have the job of transferring the fuel/air mixture from the crankcase into the cylinder. That sounds simple enough but, after we consider all of the factors involved, you will better appreciate what a mammoth task this really is.

39

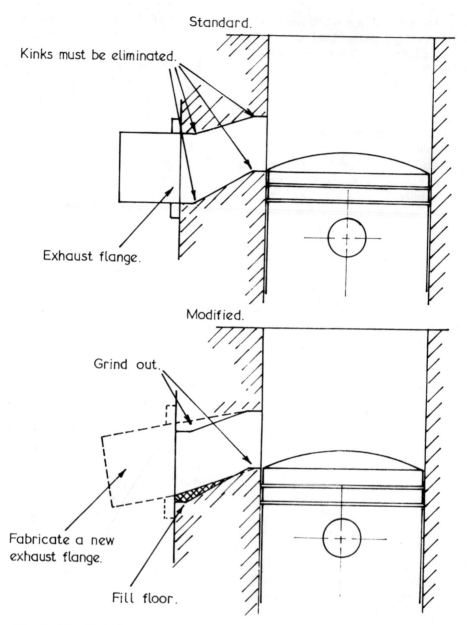

Fig. 3.14 Exhaust port must be correctly modified to assist flow.

In an average racing engine the induction cycle will take place during around 190° of crankshaft rotation. The exhaust cycle will occur over a period of 200°. The transfer phase, however, has to be completed through 130° of crankshaft movement. Not only do the transfers have an extremely short time in which to recharge the cylinder with fuel/air mixture, they must also control the flow pattern of the charge to prevent mixture loss out of the exhaust, and drive exhaust gases from the rear of the cylinder towards the exhaust port.

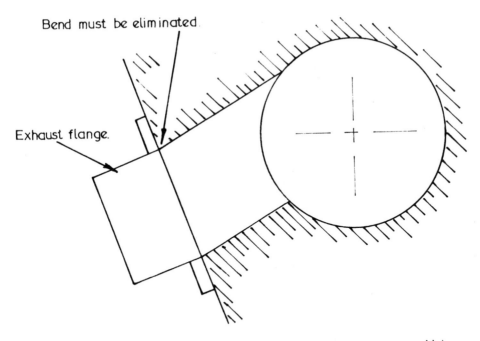

Bend must be eliminated.

Exhaust flange.

Fig. 3.15   Flange must be in line with exhaust port to stop eddying.

During the '60s, when Suzuki and Yamaha dominated Grand Prix racing, their engineers revived a myth which surfaced from the development of BSA Bantam and Villiers engines for racing just after the war. These engines had massive spaces in the crankcase and tuners reasoned, rightly enough, that filling the crankcase with a variety of 'stuffers' would reduce crankcase volume and hence increase crankcase compression when the piston descended to BDC. Increasing crankcase compression naturally enough results in higher crankcase pressure which, all else being equal, raises transfer flow and improves maximum hp output. Tuners cited the reason for this as being due to the transfer streams erupting under considerable pressure into the cylinder. Because of this the fuel/air charge tended to behave like a wedge on entering the cylinder. It didn't break up and mingle with the exhaust gases, but pushed them out of the cylinder with considerable force.

So effective was this method of cylinder scavenging that the fuel/air 'wedge' was actually being partly lost out of the exhaust before the port closed. Two-stroke tuners overcame this problem by opening the transfer ports later and closing them earlier, reducing traditional transfer duration from 130° down to 120°. Because of more fuel charge being contained within the cylinder, power increased. This encouraged engineers to further increase crankcase compression and reduce the transfer open period to less than 110°. Horsepower again rose, instilling in Japanese engineers the idea that dominance in Grand Prix racing would depend on them reducing transfer duration to contain charge loss out of the exhaust and increasing crankcase compression to ensure efficient pumping of the fuel/air mixture from the crankcase into the cylinder.

The theory sounds good, but in practice there were problems. True, power outputs rose to levels previously unknown from two-strokes, but the power bands became razor 41 thin and engine speeds rose to incredible levels. Not to be deterred, the Japanese engineers embarked on a scheme of cylinder size reduction to enable very high rpm to be attained reliably. Again power levels increased, providing a further stimulus to reduce cylinder displacement. This led to the development of such machines as the three cylinder 50cc Suzuki and the four cylinder Yamaha 125 which produced 40hp at 18,000rpm. At this time road racers had from ten to eighteen gears, such were the power characteristics of these engines.

The problem was that in spite of the very limited transfer open periods employed, at lower engine speeds too much charge was being lost out of the exhaust. This occurred because the transfer charge entered the cylinder under so much pressure that it had time to spurt right out of the exhaust at low rpm. Hence little power was produced at speeds below maximum hp revs. At higher rpm, power was again restricted, due to the transfer ports being too small to flow a larger volume of fuel/air mixture in the available time.

Today, the very same problem occurs when very short transfer periods are employed. Generally, you will find that bikes which are 'pipey', coming onto the power too quickly or exhibiting a narrow power range, are that way because the transfer ports are too low (i.e., short duration) or because the ports are incorrectly aimed.

Fortunately, manufacturers have mostly got away from the idea of using high crankcase compression to push the fuel charge through the transfers into the cylinder, so we can forget about crankcase compression and concentrate on the transfer ports. However, for those who are interested, primary compression or crankcase compression is calculated using this formula:-

$$PC = \frac{CCV}{CCV - CV}$$

where CCV = crankcase volume at TDC
CV = cylinder volume

To measure the crankcase volume (CCV), first turn the engine onto its side, with the inlet port facing up, and rotate the crank to bring the piston up to TDC. Then, using a burette filled with liquid paraffin (kerosene) and engine oil, mixed 50-50, fill the crankcase up to the cylinder wall face of the inlet port. If this equals, say, 425cc, and the engine has a 125cc cylinder, the primary compression ratio will be 1.42:1.

At this time, instead of relying solely on crankcase pressure to push the fuel/air mix into the cylinder, we also use the suction wave produced in the expansion chamber to pull the intake charge up through the transfers. If we use an expansion chamber with shallow tapers, maximum power will be suppressed, but the suction wave will be active in drawing mixture into the cylinder over a wide rpm range. On the other hand a chamber with steeper cones will produce a stronger suction wave, raising peak hp, but it will be effective over a much narrower rev range.

Obviously the longer we leave the transfer ports open, the larger the rpm range will be over which the exhaust pulses effectively pull up fresh mixture from the crankcase. Conversely, if transfer duration is kept short, we have to rely more on crankcase compression to shift the fuel/air charge, as the suction pulse in the exhaust will only arrive at the right time to draw up fuel over a limited rpm range. It stands to reason, if the transfer port is closed when the pulse wave arrives, it will not do any good. On the other hand, if we keep the port open for as long as possible we have a better chance of having pulse waves arrive at the right time, over a wider range of engine speeds.

With this idea in mind, we should realise that the transfer duration will vary for high and low speed engines. A high speed engine (i.e. 13,500rpm) will want the transfer ports open for 140-142° while an engine running at 6500rpm will be happy with a duration of 120-124° when exhaust port open periods are close to those in TABLE 3.1. At higher engine speeds there is less time for cylinder filling so we need a longer transfer period, but at lower speeds a long transfer period will allow too much charge to escape out of the exhaust so a shorter duration is in order for low speed engines. TABLE 3.2 sets out the transfer durations which I have found to allow good engine breathing at the speeds indicated. To pick up mid-range power the shorter duration should be chosen. The engine won't rev far past maximum hp revs but the power output below maximum will be superior. For good power past maximum rpm the longer transfer period is desirable. If exhaust port durations longer than those indicated in TABLE 3.1 are used, then more transfer timing may be necessary otherwise the engine could become too 'pipey'.

One ploy which is very effective in giving the engine good power over a wide range is to use staggered transfer durations. The old MZ 125 racer had the two main transfer ports open for 136°, while the third transfer port in the rear of the cylinder had a much shorter duration of 128°. Many of the Italian go-kart engines also used this type of porting in past years. When Honda introduced the MT-125RII production racer in 1977, they took this principle one step further. The main transfers opened 39.2mm from the top of the cylinder (126° duration), the secondary transfers opened a little earlier at 38.5mm (130° duration) and the boost port in the back of the cylinder opened the last, 39.7mm down (123° duration).

Tuners reasoned that as the back port aimed its flow towards the exhaust port there would be some loss of charge, unless steps were taken to prevent this occurring. Therefore the back port was opened around 1mm after the main transfers, so that flow from the main transfer ports, being aimed towards the rear of the cylinder, would actually form a wall of mixture in front of the boost port and thus prevent a loss of charge out of the exhaust. Furthermore, it was felt that delaying the opening of the rear port would allow crankcase pressure to 'blow down' through the main transfers. Hence

TABLE 3.2   Transfer port duration

rpm	Transfer duration (°)
6500	120-124
8000	124-128
9000	126-130
10000	128-132
11000	130-134
12000	132-136
13000	134-140
14000	136-142

Note: The transfer duration refers to the open period of the main transfer ports in particular. The secondary transfers and the boost port may beneficially use durations longer than shown. 43

a high pressure stream would not erupt from the back port and head right out of the exhaust.

Today those theories have been forgotten. The majority of engines come from the manufacturers with all the transfer ports at the same height. However, this does not mean that staggered porting does not work. Most tuners recognise that it does; but the transfers are staggered in reverse to the old school of thought. At this time, when a cylinder is modified, the back port is often opened 1.0 to 1.5mm earlier than the other transfers. Also I have found that opening the secondary transfers 0.8mm before the main transfers benefits the power curve as well.

There are several reasons why staggered-type porting works so well at this time. For one thing the manufacturers have forgotten their preoccupation with high crankcase pressure. Therefore, the transfer charge enters the cylinder in a more orderly and controlled manner. Additionally, the transfer ports have been re-aimed. Whereas the ports were tilted upwards so that the mixture streams from opposite sides of the cylinder gently met at a point in the cylinder just slightly higher than mid-stroke, today's ports are tilted very little or not at all (FIGURE 3.16). This means that the flow streams hug the piston crown, rather than shooting up towards the head to mingle with exhaust gases. Instead, the streams crash into each other, dissipating much of their energy. The mixture then rises relatively slowly in the cylinder, where it is trapped as the exhaust port closes. For these reasons, we can open the boost port and the secondary transfer ports a little earlier, as there is less risk of mixture escaping out of the exhaust, even at lower speeds when there is more time for this to occur. If the main transfers were opened earlier, exhaust flow would tend to turn the transfer flow around and direct it out of the exhaust port, but flow through ports further away from the exhaust port are not influenced to such an extent by the direction of exhaust flow.

When staggered porting is employed, it is usual for mid-range and maximum power to increase, due to the longer transfer periods improving cylinder filling, particularly at high rpm. Much of the mid-range power gain, I feel, is due to the cylinder being scavenged better. With the new type of transfer porting, a pocket of

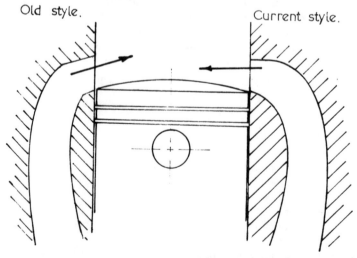

Old style.   Current style.

Fig. 3.16 Old & new transfer port designs.

exhaust gas can be left unscavenged high up in the cylinder at lower engine speeds. Opening the boost port early would tend to get this pocket of stagnant gas moving, because its flow stream is still directed upwards at 45° to 60°. Some fuel charge is possibly lost out of the exhaust but, because this pocket of exhaust gas is purged out of the cylinder, there is less dilution of the remaining fuel/air mixture. Consequently combustion will be faster and more complete, raising the hp output.

Because the direction of transfer flow is so very important in obtaining a high power output and a good power range, only very experienced tuners should attempt to modify the top section of transfer ports. If you don't know what you are doing, you could easily render the cylinder useless. When the transfer duration is too short, raise the barrel using an aluminium spacer of the required thickness, and fit a base gasket on each side to ensure a good seal. Naturally the compression will have to be restored by turning an amount equal to the thickness of the spacer, plus the thickness of one base gasket, from the barrel or cylinder head. Keep in mind, when the cylinder is raised, that the piston rings may become exposed in the inlet port. This is of no consequence providing the top of the port is correctly shaped and providing the ring ends are not exposed. If just the bottom ring is opening into the inlet port, it can be removed if the engine is usually operated at 8000rpm plus. In piston-ported engines, raising the barrel will shorten the inlet open period so the inlet port will have to be lowered to compensate.

Cylinders employing the type of boost port usually found in reed valve engines (eg. Yamaha) are quite easy to modify. This type of back port can be raised or increased in width, using hand files. Take care that you don't nick the bore wall with the file and do not make the port so wide that it opens out to the piston ring pegs. A width equal to that of the main transfer port is close to what is required, but always check to be sure.

The secondary transfers should be raised by a professional tuner with good knowledge of the subject and good equipment to do the job. The alternative, which works very well, is to file metal off the piston crown (see FIGURE 3.11) in the manner described for increasing exhaust port duration. If the piston is fitted with a Dykes ring high up (eg. Bultaco) this method will not work, as the piston ring and not the piston crown actually controls the exhaust and transfer opening.

The safest part of the transfer port for you to modify is the bottom of the port where it joins the crankcase. Cut the base gasket to match the crankcase cut-outs and then match the transfers to the base gasket. This will ensure that there is no step in the port to disrupt flow. Then carefully smooth the transfers, removing all casting imperfections. The piston cut-out below the gudgeon pin is also a part of the transfer port, so dress it up too.

Thus far we have only discussed working with the ports provided by the manufacturer, but extra transfer ports can often be added. Here there are two approaches which we can take, depending on whether we want a small increase in performance and good piston cooling, or a larger power rise without the benefit of improved piston cooling.

We will deal with the cool piston approach first, which can be applied to many engines regardless of the type of induction system employed. I first saw porting like that illustrated in FIGURE 3.17 on the old 250 Bultaco Pursang and Matador. As you can see, two boost ports are machined the depth of the cylinder liner about 7-9mm wide, on either side of the inlet port. These ports are fed through two holes in the 45

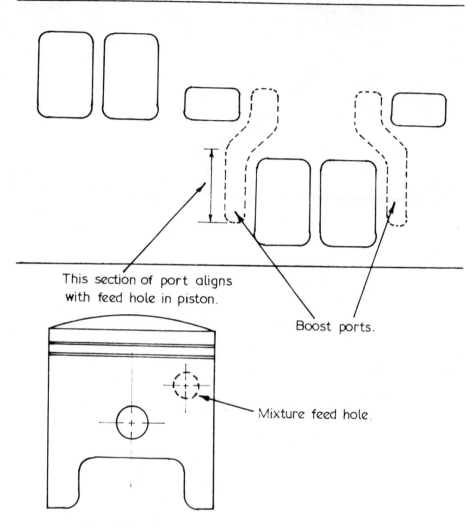

This section of port aligns with feed hole in piston.

Boost ports.

Mixture feed hole.

Fig. 3.17 A common type of boost porting.

piston. The flow of mixture past the little end and under the piston crown does much to reduce their temperatures. Desert racing engines in particular benefit from this type of porting. There isn't a huge increase in power, but usually a couple of horsepower will be picked up at the top end of the power band.

The next type of boost porting also improves little end lubrication and piston cooling (FIGURE 3.18). It is intended for piston-ported engines which have a lot of cylinder wall height between the top of the inlet port and the piston crown at BDC. Two boost ports are machined into the cylinder, generally with a 13mm cutter tilted at 25°. Ensure that the boost ports are at least 1.5mm above the inlet port, to ensure an effective seal.

The third type of boost porting shouldn't really be called boost porting (FIGURE 3.19). It doesn't do anything to increase hp output, but it will extend piston and little

Boost port/s.

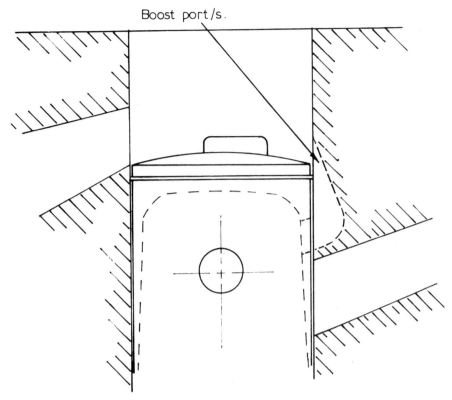

Fig. 3.18 Some engines may utilise boost ports above the inlet port.

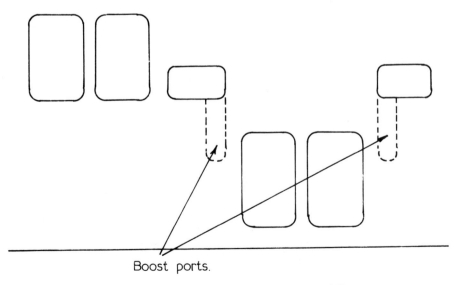

Boost ports.

Fig. 3.19 Boost porting for desert bikes.

end life in desert bikes. I call it 'last resort' porting. Two 9mm wide slots are machined the depth of the cylinder liner to join with the main transfers. Holes in the piston feed these ports as in the first example.

The final type of boost porting can only be used with reed valve induction. (FIGURE 3.20). When the inlet port is bridged, two ports are milled with a 13mm cutter tilted at 25 to 35°. If the cylinder had a single inlet port, overlapping cuts would be made to form a single port of about 18 to 20mm width.

When there is sufficient cylinder wall space available, two types of boost porting may be employed together. The porting shown in FIGURE 3.17 can often be combined with the arrangements shown in either FIGURE 3.18 or FIGURE 3.20. The resulting increase in transfer area improves transfer flow and it reduces the velocity at which the fuel charge enters the cylinder. This minimises charge loss out of the exhaust and improves cylinder scavenging.

Except in road racing, piston controlled induction systems have fallen from favour; but, as it is the most basic two-stroke inlet arrangement, we will consider it before reed valve and rotary disc valve systems. In this way you will better appreciate

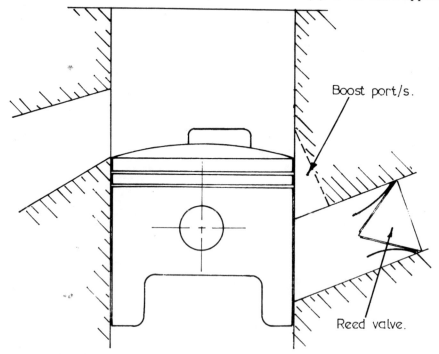

Boost port/s.

Reed valve.

Fig. 3.20 Boost porting for reed valve engines.

why these other designs have been developed and what their respective advantages and disadvantages are.

Piston controlled inlet ports have the advantage of simplicity, but they are handicapped to some extent due to the port opening and closing points being symmetrically disposed before and after TDC. As the piston rises in the cylinder, the inlet port opens, usually at around 70° before TDC in low speed engines, and 100° before TDC in high speed engines. The rising piston creates a depression in the crankcase, thus air rushes down the inlet tract to fill the crankcase. However, at TDC the port is still open so, as the piston descends, fuel/air mixture will be pushed out of the crankcase through the open inlet port. Fortunately, reverse flow occurs only after the piston has travelled about 50° past TDC at engine speeds around 4,000rpm. Therefore, if the inlet port closes at 70° after TDC, only a small amount of fuel charge will be lost. At higher engine speeds there won't be any loss of mixture, as the combined force of pulse waves and the inertia of the high velocity mixture is stronger than the pressure created in the crankcase by the descending piston. For this reason we can employ longer inlet durations in high speed engines, but at lower rpm they suffer from such a bad dose of the blubbers that they will hardly run.

The poor low speed running is partly due to not enough fuel/air mixture being available in the crankcase to adequately fill the cylinder, but there is another reason. The low rpm blubbers and stumbles are basically due to flooding. When the mixture is pushed out of the crankcase and up the inlet tract, it eventually passes through the carburettor. On its way through it picks up another load of fuel, then when the inlet port again opens the fuel/air mixture reverses and travels back through the carburettor, collecting yet another load of fuel. The rich mixture which results burns slowly and wets the spark plug.

The inlet durations set out in TABLE 3.3 will give good power at the speeds indicated. The shorter duration will improve mid-range pulling power and the longer duration for each speed will enable the engine to produce more power at rpm in excess of maximum hp revs. Motocross and enduro engines such as the RM and PE series Suzukis, with crankcase type reed valves, would normally want inlet durations 15° and 25° shorter respectively. When RM Suzuki engines are used for flat track and road racing, the inlet open period is as indicated in TABLE 3.3, as mid-range power is not so important.

TABLE 3.3   Inlet port duration

rpm	Inlet duration (°)
7000	150-155
8000	155-160
9500	165-170
11000	185-190
12000	195-200

The inlet duration is calculated using the formula:-

$$D = (\text{Cos}\ \frac{P^2 + R^2 - L^2}{2 \times P \times R}) \times 2$$

where
$R =$ stroke divided by 2 in mm

$L =$ con rod length centre to centre in mm (usually the stroke multiplied by 2)

$C =$ deck clearance in mm (i.e., the distance the piston is below the top of the barrel at TDC)

$H =$ piston height in mm (i.e., the length of the piston on the inlet side)

$F =$ inlet floor depth (i.e., the distance from the top of the barrel to the bottom of the inlet port)

$P = R + L + H + C - F$

For example, the inlet open period of the Yamaha KT-100S kart engine (FIGURE 3.21) is as follows:-

$$R = \quad 23mm$$
$$L = \quad 100mm$$
$$C = \quad 0.2mm$$
$$H = \quad 56mm$$
$$F = \quad 77mm$$
$$P = \quad R + L + H + C - F$$
$$= \quad 102.2$$

$$D = \left(\text{Cos } \frac{102.2 + + 23 + - 100 +}{2 \times 102.2 \times 23}\right) \times 2$$

$$= \left(\text{Cos } \frac{973.84}{4701.2}\right) \times 2$$

$$= \text{Cos } .20715 \times 2$$
$$= 78 \times 2$$
$$= 156°$$

Because of the bad effect long inlet periods have on mid-range power, it is always preferable to first enlarge the inlet port and see if that change gives the required improvement in high rpm power. It is impossible to say how wide an inlet port can be, as cylinder designs vary so much. However, I will say that if the port has a nice concave floor like that shown in FIGURE 3.21, even cylinders with very weak lower cylinder walls (eg., YZ80 Yamaha) will be reliable with a port 0.65 the bore size, whilst cylinders with the lower wall well supported will accept port widths up to 0.75 the bore diameter. If the inlet port is bridged, the port width can be up to 0.85 the bore size.

The piston bears quite heavily against the inlet side of the cylinder, so always increase the width by no more than 2mm initially and progress slowly from there. Before you widen the port, check to see that the piston skirt is wide enough to cover and seal the port window. There must be 2mm down each side of the inlet port against which the piston will effect a seal. If the rings run into the port at BDC, you will have to ensure that you do not increase the width so much that the ends of the ring become exposed. However, if you decide to run just the top ring, and it is the second ring which is running into the inlet tract, you won't have to worry about this.

Beside reducing frictional losses and bore wear, discarding the second ring can also have another benefit. With the second ring out of the way it is possible, in many instances, to increase the inlet port height. At times this won't work without also increasing the port timing, as the piston skirt will block the top of the port at TDC, unless it is shortened. Actually, the first check that you should make before lowering the inlet port to increase the port open period is to see that the lower edge of the piston skirt does not protrude into the top of the port with the crank rotated to TDC. When the skirt is shortened, cut off just the inlet side and be sure to put a good chamfer on the skirt so that it encourages lubricant to stay on the cylinder wall.

All dimensions in mm.

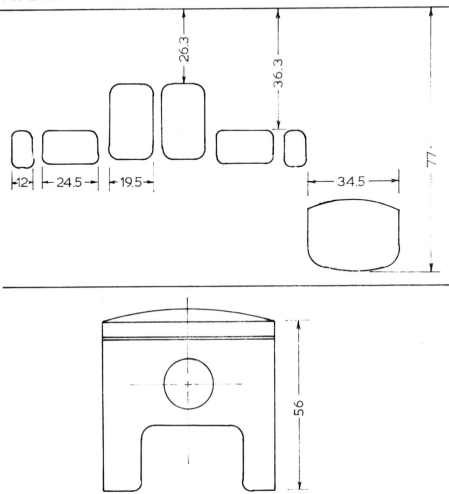

Fig. 3 . 21 Yamaha KT-100S porting & piston dimensions.

A lot of tuners lengthen the inlet timing just by shortening the piston. Sometimes there is no alternative, as the cylinder may be too weak to stand having metal removed, but, generally, skirt cutting is the easy way out. Even though cutting 3mm off the skirt will increase the inlet duration to the same figure as lowering the inlet floor by 3mm, you will find that maximum hp will not be as high and the engine will not rev as far past maximum hp revs. The simple truth is that the port area, as well as the duration, must be increased to flow the amount of air necessary to improve the power output. I have found, as a general rule, that the piston skirt will have to be shortened by 4mm to give the same high speed power characteristics as obtained by lowering the port 3mm. However, mid-range power is not as good, due to increased blow-back caused by the longer duration. For maximum power, the inlet port area should be about 10 to 15% larger than the area of the carburettor bore.

When the inlet floor is lowered, the full length of the port floor right back to the 51 carburettor will have to be reworked. (FIGURE 3.22). If this isn't done, the port will not flow any better than the standard port. In fact, an abrupt increase in area close to the port window will cause eddying and actually decrease flow.

To encourage air flow in the inlet tract, it must be smooth and free of obstructions. Casting flaws, bumps and hollows must be eliminated by grinding or filing. The carburettor should be matched to the inlet manifold and in turn the port must be matched with the manifold. In the case of road race engines, high speed air flow is very important, so investigate if it is possible to raise the carburettor to eliminate the kink which usually exists in the inlet tract (FIGURE 3.23). If there is room to raise the carburettor, this can be done either by inserting a wedge-shape spacer between the inlet manifold and barrel, or by remachining the face of the inlet port at a suitable angle.

Rotary disc valve induction, normally called rotary valve induction, neatly solves the problem of low speed blow-back experienced with piston-port induction, but in doing so introduces a couple of other relatively minor problems. Because of additional mechanical complications, rotary valve engines cost a good deal more to produce than piston-port or reed valve engines and, unless special measures are taken, they are much wider, physically, than other types of two-strokes. These considerations aside, rotary valve induction is definitely the best type of inlet system currently available for two-stroke engines. A rotary valve engine will produce more power and a better spread of power. This is principally because it doesn't present the high speed flow resistance which stifles maximum hp output in reed motors. Because it is free of low rpm blow-back problems, the induction period can be longer than for engines with piston-controlled inlet ports.

As shown in FIGURE 3.24, the rotary valve is most commonly driven off the end of the crankshaft, with the induction tract entering the side, rather than the rear of the engine. The cutout in the disc valve and the width of the inlet port actually determine when the induction period will commence and finish. Because of this, we can start the inlet cycle much earlier than in a piston-ported engine and we can also close the inlet port much sooner after TDC.

It is usual, when good low speed power is required, to open the inlet port about 5

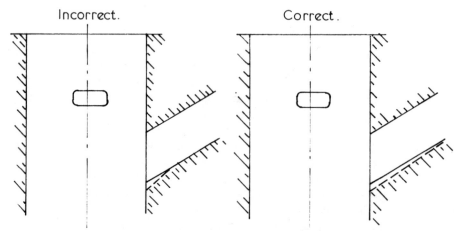

Incorrect.   Correct.

Fig. 3. 22 Inlet port floor must be correctly lowered.

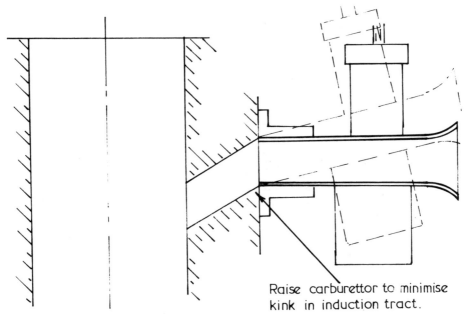

Raise carburettor to minimise
kink in induction tract.

Fig. 3 . 23 Raise carburettor to improve inlet flow.

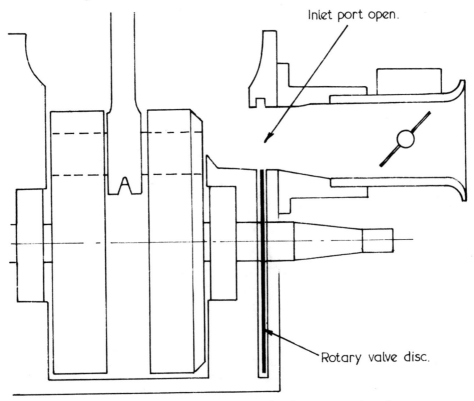

Inlet port open.

Rotary valve disc.

Fig. 3 . 24 Rotary valve induction arrangement.

to 10° before the transfer port closes (i.e., 120 to 130° before TDC) and to close the inlet port at about 55 to 60° after TDC. This results in an inlet duration of around 180 to 190°. For more power at the top end of the power curve, the duration is increased to something like 200 to 210°. There will, however, be some loss of low speed power and the engine won't take a fistfull of throttle at low revs without stumbling. The increase in duration can be obtained in two ways. Either we can have the rotary valve open a little earlier at 135 to 140° before TDC and close a little later at 65 to 70° after TDC, or we can leave the valve opening point alone and pick up the extra duration by closing the port at 70 to 80° after TDC. The effect on the power curve will be quite different, even though the inlet open period is the same. Opening the valve at, say, 140° before TDC and closing it at 65° after TDC (205° duration) will tend to lift maximum power a little, but the main effect will be to considerably increase power in the upper mid-range. Leaving the opening point at 125° before TDC and shifting the moment of closing to 80° after TDC (205° duration) will reduce mid-range power due to increased blow back, but there will be a good power rise right at the top end of the power curve (FIGURE 3.25).

In high rpm road racing engines, where mid-range power is of only minor concern, the inlet duration is increased to about 220 to 235°. The rotary valve will open at 135 to 150° before TDC and close at 80 to 90° after TDC. The main concern here is that the inlet duration is of sufficient length to ensure complete crankcase filling at the rpm where maximum horsepower is desired. If we want peak power at 14,000rpm then the

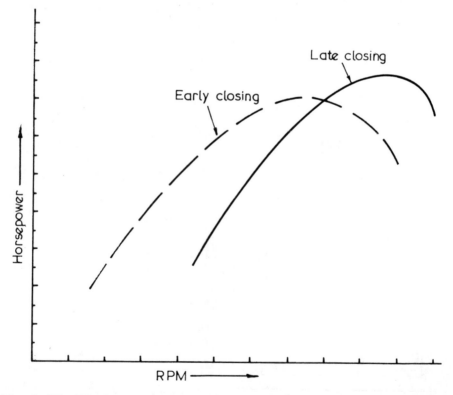

54   Fig. 3.25 Effect on power curve of changing rotary valve closing angle.

duration will be around 235°, but if we want peak power at 11,500rpm the duration will be close to 220°.

TABLE 3.4 sets out the rotary valve timing for a number of go-kart and bike engines. All of the 100cc kart engines have fixed gearing.

Before you set about altering the valve timing, check to see that the inlet port is of the correct shape and that the valve cover perfectly matches the inlet port in the crankcase. Any obstruction here will disrupt air flow. You will find in many engines that the port in the valve cover does not align with the crankcase port. Grinding the port in the valve cover or the crankcase will affect the inlet timing. In some engines the inlet port opens and closes slowly because the sides of the port are the wrong shape. The port illustrated in FIGURE 3.26 should be reshaped as shown. The port area is increased and it will open and close more abruptly, generating beneficial pulse waves in the inlet tract.

The actual side profile of the inlet port is very poor in many rotary valve engines. In FIGURE 3.24 you can see a common mistake made by manufacturers which is very disruptive to air flow. The mixture rushes straight down the inlet port and proceeds to bang right into the crankwheel, losing a good deal of inertia. Some of the mixture will slowly rise up and around the crankwheel into the crankcase and a little of the air will form into a turbulent eddy current. When this kind of situation exists, air flow into the engine is severely restricted at high rpm. To increase air flow, and consequently high speed hp, there are two options open. Either the inlet port open period can be

TABLE 3.4   Rotary valve timing

Engine type	Capacity (cc)	Valve timing	Transfer closing
Arisco C-75 kart	100	155/43	124
BM K96-3 kart	100	115/60	123
BM FC-52 kart	100	115/60	120
Can-Am MX-6 bike	125	140/85	113
Can-Am MX-3 bike	250	140/85	125
Can-Am MX-6 bike	250	140/85	113
Can-Am Qualifier bike	175	137/75	113
Can-Am Qualifier bike	250	137/75	116
Can-Am Qualifier bike	350	137/75	116
DAP T81 kart	100	132/58	117
DAP-JM T71 kart	100	120/55	113.5
Komet K78 kart	100	132/60	118
Komet K78 TT kart	100	132/60	117
Morbidelli 125 bike	2×62	150/79	109
MZ 125 bike	125	135/70	112
Rotax 124 LC kart	125	120/87	113
Sirio ST50 kart	100	134/75	116.5
Sirio ST504 kart	100	135/65	120
Sirio ST52 kart	100	134/75	117.3
Zip ZED1 kart	100	140/66	121.5

Note: The first valve timing figure refers to the opening point in degrees before TDC and the second figure is the closing point after TDC. The transfer closing figure refers to the closing point in degrees before TDC.

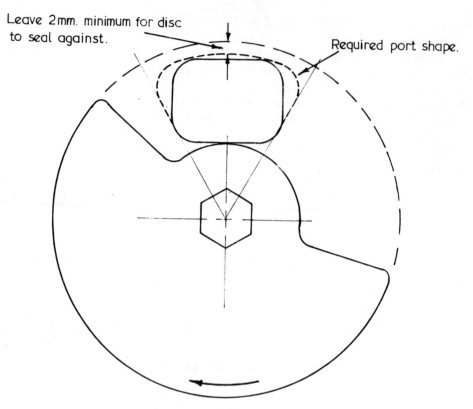

Leave 2mm. minimum for disc to seal against.

Required port shape.

Fig. 3.26 Modifying inlet port shape without affecting rotary valve timing.

increased, which will reduce mid-range power, or we can reprofile the inlet port and increase air flow in this way. Top end power will improve and often mid-range power rises too.

What we must do is change the shape of the inlet port, so as to encourage the mixture to turn up and over the crankwheel. In effect, the edge of the crankwheel has to become a part of the inlet tract floor, instead of a barrier at the end of a hole. In FIGURE 3.27 you can see the shape we have to aim for. The floor of the port is built up to blend into the crankwheel, and the lip formed by the port roof and the transfer cutout is radiused. The port can be built up using Devcon F aluminium epoxy. It contains 80% aluminium, is heat resistant to 250°F and is not attacked by petrol, methanol, oil or toluol.

Ideally, manufacturers should turn to the use of larger disc valves so that the inlet port floor could be in line with the top of the crankwheel. In this situation the fuel/air charge would flow straight into the crankcase unimpeded. In addition to this, there is another advantage in the use of large diameter discs, which is the primary reason for their existence on the works Minarelli and Morbidelli Grand Prix racers. When the rotary disc diameter is increased, there is a corresponding decrease in the duration angle actually taken up by the inlet port itself, assuming the inlet port width is not altered. This allows for a longer duration angle with the large disc without increasing the actual inlet port open period. The power output then goes up, because the inlet port

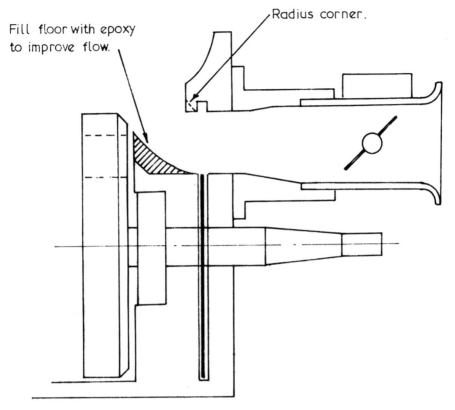

Fill floor with epoxy
to improve flow.

Radius corner.

Fig. 3.27   Modify inlet port to increase flow.

is fully open for a greater number of degrees, without being partially closed by the disc, or as the engine sees it for more time, so more air flows into the crankcase. Conversely, if the engine is already producing ample power at the top end of the rpm range, then the inlet open period can be reduced with the large diameter disc. In this way peak power will remain the same, but the mid-range to upper mid-range will rise appreciably.

Trying to get the sense of this is quite hard just using words, so I will help you to reason it out with an example and an illustration (FIGURE 3.28). As you can see, both engines have an inlet port 34mm wide and an inlet duration of 200°. The engine with the small 100mm diameter disc (engine A) has an inlet port and rotary disc which takes up 40° and 160° respectively of the 200° inlet cycle. On the other hand the inlet port and disc occupy 27° and 173° respectively when a 150mm disc (engine B) is used. This means that the inlet port is not obstructed in any way by the rotary valve for 120° (200 − [2 × 40] = 120°) in the case of engine A and for 146° (200 − [2 × 27] = 146°) for engine B. In other words the inlet port will be fully open for 26° or 22% longer. As regards time this represents 0.00166 sec. for engine A and 0.00203 sec. for engine B at 12,000rpm.

Before you modify the rotary valve to change either the inlet opening or closing points, it is a good idea to find out exactly what the standard timing is for your engine and then compare that with the manufacturer's specifications. At times there can be 57

Engine "A"

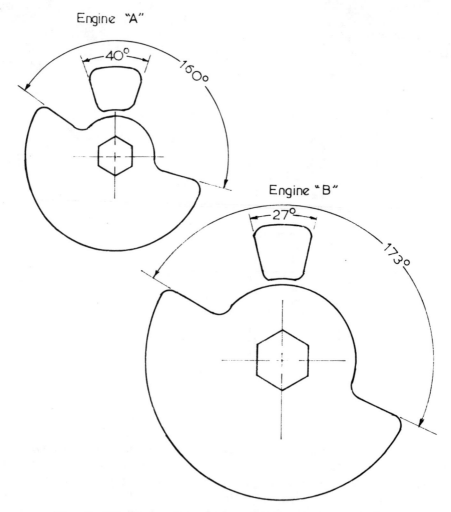

Fig. 3.28 Comparison of small & large rotary valves.

variations, because a keyway or master spline is cut slightly out or, in some engines, it is possible that the disc valve has been fitted one tooth out on the drive gear either during manufacture or when the engine has been repaired.

To check the valve timing you will require a 360° timing disc or, if you can't obtain one of these in your area, buy a large 200mm diameter protractor and drill a suitable size hole exactly in the centre so that it fits the end of the crankshaft. You will also need a good solid pointer which can be fixed under a stud in the crankcase. If you don't have a dial timing gauge to find TDC, then you will have to make a positive stop to prevent the piston rising to the top of its stroke. The best positive stop is one made out of an old Bosch spark plug and a length of 6mm mild steel rod. A Bosch plug is preferred as its insulator is very easy to remove. Under the hexagon shaped part of the plug shell you will see a groove running right the way around. Cut through this groove with a hacksaw and the insulator can be pulled out. Then weld a piece of rod into the plug shell, just long enough to stop the piston reaching TDC.

58

Using a dial gauge find TDC and rotate the timing disc to align the zero mark with the pointer. Lock the disc in place on the crank and again check that the pointer points to zero when the dial gauge indicates TDC. Then simply rotate the crankshaft in the normal direction of rotation, noting at what angle the inlet port opens and closes. When making this check it is necessary to shine a light down the inlet port so it can be clearly seen when the valve opens and closes.

Using a positive stop, the procedure is a little different. Rotate the engine in one direction until the piston contacts the stop. Note the angle and then rotate the crank in the opposite direction until the piston contacts the stop. Again note the angle. Midway between these two angles TDC is located. Let's say that there is 36° difference between the two angles. In this case TDC will be 18° (36÷2=18°) around from where the crankshaft is now stopped. Therefore loosen the timing disc and move it around until the pointer indicates 18° or 342° depending on which way the crankshaft is being rotated. Having done that, lock the timing disc in position and again rotate the crank one way and then the other until the piston contacts the stop. If in one direction the pointer indicates 342° and in the other direction it indicates 18°, you can be sure that the timing disc is locked onto the crank in the correct position. After this, remove the positive stop and make a note of the rotary valve's opening and closing angles.

Instead of using a degree wheel to physically determine the valve timing, it may be calculated mathematically using this formula if the engine has a Dykes ring fitted right at the top of the piston:-

$$A = \text{Cos}\left(\frac{T^2 + R^2 - L^2}{2 \times R \times T}\right)$$

where T = R+L+C−E
R = stroke divided by 2 in mm
L = con rod length in mm centre to centre (usually the stroke multiplied by 2)
C = deck clearance in mm (i.e., the distance the piston ring is below the top of the barrel at TDC)
E = distance from the top of the barrel to the piston ring at the instant of inlet opening or closing.

For example the inlet timing of the Rotax 124LC is as follows:

R = 27mm
L = 110mm
C = 1.8mm
E = 44.7mm (valve opening)
= 31.9mm (valve closing)
T = 27+110+1.8−44.7 (valve opening)
= 94.1
and T = 27+110+1.8−31.9 (valve closing)
= 106.9

continued over 59

$$\text{valve opening A} = \text{Cos}\left(\frac{T^2 + R^2 - L^2}{2 \times R \times T}\right)$$

$$= \text{Cos}\frac{(94.1^2 + 27^2 - 110^2)}{2 \times 27 \times 94.1}$$

$$= \text{Cos} \ .49518$$
$$= 119.7° \text{ before TDC}$$

$$\text{valve closing A} = \text{Cos}\frac{(106.9^2 + 27 - 110^2)}{2 \times 27 \times 106.9}$$

$$= \text{Cos} \ .00981$$
$$= 89.4° \text{ after TDC}$$

When you have the timing figures for your engine, check them against the manufacturer's figures. If the makers state that the valve opens 130° before TDC and closes 65° after TDC and yours opens 132° before TDC and closes 63° after TDC, then you know that the timing has been advanced 2° due to manufacturing errors. This will have the effect of slightly increasing mid-range power at the expense of a reduction at the top end. Obviously, if you are after more top end power, the first move should be to machine the disc to move the closing angle to 65° after TDC. If, after this, you want still more power at high engine speeds, move the closing point 2° at a time, but stop once you reach about 76°. Then go back and add 4° to the opening angle to bring it up to 136° and see how the engine responds. If the engine reacts favourably, but you are after still more power, move the opening angle another 4° to 140°. After this, you can go back to delaying the angle of closing in increments of 2° at a time. Normally, the only time that the valve characteristics would be altered to this extent would be when a motocross engine was modified for use in a road race go-kart.

If, after checking your timing against the maker's figures, you find that the disc valve has been retarded by, say, 6° and the bike is very 'pipey', coming onto the power with a sudden rush, then it is probable that the power curve can be improved by getting the inlet timing back to what the manufacturer originally intended. (A disc retarded by 6° would be indicated by manufacturer's figures of, say, 130°/65° and your figures being 124°/71°). The only way to cure a problem such as this, which fortunately occurs infrequently, is to relocate the rotary valve cover, moving it around 6° in the opposite direction to crankshaft rotation. To calculate how far the cover has to be rotated, first measure across the valve cover from the centre of one retaining screw to the screw opposite it. Say this dimension is 145mm. In this instance the cover will have to be rotated by 7.6mm which is calculated using this formula:-

$$X = \frac{D \times \pi \times A}{360}$$

where D = diameter across cover retaining screws

A = angle of timing error

In this example D = 145mm and A = 6°, therefore

$$X = \frac{145 \times \pi \times 6}{360}$$

$$= 7.6mm$$

The idea is to then drill a new set of fixing holes in the valve cover 7.6mm from the original hole centres. Having done this, refit the cover and check when the rotary valve opens and closes the port in the valve cover. Actually, the port timing figures should always be taken off the valve cover, never the crankcase port. If the timing is correct, it is advantageous to take the machine for a test run before you spend a lot of time matching the ports. Naturally, the engine will be down on top end power, but it is its 'pipeyness' which you are checking, not top end power. If the results are satisfactory then match the ports, filling one side with Devcon F as shown in FIGURE 3.29 and grinding the other side out.

It is not always necessary to relocate the rotary valve cover to correct valve timing errors. Some engines, for example those made by Rotax, have the rotary valve driven by a hub which is located on the crankshaft by a key. In the case of Rotax motors the hub is cut with 22 external gear teeth so moving the rotary valve one tooth on the hub will alter the timing by 16.4° (360° ÷ 22 = 16.4°) which isn't of much use to us. However, by machining a new keyway in the hub and by moving the valve around the appropriate number of teeth timing errors can be corrected.

For example, machining a new keyway 90° around from the original and moving the valve around by 5 or 6 teeth (depending on whether the timing is advanced or retarded) will correct an 8° timing error. That is quite an easy one to work out, but

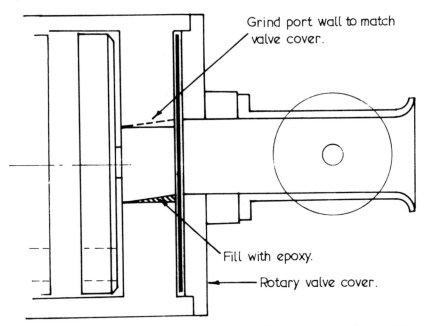

Grind port wall to match valve cover.

Fill with epoxy.

Rotary valve cover.

Fig. 3.29 Match inlet port after relocating rotary valve cover.

what if the timing is retarded by 6°? To calculate how many degrees around the new keyway has to be cut, add the angle of error to 90° and subtract 8°, which equals 88° (90° + 6° − 8° = 88°.) The new keyway will therefore have to be cut 88° around from the original, but will it be to the left (counter-clockwise) or right (clockwise) of the original? Since the valve is presently retarded it will have to be advanced to correct the timing error. The engine turns counter-clockwise so the new keyway will have to be machined 88° to the left of the original keyway, which will advance the hub by 88°. Retarding the rotary valve (i.e., moving it in the same direction as crank rotation) by 5 teeth will retard the timing by 82° (16.36° × 5 = 82°), consequently the timing will finish up being advanced by 6° (88° − 82° = 6°) from what the original timing figure was, which should be the figure specified by the manufacturer. You must be very careful that this type of work is carried out by only a top class machinist as it is exceedingly difficult to work to such fine tolerances in a bore as small as that found in the hub of a rotary valve.

To change the opening and closing points of the rotary valve disc proper is a little difficult, unless you make a special setting-up template of white cardboard or cartridge paper. In the centre of the template draw a cross (+) with lines about 150mm long intersecting at exactly 90°. Using the cross as the centre, draw a circle exactly the same diameter as the rotary valve disc. Carefully lay the rotary valve on the template within the confines of the circle which you just drew and using a sharp pencil draw the disc cut-out. (Be sure that the outside face of the disc is facing up.). Now draw another circle, using the cross as the centre, about 50mm larger in diameter than the rotary valve. After this, set a large (100mm or larger) protractor exactly on centre and note the angle of the disc's opening and closing points. Now carefully mark in the new opening or closing angle which you want. Draw a line from the centre through this point right out to the edge of the large circle. Lay the disc back onto the template, the correct way up, being careful to line it up within the boundary formed by the small circle and the original opening and closing lines. Now scribe a line across the disc exactly in line with the line you drew to show the new opening or closing angle. With that done, the disc can be modified to change the inlet timing.

The clearance between the valve cover and the rotary disc is very important. If the clearance is too tight, power is lost due to friction and, if the clearance is excessive, low speed and mid-range power is lost due to fuel/air charge leakage out past the valve. Unless otherwise specified, the clearance should normally be between 0.25mm and 0.35mm. If it is less than 0.25mm the face of the valve cover will have to be machined the appropriate amount. On the other hand, if the clearance is greater than 0.35mm the mating surface of the cover will require machining.

Reed valve induction was first introduced to the motorcycle world in 1972 when Yamaha released their range of 'Torque Induction' bikes (FIGURE 3.20). The reed valve functions as a simple check valve and prevents blow-back in the inlet tract. Therefore, a reed engine can be lugged down to very low rpm (depending on the exhaust timing), as the air flowing down the inlet tract is trapped once it passes the reed valve. Low speed cylinder filling improves and, because the air passes through the carburettor just once, the fuel/air ratio remains correct. This results in good low speed combustion.

Reed valve induction, however, is not entirely free of problems. Until very recently, the stiffness of the reed petals was severely compromised. To ensure good low speed crankcase filling, the reed petals must be thin and flexible so that they open easily and do not unduly restrict air flow. On the other hand the petals must be thick and stiff, otherwise crankcase filling at high speeds is not good. At high speeds thin, flexible petals flutter, allowing reverse flow out of the crankcase. They tend to close and then rebound from their seats due to inertia and/or resonance in the induction tract.

A dual reed assembly patented by Eyvind Boyensen reduces this compromise a considerable amount. The presence of a reed cage and petals in the induction tract still reduces high speed air flow below that possible with rotary valve or piston ported induction, but the difference is not so great as before. The Boyensen assembly comprises a thin 0.25mm reed, riding on top of a thicker 0.7mm reed. The thin reed opens easily under a low pressure drop and the thicker one takes over at higher rpm. This gives the benefits of good low speed air flow, as well as an absence of high speed petal flutter. As an added benefit, the ribs in the reed cage can be cut out when the Boyensen assembly is fitted, such is the design of the thick petal. This alone improves air flow and crankcase filling at higher speeds.

Over the years a lot has been said about the benefits of reed valve induction, but it seems that very few people realise the very high power outputs now being produced by motocross and enduro engines are not a direct result of reed valve induction. A lot seem to think that, because the piston is cut away, or has windows in it, allowing in some engines up to 360° inlet open period, this automatically results in a high power output. I can assure you that this is not so. In itself a reed valve improves low speed and mid-range power only, by preventing blow-back.

To give you some proof of why I say this, we will have a look at the effect of adding a reed valve to an old 250 Bultaco Matador. In standard tune the engine had exhaust, transfer and inlet open periods of 170°, 126° and 150° respectively. As shown in TABLE 3.5, the engine has a gentle power curve. It pulls very well at low speed and produces a maximum of 25.8 hp at 7000rpm. In test 2 a reed valve was added and four 16mm holes were drilled in the piston skirt, increasing the inlet timing to 360°. As you can see, there has been very little increase in power at the top end in spite of the fact that a 34mm Bing carburettor was fitted to replace the stock 32mm Amal. Note, too, that there has been only a marginal decrease in low speed power, due to the reed valve offsetting to some extent the bad effect the larger carburettor would have had at low rpm.

In test 3, however, you can see that power right through the range has risen by an average of 1.5 hp below 5500rpm, and by up to 3.1 hp between 6000 and 7000rpm. What brought about such a sudden power increase? In this test, two boost ports were added in the rear of the cylinder. The ports were cut with a 13mm cutter tilted at 30°. So it was the increase in transfer port area which picked up power significantly, not the addition of a reed valve.

In test 4, there was an increase in power above 6500rpm, but a decrease at lower speeds. For this test, a new piston was fitted which had 13mm removed from the bottom of the inlet skirt to give an inlet open period of 200°. This means that the piston exercises control over which direction transfer flow will take. In test 3, the boost ports are always connected with the crankcase (i.e., for 360°) but in test 4 the boost ports are isolated from the crankcase (see FIGURE 3.20) once the piston skirt drops below the level of the inlet port floor. Thus, any flow through the reed valve will be diverted up 63

TABLE 3.5   Effect of reed valve induction

rpm	Test 1 (hp)	Test 2 (hp)	Test 3 (hp)	Test 4 (hp)
3000	6.8	6.4	8.3	7.9
3500	7.9	8.1	10.9	10.4
4000	11.9	11.3	12.1	11.8
4500	14.2	13.6	14.8	14.6
5000	16.0	15.6	17.0	16.6
5500	18.1	18.0	19.7	19.3
6000	22.6	22.9	26.0	25.7
6500	23.3	24.9	27.2	27.1
7000	25.8	26.7	27.8	28.4
7500	25.6	25.1	26.3	27.6
8000	23.7	24.8	25.5	26.2
8500	18.1	20.6	22.1	22.8

Test 1 — *standard Bultaco Matador 250cc*

Test 2 — *reed valve assembly and 34mm Bing carburettor added; piston modified to give 360° inlet open period.*

Test 3 — *as above, with the addition of two boost ports in rear of cylinder.*

Test 4 — *as above but with piston modified to give 200° inlet open period. i.e., 'power ported'.*

through the boost ports once the piston closes the inlet tract off from the crankcase. With this arrangement, low speed power falls away, because the boost ports flow only if the exhaust pulses create a depression low enough to open the reed valve and pull fuel/air mixture up through the boost ports. However, at higher speeds, peak power is increased with this system, because the piston closes off the crankcase from the inlet tract, preventing back flow out of the crankcase as the piston descends to BDC. Without the effects of reverse flow to fight against, mixture will continue on flowing through the reed valve and up through the boost ports until cylinder pressure equals pressure in the inlet tract, causing the reed valve to close.

When this latter type of 'power porting' (i.e., test 4) is applied to more modern two-stroke engines, there is often little or no loss of low speed power because of larger transfer port areas being employed today. However, on some bikes the power curve can become very peaky, making the bike difficult to ride. This is why you will seldom see this arrangement employed on anything but small displacement motocross bikes and reed valve road race engines. Of course, with many engines there isn't much you can do to convert from the conventional type of boost porting to power porting, unless you can find a suitable piston from another engine which doesn't have windows in the skirt. However, with some engines, such as the Honda CR125R, it is possible to convert easily to power porting. These engines have two small passages, instead of piston skirt windows, which connect the inlet tract with the crankcase. If these boost passages are filled with an epoxy such as Devcon F, the inlet tract will be isolated from the crankcase when the piston skirt closes the inlet port allowing the engine to operate
64 as a power ported engine.

In TABLE 3.6 you can see the effect which such a modification had on a Honda CR125R equipped with a Mugen air cooled hot-up kit. As you can see, low speed power has not been affected by blocking up the two small crankcase feed passages. From 7500rpm up to maximum rpm, there is a steady power increase. Peak power is up 0.9 hp, but at higher speeds the power rise is more dramatic. It is up by 2.2 hp and 5.1 hp at 10,500rpm and 11,000rpm respectively, and at 11,500rpm the engine is still making 15.8 hp. I must point out that some of this high speed power increase also comes about due to changes in the transfer open period. When the cylinder was converted to power porting the auxiliary transfers were raised 0.8mm and the boost port was raised 1.2mm. These modifications probably accounted for about 50% of the power increase from 10,500rpm up. In both tests the engine was equipped with a 34mm Mikuni carburettor bored out to 35.3mm and a special expansion chamber was used. Without these additions, power above 10,500rpm would have been suppressed in both tests.

In 1976, Suzuki introduced us to a new type of reed valve system with the release of their 'A' series RM motocross bikes. The 'Power Reed Intake System', as it is called by Suzuki, or more commonly a case reed, is an attempt to combine good features of both reed induction and piston-ported induction (FIGURE 3.30). With the case reed system, both the reed valve and the action of the piston opening and closing the inlet port controls mixture flow into the crankcase. Even a very potent engine like the little RM125 has an inlet open period of only about 150°, which is very short when compared with the average 125 piston port engine employing 170° inlet duration. When a short inlet duration is used, there is very little blow back at low speeds, so

TABLE 3.6   Effect of power porting

| rpm | Standard boost porting | | Power porting | |
	hp	Torque (lb/ft)	hp	Torque (lb/ft)
3000	2.5	4.4	2.6	4.5
3500	3.0	4.5	3.9	5.8
4000	4.0	5.3	4.5	5.9
4500	4.8	5.6	5.0	5.8
5000	5.9	6.2	6.4	6.7
5500	6.7	6.4	7.1	6.8
6000	7.7	6.7	7.8	6.8
6500	8.9	7.2	8.5	6.9
7000	9.3	7.0	8.9	6.7
7500	10.4	7.3	11.3	7.9
8000	14.5	9.5	16.1	10.6
8500	18.0	11.1	18.3	11.3
9000	19.0	11.1	20.0	11.7
9500	21.3	11.8	22.1	12.2
10000	22.1	11.6	23.0	12.1
10500	20.8	10.4	23.0	11.5
11000	16.5	7.9	21.6	10.3
11500			15.8	7.2

Note: Inlet port open period was 230° with power porting.

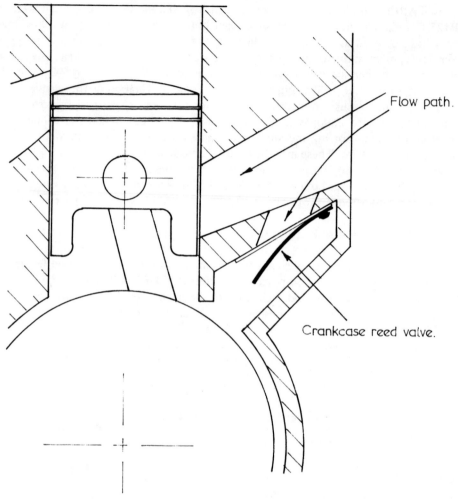

Fig. 3.30 Crankcase reed valve assembly.

throttle response and low speed running is good. As shown in FIGURE 3.31, the reed valve operates even at low rpm, ensuring good crankcase filling. Then at higher speeds the reed valve stays open until after the piston timed inlet tract has closed, ensuring good high speed hp.

What is the difference in performance between case reed induction and conventional reed induction? When I first saw the Suzuki system, I was convinced that it would enable much higher power outputs than a conventional reed engine, but since then I have been proved wrong. Even in road race go-kart applications, where the unobstructed inlet tract of the Suzuki should assist air flow, an engine like the YZ Yamaha with conventional reed induction will pick up one or two lengths on a Suzuki down the longer straights, or up hills. However, out of corners, the Suzuki will run all over a Yamaha, showing superior mid-range power. Of course the Suzuki case reed system was originally designed for motocross and later enduro bikes. It is in these applications where this type of induction is in its element. With fairly conservative

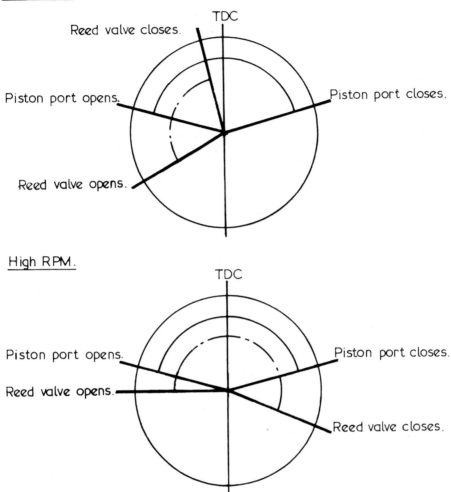

Low RPM.

TDC

Reed valve closes.

Piston port opens.

Piston port closes.

Reed valve opens.

High RPM.

TDC

Piston port opens.

Piston port closes.

Reed valve opens.

Reed valve closes.

Fig. 3 . 31 Crankcase reed valve opening/closing angles .

porting, the case reed engine will make the same power as a conventional reed engine, but in the mid-range it is much stronger and it delivers the power to the rear wheel more smoothly.

When you make a more careful examination of a case reed engine like the Suzuki (KTM and Rotax also use a case reed on some of their engines), you can see why it will not make as much power as a Yamaha or Honda in all-out applications like flat track racing or go-kart road racing. It highlights, once again, the importance of the transfer ports. With conventional reed engines the back transfer port, or boost port, can be made very large and, as it enters right into the inlet port and is free of obstruction, it flows well. Case reed engines have two tiny boost ports and, because the transfer passages which feed these ports enter at such a strange angle, directional control of the transfer streams is not good.

Regardless of the type of reed employed, the same basic principles apply for the modification of reed valve systems. Naturally, the entrance of the reed cage must be perfectly matched to the inlet manifold to ensure minimal air flow disruption. If the reed fixing screws protrude into the air stream, grind them off flush with the reed cage. However, if the screws are well below the surface, fill the holes with Devcon F. Be sure to put a drop of Loctite (blue grade) on the fixing screws each time that they are refitted.

Within the reed cage you will often find little steps and ridges which can be filed out. When you do this, be sure to leave a 1mm wide seat for the reed to seal against and, when you refit the reed petals, carefully line them up with the cage openings. Unfortunately, some manufacturers make the petal fixing holes so much larger than the diameter of the fixing screws that the petals can be fitted seating over an area 2mm wide on one side and barely covering the cage opening on the other side.

If you are not after a huge increase in high speed air flow, then I would recommend that you retain the standard reed cage and fit phenolic reed petals or, better still, a set of dual Boyensen petals. Phenolic petals wear out fairly quickly, which is why most bike manufacturers prefer stainless steel petals. However, phenolic petals respond to the air requirement of the engine more quickly and they do not flutter and rebound off the cage to the same extent as stainless steel petals. To increase the life of phenolic petals they should be carefully sanded around the edges, using 600 grit wet and dry carborundum paper, before being fitted. Some petals are smooth on one side only, so be sure to fit these with the smooth side sealing against the reed cage.

When a large increase in high rpm air flow is required, a larger reed valve assembly will be necessary. There are special assemblies available for some engines but often it will be necessary to adapt a reed valve from a larger, or more potent, engine. This can be quite frustrating, as you won't find many dealers with reed valves in their parts bins for you to inspect for size. The best way is to go to a motorcycle wrecker, cylinder in hand, and look through his range of reed valves. Don't look for a reed valve which will drop straight into the inlet tract of your cylinder, as it probably won't be much bigger than the standard assembly. Instead, look for a valve which is a little wider and perhaps a little higher than standard. The fixing holes probably will not line up with the holes in your cylinder, but that is not a great problem providing the wrecker has the inlet manifold which matches the reed valve. Check that the inlet manifold has a hole of the correct size to suit your carburettor; if it does, you are in business.

The next problem is enlarging the inlet cavity to suit the bigger reed cage. To accomplish this, you will have to use your judgement. Start by measuring the reed assembly and comparing its size with the reed cavity in the inlet port. If it's 4mm wider, then grind 2mm off each side of the cavity and so on.

When the reed valve fits the cavity, you can then decide what has to be done to fix the reed valve and manifold to the cylinder. If the fixing holes are close, then it may be possible to elongate the holes in the reed cage and manifold to align with the cylinder. In some cases, it will be a matter of filling the stud holes in the cylinder and then drilling and tapping new fixing holes. Probably the most extreme case is when the Yamaha RD350 or 400 is fitted with TZ 750 reeds. In this instance, an aluminium plate with fixing holes to suit the TZ reeds is welded to the RD cylinder face.

Before some special replacement reed assemblies are fitted, they have to be modified in ways different to that outlined on preceding pages. One such reed which comes to mind is the R & R Hi-Volume reed for RM and PE model Suzukis. This reed flows very well but it falls short in two areas, which could easily catch the unsuspecting tuner out. The first problem is that the screw heads on the lower side of the reed prevent the cage from seating properly against the base of the cylinder. Thus an air leak can develop and spoil engine performance. What must be done is file the edges of the screw heads flush with the cage mounting face, so that the cage can seal against the cylinder base. The other problem involves the reed stop for the main (i.e., bigger) reed petal. The stop is too flexible and actually rebounds the reed petal when it comes against the stop. This sends the petal into flutter and reduces high speed power. To cure this, the R & R stop should be removed and the standard Suzuki reed stop fitted. You will note that the Suzuki stop is much thicker, so longer fixing screws are required. If these are unobtainable, the holes in the stop can be countersunk to give the screws more bite.

Before we close the subject of reed valve induction, there are a couple of don'ts which you should keep in mind. Don't ever bend the reed stops to increase reed lift and don't ever fit a spacer under the stop to increase reed lift. Either practice will cause petal flutter at higher rpm, because the reed becomes unstable (i.e., out of control). On the average 125 motocrosser, increasing reed lift by just 0.7mm will knock 2 hp off the top end between 9000 and 10,500rpm.

The other don't is this: don't waste your time cutting the back out of the piston or enlarging the skirt windows. This weakens the piston and there is little or no gain in hp anywhere in the power range. The only exceptions to this rule would be in the case of desert racers, or bikes which are very pipey, if they don't have any holes high up on the piston skirt. Drilling a pair of round holes just below the ring land will help cool the piston crown and little end, or if the bike is very peaky and nothing else has tamed the push of power, maybe a pair of holes will help. The holes shouldn't be too large: 10 to 13mm is plenty big enough for a 125 or 175, and larger engines could use holes about 14 to 16mm in diameter. After the holes are drilled, carefully chamfer them on the inside and outside of the piston, then dress the holes with 180 grit wet and dry. These precautions will help prevent premature cracking of the piston skirt.

Chapter 4
The Exhaust

IT IS TRUE to say that the largest contribution towards achieving the current high power levels from the two-stroke engine has come from increasing knowledge in the area of exhaust system design. Originally, the exhaust pipe was designed to get burnt gases out of the engine as quickly as possible. Then, as designers learned more about pressure waves, they attempted to make use of them to scavenge the cylinder of exhaust gases.

The basic theory of pressure waves is quite easy to understand, but the practical application of pressure wave phenomenon is very difficult to formulate. Fortunately, the experimental work done by two-stroke engineers during the past twenty years has made the task of building an effective exhaust well within the grasp of any two-stroke engine tuner. This is not to imply that the first exhaust you fabricate will be perfect. The Japanese manufacturers, and in particular Yamaha and Suzuki, know as much as anyone about exhaust tuning, but you will find they are constantly updating the expansion chambers on both their works and production racers, proving they are still looking for the best design.

Understanding exhaust design begins with an appreciation of the behaviour of sonic waves travelling through a pipe. These waves travel at a speed determined by the temperature and pressure of the outflowing exhaust gas. This speed always equals the speed of sound, which averages around 1675ft. per second in hot exhaust gas.

Sonic waves have the strange property of being reflected back along the pipe they are travelling through, regardless of whether the pipe has an open or closed end. Even more peculiar is another fundamental law of acoustics which causes a pressure wave to invert its sign on reaching the open end of a pipe. A positive pressure wave, on reaching the pipe's open end, goes back up the pipe as a negative wave, and vice versa. Reflection from a pipe's closed end does not change sign, a positive wave stays positive.

The earliest exhausts were a piece of straight pipe, but these were not able to take full advantage of pulse waves to 'suck' exhaust gases out of the cylinder. In this type of system a positive pressure wave charged down the pipe immediately the exhaust port opened. On reaching the end of the pipe it was reflected as a negative wave, but with reduced intensity because much of its wave energy was lost to the surrounding atmosphere. However, some energy did remain and if, when the negative wave reached the exhaust port, the port was still open, it would assist in a small way in evacuating the cylinder. This being the case, the wave would turn round and travel back down the exhaust still negative, then, on reaching the open end of the pipe, be reflected up again as a positive pressure wave. If the exhaust was of the correct length, the positive wave should have arrived back at the exhaust port just before it closed, forcing any fuel/air mixture that had spilled into the exhaust back into the cylinder to be burned.

In theory it sounds good, but in practice the straight pipe exhaust never worked too well, primarily because so much kinetic energy was lost each time the sonic wave reached the open end of the exhaust pipe. A two-stroke engine requires strong pressure pulses to work efficiently, so engineers added a megaphone to the end of the straight pipe.

A megaphone, more correctly called a diffuser, is in effect a relatively efficient energy inverter. In a diffuser the walls diverge causing the sonic wave to react just as though it had reached the open end of the exhaust. However, the reflected wave retains most of its energy and can create a vacuum as low as 6 psi. Obviously a pulse wave of this magnitude can be very effective in drawing exhaust gas out of the cylinder, and in pulling the fresh charge from the crankcase up through the transfer ports.

The problem with this system is that much of the time the strong negative pulse wave will arrive at the wrong moment, and draw a considerable amount of fuel/air mixture into the exhaust. The exhaust port will close before the reflected positive wave arrives, to force the mixture back into the cylinder.

The next step was to add a reverse cone with a small outlet to the diffuser, and this proved to be the real break-through in two-stroke exhaust design. This type of exhaust is referred to as an expansion chamber. The addition of the reverse cone with a small bleed-off hole acts as a closed pipe, giving the exhaust a double pulse action. When the positive wave reaches the diffuser, part of the wave is inverted and reflected as a negative wave to evacuate the cylinder. However, part of this wave continues on to be reflected by the reverse cone. Because of the pressure buildup caused by the small bleed hole, the reverse cone acts like a closed pipe, reflecting the wave with the same positive sign. This strong positive pulse arrives just before the exhaust port closes, forcing any escaped mixture back into the cylinder, increasing power output and reducing fuel consumption.

On paper that theory, too, sounds very simple, but there is much more involved when we actually set about designing a system. Obviously the expansion chamber must be of the correct length to ensure the pulse waves are reflected to arrive at the exhaust port at the proper time.

The formula we use to determine the tuned length of the exhaust is:-

$$L = \frac{ED \times 42545}{rpm}$$

where L = tuned length in mm
   ED = exhaust duration in degrees
  rpm = engine speed exhaust is tuned to work best at

Assuming we had an engine with an exhaust duration of 196° and producing maximum power at 11,000rpm, the tuned length would be:

$$L = \frac{196 \times 42545}{11,000}$$

$$= 758mm$$

The length of 758mm is measured from the piston face to the assumed reflection point of the reverse cone. This point is half way along the cone but, because the top is cut from the cone, the point must be calculated mathematically. (FIGURE 4.1).

The first part of the expansion chamber, the header pipe, may be either a straight pipe with parallel walls, or a tapered pipe with diverging walls. A tapered header pipe is to be preferred, as it will improve the power and power range; however, it is much more difficult to fabricate than the straight pipe. For this reason, some designs utilise a parallel-wall header. Most go-kart headers, and also the Honda CR250R expansion chamber for example, have a non-diverging header pipe. (FIGURE 4.2).

The actual length required for the header pipe can only be determined accurately by testing. Over the years, I have devised and tried all kinds of formulae to calculate the length of the header, but I've never found one that works too well. It has been my experience that it is much quicker to make an educated guess and work from there.

In TABLE 4.1, I have set out what I consider to be a good starting point in working out the header pipe length. For example, if you are building a chamber for a road race 125 with an exhaust port inside diameter of 38mm and you intended to fabricate a multi-stage diffuser, then the header would be between 247mm and 285mm long. However, if you were to use a single stage diffuser, the header would be a little longer at 296 to 323mm. Usually, you will find the shorter length in both instances to be very close to what is required for best performance. Lengthening the header has the effect of increasing mid-range power at the expense of a drop in maximum hp.

It is important to note that the above rule for calculating the header length can work only if the exhaust port is of a standard diameter for that particular size of engine. If the engine has a port size outside that shown in TABLE 4.2, then it will be

TABLE 4.1   Calculating header pipe length

| | Multiplying Factor | | | |
| Cylinder size (cc) | Road race | | Motocross & Enduro | |
	single stage	multi-stage	single stage	multi-stage
50-80	8.5-9.5	8-9	10-11	8.5-9.5
100-125	7.8-8.5	6.5-7.5	7.8-8.5	6.5-7.5
175-250	7.3-8.3	6.5-7.5	9-10	8.2-9.2
350-500			8.5-9.5	7.5-8.5

Note: To calculate header pipe length multiply exhaust port diameter by the appropriate multiplying factor.
Single stage refers to a single stage diffuser.
Multi-stage refers to a multi-stage diffuser.

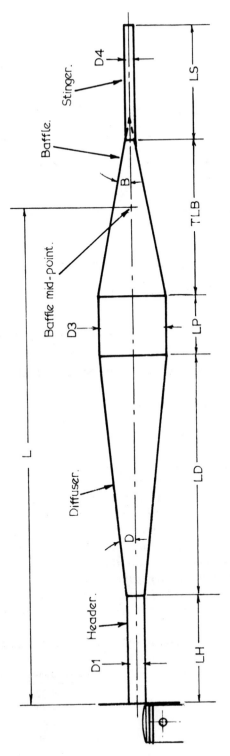

Fig. 4.1   Basic two stroke expansion chamber.

Hartman go-kart pipe.

All dimensions in mm.

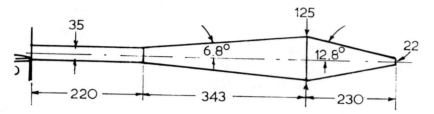

Yamaha MX360 pipe.

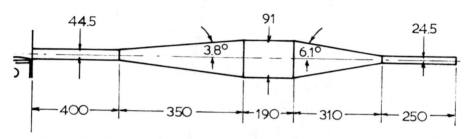

Fig. 4.2 Expansion chambers with parallel-wall header pipes.

necessary to work out the length based on a standard port diameter. Also, keep in mind that the calculated length of the header is the measurement from the piston to the end of the header pipe. Therefore, when you fabricate the pipe, remember to subtract the length of the exhaust port.

Over the past ten years the majority of manufactures have realised the benefits to be gained from a tapered-wall header and have gone over to this design. In the first instance it increases chamber volume, which effectively broadens the power range. Secondly, its diverging walls reduce flow resistance both in and out of the cylinder. The burnt gases flow out easily with a minimum of turbulence and any fuel mixture which has spilled into the exhaust is rammed back into the engine more efficiently. Thirdly, and this is the most important reason for the justification of tapered headers, the shallow taper allows the exhaust gas to expand and cool more gently. This results in less loss of kinetic pulse energy than if the gases were to expand rapidly and abruptly on passing from a straight header into the diffuser section of the expansion chamber. With

TABLE 4.2   Standard exhaust port diameter

Cylinder size (cc)	Port inside diameter (mm)
62-80	30-32
100	34-37
125	37-40
175	42-46
250	44-48
350-500	45-50

more pulse energy available, a stronger evacuation wave to scavenge the cylinder, and a stronger wave to ram spilled mixture back into the cylinder, is produced.

The taper of the header is normally between 1.15° and 1.5°. However, some manufacturers have used tapers as shallow as 0.8° and as steep as 2.3° in certain circumstances. If the diffuser taper is very shallow (i.e., 2.8° to 3.25°) then a 0.8° header taper is at times in order. Conversely, if the exhaust port and flange is very long (i.e., 75mm to 100mm) a steeper 1.7° to 2.3° header may be necessary. (FIGURE 4.3).

To work out the physical size of a diverging header pipe of a particular length and taper, we use this formula:-

$$D_2 = \left(\frac{LH \times 2}{Cot\ H}\right) + D_1$$

where D_2 = header pipe major inside diameter

D_1 = header pipe minor inside diameter

LH = header pipe length minus the length of the exhaust port and flange

$Cot\ H$ = cotangent of header pipe's angle of taper

We will assume our road racer has a cylinder volume of 125cc and an exhaust port and flange 70mm long by 40mm id. The total length of the header will be $(40 \times 6.5) - 70 = 190mm$. The taper of the pipe will be 1.5°, which has a cotangent of 38.19 (from TABLE 4.3)

$$\text{Therefore } D_2 = \left(\frac{190 \times 2}{38.19}\right) + 40$$

$$= 50mm$$

TABLE 4.3   Useful Cotangents

Angle	Cotangent	Angle	Cotangent	Angle	Cotangent
0.8	71.62	6	9.5144	11	5.1446
1	57.29	6.5	8.7769	11.5	4.9152
1.25	45.83	6.75	8.4526	12	4.7046
1.5	38.19	7	8.1443	12.5	4.5107
1.75	32.73	7.25	7.8712	13	4.3315
2	28.64	7.5	7.5958	13.5	4.1653
2.5	22.90	7.75	7.3498	14	4.0108
3	19.08	8	7.1154	15	3.7321
3.5	16.35	8.5	6.6912	16	3.4874
4	14.30	9	6.3138	17	3.2709
4.5	12.71	9.5	5.9758	18	3.0777
5	11.43	10	5.6713	19	2.9042
5.5	10.39	10.5	5.3955	20	2.7475

Yamaha TZ750C pipe.

All dimensions in mm.

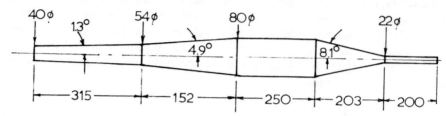

Morbidelli 125 production racer pipe.

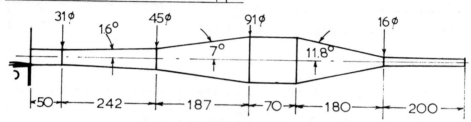

Fig. 4.3 Expansion chambers with tapered header.

The next stage of the expansion chamber, the diffuser, is, as we mentioned earlier, a wave inverter. The duration and intensity of the inverted return wave is determined by the diffuser taper. A shallow taper returns a wave of long duration and low intensity. This has the effect of cutting maximum power but, beneficially, it boosts mid-range power by allowing the expansion chamber to stay 'in tune' with the engine over a larger rpm band. (FIGURE 4.4).

Conversely, a steeply-tapered diffuser reflects a pulse of high intensity and short duration. Maximum power will be increased but at the expense of narrowing the power band. In applications such as road racing this may be acceptable if the machine has a close ratio 6-speed gearbox and the rider has the necessary riding skill to ride a bike with a narrow power range and a sudden rush of power.

In TABLE 4.4, you can see the sort of angles that I recommend for diffusers. Some people build expansion chambers with larger diffuser tapers, but I tend to value good mid-range power and a wide, easily managed power band much more than all-out power.

The length of the diffuser is determined by the diameter to which it expands, which should normally be 2.5 times the exhaust port diameter. If you have room on the bike, and you wish to experiment, you may be able to spread the power range by making the diffuser taper to 2.7 – 2.9 times the port diameter. This move will at times suppress maximum power, but the improvement lower down the scale usually compensates. On many bikes, it is difficult to find room for a large diameter exhaust, so you may have to be satisfied with a less than perfect chamber. Most bikes have trouble catering for an exhaust in excess of 110mm diameter, so this could restrict the diffuser outlet to something closer to 2.2 times the port diameter in bikes over 175cc.

Going back to our previous example, we calculate the diffuser size based on a 7° taper (i.e., 14° divergence) and 2.5 times the port diameter (i.e., 40mm × 2.5 = 100mm).

The formula is:-

$$L_D = \left(\frac{D_3 - D_2}{2}\right) \times \text{Cot } D$$

where L_D = diffuser length

D_3 = diffuser major inside diameter

D_2 = header pipe major inside diameter

Cot D = cotangent of the diffuser's angle of taper

Therefore $L_D = \left(\frac{100 - 50}{2}\right) \times 8.1443$

$$= 204\text{mm}$$

Today, instead of relying on a single taper diffuser, we are using multi-stage diffusers. Generally, a two or three section diffuser is utilised, although some tuners

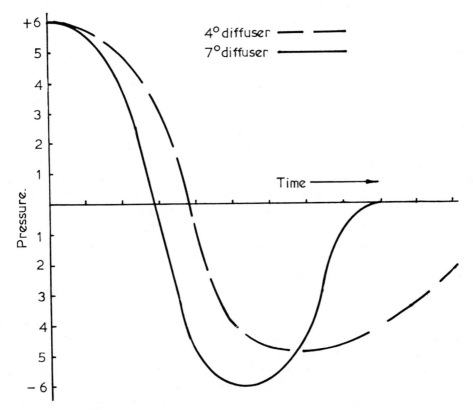

Fig. 4.4 Effect of diffuser taper on intensity & duration of return wave.

TABLE 4.4   Diffuser tapers

Diffuser angle (degrees)

Cylinder size (cc)	Road race			Motocross & Enduro	
	single stage	*two stage*	*three stage*	*single stage*	*two stage*
50-80	6.5 to 7	4.5 & 7	4 & 6 & 8	3 to 3.5	3 & 5
100-125	6.5 to 7.5	4.5 & 7.5	4.5 & 7 & 9	4 to 4.8	3.3 & 6
175	6.5 to 7.5	4.5 & 7	4.5 & 7 & 10	3.5 to 4.5	3.5 & 6
250	7 to 7.5	4.5 & 7	4.5 & 7 & 10	4 to 4.5	4 & 7
350-500				4 to 5	3.5 & 6

and manufacturers are turning to the use of four stage diffusers. For motocross and enduro bikes, I usually work with a two-stage diffuser as relatively shallow tapers are involved. Road race engines and 125 motocross engines with near road race porting require a three stage diffuser, due to the need for steeper angles of taper to pick up peak power.

A multi-section diffuser allows the exhaust gas to expand and cool more gradually, which means there is less loss of kinetic pulse energy than if the gases were allowed to expand more rapidly in a single taper diffuser. With extra pulse energy available, the expansion chamber can do a better job of scavenging exhaust gases out of the cylinder and drawing up the fresh fuel/air charge through the transfer ports.

In TABLE 4.4 you will note the diffuser angles which I have found to work well when multi-stage diffusers are utilised. For example, a twin cylinder road race 250 would use a diffuser with the first section tapering at 4.5°, the second section at 7° and the third section at 9°. Just how long each section should be is a secret most two-stroke tuners keep to themselves. However, I will tell you this: motocross and enduro bikes using a two-stage diffuser will usually require the first section to be 200 to 240mm long; road race bikes with a two-stage diffuser will usually require the first stage to be 140 to 160mm long and, with a three-stage diffuser, the first stage will be 110mm to 140mm long. If, after building an expansion chamber with a diffuser like this, you find that the engine is too peaky, then increase the length of the first stage of the diffuser. This will broaden the power band. Conversely, if the engine lacks peak power, decrease the length of the first diffuser section and lengthen the second stage. In FIGURE 4.5 you will note the diffuser designs which a variety of manufacturers are using.

The parallel belly section of the expansion chamber naturally has the same diameter as the diffuser outlet, but we cannot calculate its length until we have arrived at a suitable size for the rear baffle cone. After that, the mid-section fills the gap to give the chamber its correct tuned length.

As noted earlier, the baffle cone (or reverse cone) reflects a wave of like sign to stuff the fuel/air charge back into the cylinder. A flat plate could do the same job but the wave duration would be so short that this would only occur over a very narrow rpm range. A cone, on the other hand, extends the duration of the pressure pulse, although reducing its intensity. This serves to broaden the engine's useful power band.

Again, the actual taper of the baffle cone affects the pulse time/intensity factor just as in the case of the diffuser. A short, sharp baffle will increase maximum power, but the motor will lose out in the mid-range; also it will tend to cut dead at just a couple of hundred revs past maximum power rpm. A shallow taper baffle reduces top end

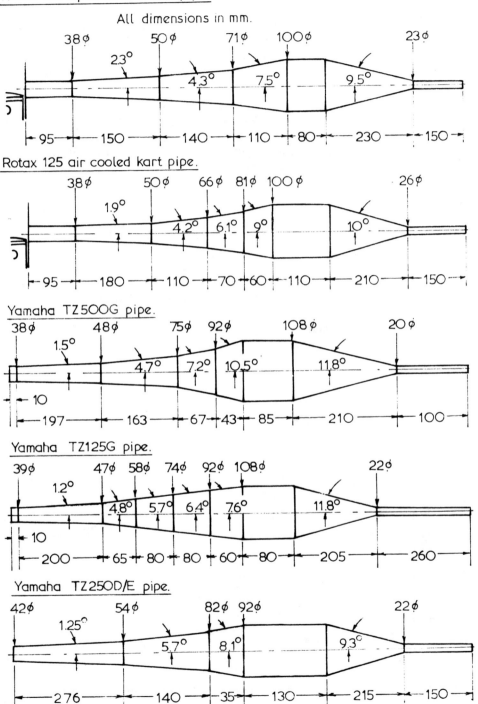

Rotax 125 liquid cooled kart pipe.

All dimensions in mm.

Rotax 125 air cooled kart pipe.

Yamaha TZ500G pipe.

Yamaha TZ125G pipe.

Yamaha TZ250D/E pipe.

Fig. 4.5 Expansion chambers with multi-stage diffusers.

power, but the engine will develop more power lower down the rpm range and it will rev on well past the maximum power engine speed. This broadens the engine's effective power range and means that the bike's speed down the main straight will be less affected by changing wind conditions during a race. If a head wind blows, the engine will have enough power below maximum to fight against it and, if a tail wind comes in, the shallow baffle will enable the engine to over-rev and pick up some more speed. (FIGURE 4.6).

TABLE 4.5 indicates the baffle cone tapers with which I prefer to work. These angles have proved to give a good power range without suppressing maximum hp excessively.

In our example, we will assume that an 11.5° baffle taper is used. The formula is:-

$$OL_B = \frac{D_3}{2} \times Cot\ B$$

where OL_B = overall length of baffle cone

D_3 = baffle major inside diameter

Cot B = cotangent of the baffle's angle of taper

Therefore $OL_B = \frac{100}{2} \times 4.9152$

= 246mm

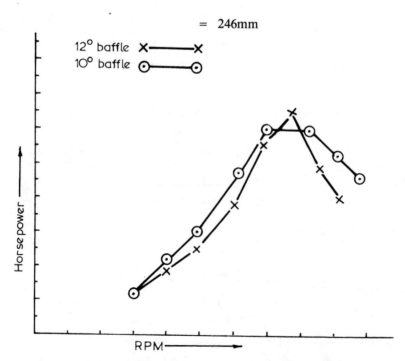

Fig. 4·6 Effect of baffle angle on horsepower output.

You will note that this calculation gives us the overall length of the cone, without allowing for a part of the top to be cut off where the stinger will be attached to bleed pressure from the chamber. By halving this figure, 246mm, we can determine the mean reflection point of the baffle and then go back and calculate how long the belly section has to be to give us the tuned length of 758mm which we originally worked out.

$$L_P = L - \left(L_H + L_D + \frac{OLB}{2}\right)$$

where $L_P =$ length of parallel section

$L =$ tuned length of chamber

$L_H =$ length of header pipe including the port

$L_D =$ length of diffuser

$OLB =$ overall length of baffle

Therefore $L_P = 758 - \left(260 + 204 + \frac{246}{2}\right)$

$$= 758 - 587$$
$$= 171mm$$

In an effort to broaden the power band on motocross bikes and small displacement road race bikes, tuners and manufacturers have been experimenting with two-stage baffles over the past few years (FIGURE 4.7). Unfortunately the results have not been as promising as expected. However, small gains have been made by some tuners working with 62cc and 125cc size cylinders. If you wish to do some experimentation along these lines, start out using a baffle which has the first stage tapering at 4.5° to 5.5° over a length of 70 to 90mm, and the second stage tapering at 12° to 14°.

The last section of the expansion chamber, called the 'stinger', is in reality a bleed pipe. Its function is to restrict gas flow out of the exhaust and create back pressure by slowly bleeding off exhaust gas. This serves to assist the positive pulse wave in pushing any spilled fuel/air charge back into the motor.

TABLE 4.5   Baffle tapers

| | Baffle angle | |
Cylinder size (cc)	*Road race*	*Motocross & Enduro*
50-80	10.5-12	8.5-9.5
100	10.5-12	9-10
125	9.5-12	8.5-10
175	10-12	8-10
250	10-12	7.5-10
350-500		9-11

Suzuki RM125B/C pipe.

All dimensions in mm.

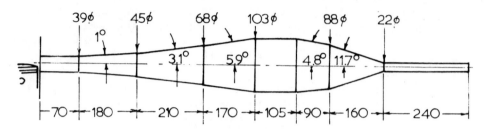

Fig. 4.7 Expansion chamber with multi-stage baffle.

TABLE 4.6 indicates the stinger dimensions which I have found to be most successful. You may find that a minor reduction in pipe diameter will raise the power output, but do be careful. A stinger pipe smaller in diameter or longer than specified could easily result in engine overheating and seizure. Therefore, I would suggest you make only small changes and then thoroughly test the pipe before going any smaller. Engine overheating, in its early stages, is indicated by the presence of oil burnt dark brown under the piston crown. On the next stage the burnt oil turns black, until finally 'death ash' appears. After this, the piston can be holed at any time.

TABLE 4.6   Stinger dimensions

Cylinder size (cc)	Stinger length (mm)	Inside dia. (mm)
50-80	205-230	17-19
100	230-250	19-21
125	265-290	22-24
175	270-295	25-27
250	280-305	26-28
350-500	285-310	27-29

Note: When using this table, first select an intermediate size in both length and diameter and work from there. Do not start with the smallest diameter and greatest length.
Most road race expansion chambers will require a stinger not more than 200mm long and of the smallest diameter indicated for each engine size.

All dimensions in mm.

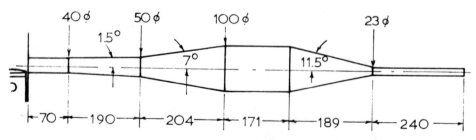

Fig. 4.8   125 road race expansion chamber.

In the example we have been using right the way through, we would select a stinger 23mm in diameter (id) and about 240mm long. The entire expansion chamber would look like that shown in FIGURE 4.8.

The addition of the stinger shortens the baffle cone; its final length can be calculated using the same formula as for the diffuser cone:

$$\text{Thus } TL_B = \left(\frac{D_3 - D_4}{2}\right) \times \text{Cot B}$$

where TL_B = true length of baffle cone

D_3 = diffuser major inside diameter

D_4 = stinger inside diameter

Cot B = cotangent of the baffle's angle of taper

$$\text{Therefore } TL_B = \left(\frac{100 - 23}{2}\right) \times 4.9152$$

$$= 189\text{mm}$$

To draw out the shape of either the diffuser or baffle cone on a piece of sheet metal is quite difficult. The cone's dimensions, when rolled out flat, can be worked out geometrically, or the sizes can be calculated mathematically. I prefer the latter method.

Assuming we were going to fabricate the baffle cone for this expansion chamber, we would calculate its size, before being rolled into a cone, in this way.

Looking at FIGURE 4.9, you will note we only know the inside diameter of the baffle's inlet and outlet, and its length through the centre. The next dimension we must calculate is the length of the cone when measured along the tapered wall, dimension AC. We use the formula:-

$$AC^2 = AB^2 + BC^2$$

where AB = 246mm

BC = 50mm (i.e., half the inside dia)

$$AC^2 = 246^2 + 50^2$$

$$AC = \sqrt{246^2 + 50^2}$$

$$= \sqrt{60516 + 2500}$$

$$= \sqrt{63016}$$

$$= 251\text{mm}$$

Now calculate the length of AC_1 using the same formula:-

$$AC_1{}^2 = AB_1{}^2 + B_1C_1{}^2$$

$$\text{where } AB_1 = 57\text{mm (i.e., } 246 - 189 = 57)$$

$$B_1C_1 = 11.5\text{mm (i.e., half the inside dia)}$$

$$\therefore AC_1{}^2 = 57^2 + 11.5^2$$

$$\therefore AC_1 = \sqrt{57^2 + 11.5^2}$$

$$= \sqrt{3249 + 132.25}$$

$$= \sqrt{3381.25}$$

$$= 58\text{mm}$$

The next calculations we make are to work out the circumference of the baffle cone's inlet using the formula:-

$$C = \pi d$$
$$\text{where } \pi = 3.1416$$
$$d = \text{diameter of baffle inlet or diffuser outlet}$$
$$C = \pi \times 100$$
$$= 314\text{mm}$$

The final calculation is worked on the formula:-

$$\theta = \frac{Arc}{r}$$

$$\text{where } r = \text{the dimension AC}$$
$$Arc = \text{C the circumference of the baffle inlet}$$
$$\text{or diffuser outlet}$$

$$r = 251\text{mm}$$
$$Arc = 314\text{mm}$$

$$\theta = \frac{Arc}{r}$$

$$= \frac{314}{251}$$

$$= 1.2510 \text{ radians}$$

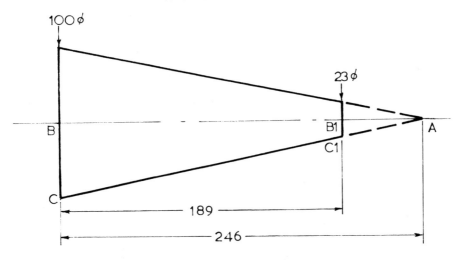

All dimensions in mm.

Fig. 4.9   Baffle dimensions.

The result, 1.2510, is in units called 'radians'. To be of any value to us we must convert it to an angle by multiplying by 57.3° (note 1.0 radians equals 57.3°). This gives the answer $\theta = 71.7°$.

The final check which we should make involves quite a simple calculation. We multiply the baffle cone (or diffuser) taper by $\pi \times 2$. In this example the baffle taper is 11.5° so the answer is 72.2°. If all of our calculations have been correct, this figure should be very similar to the angle θ, which we calculated to be 71.7°.

Now that all these calculations have been made, we have the dimensions and angles necessary to drawn the cone onto the piece of sheet metal from which the cone is to be cut. Actually, I recommend that you first make a template on a piece of stiff cardboard, and then transfer the shape to the sheet metal, as it is much easier to draw accurately on cardboard than on steel.

On your piece of cardboard, mark a cross (+) near one corner. Then adjust a pair of compasses to draw an arc, the radius of which will be equal to dimension AC, in this case 251mm. Using the cross as the centre, scribe the arc. Next adjust the pair of compasses to 58mm (dimension AC_1) and draw another arc, using the same centre (+) as previously. Then draw a straight line through the centre (+) approximately parallel with the edge of the cardboard. Position a protractor on the centre (+) and mark off the angle θ, calculated to be 72°. Draw a line from the centre through this point and you have the outline of the template. This is shown hatched in FIGURE 4.10.

Once you have a template you can go ahead and cut out the metal required for the baffle cone. (Note a similar series of calculations are required to get the diffuser cone, or tapered header pipe shape, drawn onto a template.). If you have not had any experience with sheet metal, then I would suggest that you take your templates to a sheet metal fabrication shop and get them to cut and roll the cones. When the cones are formed, you can weld all the pieces together, and you have your super home-made expansion chamber.

Actually, it is a little more difficult than that. Exhausts for go-karts, and single   85

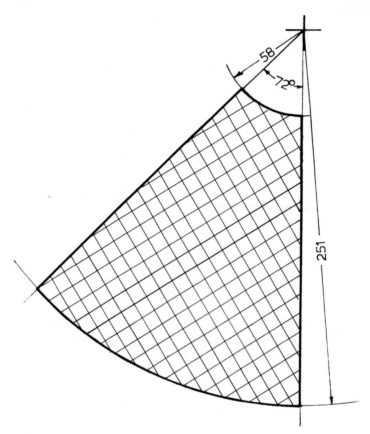

Fig. 4.10 Baffle template.

and twin cylinder road and road race bikes, are fairly straight forward, with the exception of the header pipe. Building a system for a motocross or enduro bike must be one of the worst forms of torture yet devised by man.

The main point to keep in mind, when you set about making the pipe fit, is to keep the header pipe entry into the diffuser cone smooth (FIGURE 4.11) and avoid the temptation to flatten the chamber anywhere. If the header entry is not smooth, gas flow out of the cylinder will suffer because any abrupt change in direction here, where gas velocity is very high, creates turbulence. Flattening the chamber doesn't upset gas flow, although the sonic pulse wave's effectiveness is reduced as any change in cross-sectional shape lowers the pulse's wave energy. Remember that an expansion chamber's basic function is to maintain and preserve the wave energy at a high level, so you will not want to do anything to cause a loss of this energy which is used to evacuate and recharge the cylinder.

While changes in cross-sectional shape affect pulse wave energy, abrupt bends or turns anywhere in the system do not. Sonic waves are willing to follow even the most tortuous curves without any reduction in pulse energy. Therefore, you can cut and resection the cones and parallel belly section to make the chamber fit your bike. The pulse waves will not know whether the system is straight, or bent all over the place.

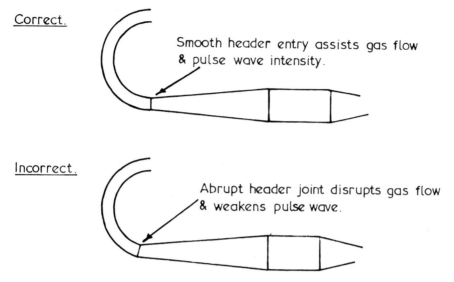

Fig. 4.11   Header joints must always be smooth.

There are two ways to cut and resection an expansion chamber to form a bend: the easy way and the right way. (FIGURE 4.12). When you cut a cone and reweld it the easy way, you will lose out in two ways. First, the length of the cone is reduced, altering the tuned length of the exhaust, and secondly wave energy will be lost as the exhaust gases will no longer be expanding at a progressive 7° (or whatever the cone taper is) along the inner wall of the cone.

The correct method to form a bend is to make the first cut right through the cone and then take the second cut only as far as the cone's centre. When the cone is resectioned, the piece which is cut out is welded into the outside of the bend. This technique keeps the length of the cone, through the centre, the same as it was when straight. There is still some change in the taper of the walls and in the cross-sectional dimensions, however, which will have a small effect on the pulse wave.

The next thing you must think seriously about is an effective muffler. I'm not too happy having to fit mufflers to a road racer, but this is what nearly all sanctioning bodies require. A muffler just adds more weight and knocks the edge off maximum power, also this requirement is just another example of discrimination against motorcycles. Racing cars are not required to be fitted with mufflers and yet bikes, running on the same road circuits and speedways, must be silenced.

On the other hand, I feel every effort should be made to silence motorcycles to a whisper when they are being used on public roads, on private and government land, deserts and reserves etc. The noise of two wheelers in these areas is upsetting a lot of people and driving wildlife back into more remote areas. This is bad for you and all other off-road riders, because every day a few more gates, which were previously always open to motorcyclists, will be closed and locked. If you want your freedom to ride in the places where you are currently permitted to ride, then you are going to have to make sure that the people who live around those areas are free of the noise of your motorcycle.

There are several choices open as to the type of silencer which can be fitted. A few   87

Correct.

Tuned length is not altered.

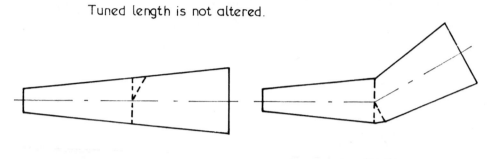

Incorrect.

Tuned length is shorter by this amount.

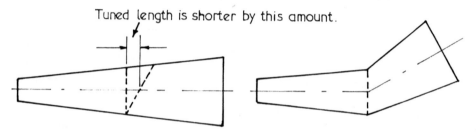

Fig. 4.12   Expansion chambers must be correctly cut & resectioned.

of the aftermarket mufflers are quite good, and relatively trouble-free, providing they are properly mounted to the bike. The Super Trapp is a particularly effective muffler, but I would suggest that you modify it in the same way Can-Am does on their motocross and enduro bikes. Instead of solidly bolting the front and rear sections together, Can-Am use four springs stretched over the silencing discs to hold the muffler together. This allows the silencing discs to work a little more effectively and slows down carbon build-up between the plates. Normally the Super Trapp is supplied with eight discs fitted, plus four spares which may be added if you want a little more power at the expense of more noise.

If you wish, you can make your own detachable muffler. It should be of similar dimensions to the one shown in FIGURE 4.13. To reduce weight and increase the silencing efficiency, consider fabricating a muffler from aluminium instead of steel tube. Steel tends to resonate more readily than aluminium and this reduces the effectiveness of a steel silencer. Riders operating very close to housing estates should seriously endeavour to reduce noise to the minimum by making their muffler double walled. Sliding another piece of tube over the muffler reduces resonance from the inner wall, hence less noise is emitted from the body of the muffler.

Mufflers for road race bikes and karts are best fabricated as part of the expansion chamber. (FIGURE 4.14). As the allowable noise level is reasonably high, usually around 96 dbA, this type of silencer does not have to be so elaborate. Preferably, the main body of the silencer should be 16 gauge aluminium.

Whatever type of silencer you choose to use, make sure that it can be easily

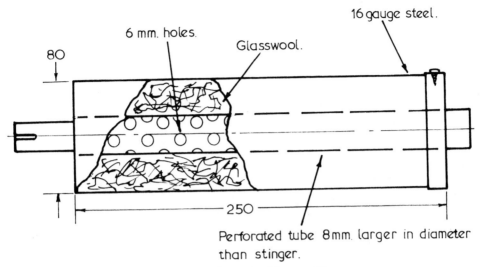

Fig. 4.13   Detachable muffler.

dismantled. Then, when the fiberglass sound-absorbing material is choked with oil and carbon, it can be easily replaced with new fiberglass to restore the muffler to its original silencing capacity.

It is not of much use if your exhaust has a good quiet muffler, but the expansion chamber is cracked and almost falling off because of incorrect mounting. FIGURE 4.15 shows the mounting arrangements that it is advisable to use. You will note in both instances, where the exhaust is attached to the machine by welded brackets, the large area over which the load is supported. This reduces the possibility of the chamber or the bracket cracking. If the mount does start to crack, a length of 6mm rod can be welded into the corners where the mount angles away abruptly from the chamber.

The third method of mounting is the system used by most go-karters. A saddle is fabricated out of fairly heavy steel, usually 4mm thick by 13mm wide, to support the chamber, which is held in place by two springs.

The exhaust flange and joint is also a mount of a kind, as well as being a gas and water-tight connection. Usually, the header pipe is secured to the exhaust flange by either a system of springs or a large flange nut. Whatever method is used, make sure the header pipe will not slip out of the flange in the middle of a race. This means if a flange nut is the method of attachment, it must be tight and properly prevented from loosening by the attachment of two springs from the header pipe to the nut as is done on the older Bultacos.

Most two-strokes use a flexible slip joint connection with the header pipe held into the exhaust flange by two or three springs. The thing to watch here is that the header and flange should overlap by at least 25mm. This reduces exhaust leakage and makes it much harder for the header pipe to jump out of the flange.

FIGURE 4.16 illustrates the two most common types of flexible slip joints. The simpler joint is used by the majority of motorcycle manufacturers for economic reasons. As you can see, if the exhaust port is made the correct diameter, the header pipe is too large, or if the manufacturer makes the header pipe the correct size, the exhaust port ends up too small. The joint I prefer is more complicated and can make 89

Low restriction muffler.

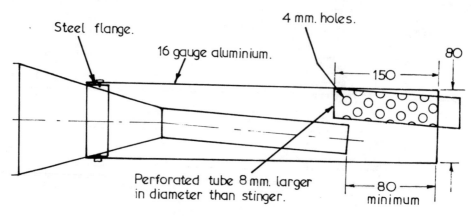

Low noise muffler.

The basic construction is similar to the low restriction muffler except the perforated tube is packed with glasswool.

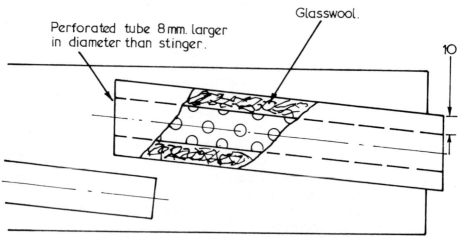

Fig. 4.14   Road race mufflers.

the expansion chamber difficult to get on and off the bike, but it does keep the port and header pipe sizes matched and it reduces leakage at the joint to a minimum.

Many people don't worry too much about exhaust flange leakage, yet every effort should be made to prevent this, as any leakage reduces the pressure in the chamber, upsetting sonic wave speed and changing the tuned length of the system. If the leak is serious enough, the chamber will cease to evacuate the cylinder properly. Instead, the suction pulse wave draws air into the chamber through the leaky joint. Then the pressure wave will push this air up the exhaust port, and into the cylinder. The fuel/air ratio is upset, power is lost and, in severe cases, piston burning and seizure is the end product.

If you are an off-road rider, you don't want an exhaust flange leak for another 90 reason. A leak that gas can find its way through will also often allow water through

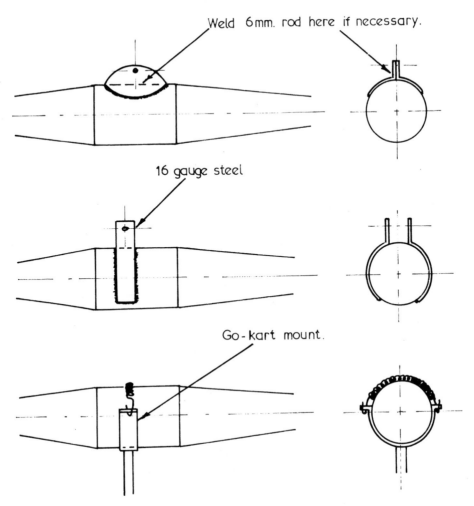

Fig. 4.15 Suitable expansion chamber mounts.

too. Every off roader, sooner or later, stalls or bogs in a creek, and when this occurs you don't want water to seep into the motor to worsen the situation in which you find yourself.

All exhaust flanges leak to some degree, but slip joint flanges appear to be the worst, until carbon begins to build up and seal the joint. Unfortunately, racing engines have the barrels and chambers removed too frequently for the carbon to seal properly, so it is necessary to use some sort of exhaust putty to stop leakage. I use Silastic RTV silicone to seal all exhaust joints.

Two-stroke exhausts are not a fit-and-forget proposition, as they require fairly frequent maintenance to clean out carbon build-up. Depending on the shape of the system, a layer of carbon 1-2mm thick may form in the header pipe after just a few race meetings and the diffuser and baffle cones usually get a good coat of oily goo at the same time. The carbon and gum deposits upset gas flow by constricting the internal dimensions of the header pipe and by creating turbulence in the system. These effects adversely alter performance, therefore the system must be regularly cleaned out.   91

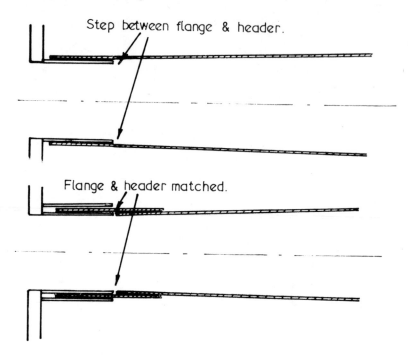

Fig. 4.16 Slip-joint header connections.

Some people use a hot caustic soda solution to scour the chamber internally, but I feel the most effective method is to burn the system clean with either an oxy-acetylene or propane gas torch. This may be done by heating the outside of the system to a red heat and occasionally directing the flame down the header pipe to ignite any oil gum present. If the chamber is made of 16 or 18 gauge steel, it is an idea to tap the chamber quite vigorously with a piece of broom handle as this will help free the carbon clinging to the walls. Wait until the chamber cools a little before you do any banging, otherwise the walls could easily be deformed.

Chambers made of 20 or 22 gauge material are much more difficult to clean, as the heating will often cause the chamber walls to deform slightly, and banging with a stick while the chamber is still hot, to loosen baked on carbon, is definitely out. About all you can do is not use an intense flame, but wait until the chamber is quite cool before attempting to free the burned carbon ash. You can tap the chamber lightly with a rod or you can throw a few rough stones or a short length of chain inside and give it a good shake.

There is something you should remember, and that is to give your exhaust a burn-out in a well ventilated area, and preferably outside your shed. The oil in the chamber gives off foul fumes, which will soon have your eyes watering and your throat hurting, so be warned.

The other part of exhaust maintenance involves a careful inspection for any sign of cracks. These usually appear in the mounting bracket proper, or around where the brackets are welded to the main body of the chamber. Chambers constructed of very light gauge material will often crack along seams in the parallel belly section, as this section tends to pulse in harmony with the system's sonic waves.

Chapter 5
Carburation

THE BASIC requirement for any carburettor is that it meters the fuel and air in such proportions as to be easily combustible and hence enable the engine to produce good power over a wide rpm band. Usually, the mixture we want is around 1:12 or 1:13, i.e., one pound of petrol (gasoline) for every twelve or thirteen pounds of air. Such a blend is just right for full throttle operation, but for other conditions, such as starting or light load operation, the fuel-air requirement is different (TABLE 5.1). Therefore, the carburettor has to 'sense' the engine's operating conditions accurately and adjust the fuel-air mix accordingly. If the carburettor is not able to do this, flat spots and engine surging will result, spoiling performance. For this reason we have to be very selective as to the type and size of carburettor we choose for our particular engine.

To understand more fully what we should be looking for in a carburettor to suit our engine's requirements, we need to go back to basics and get to know how a carburettor works. Nearly all two-stroke carburettors are a slide throttle type employing a fuel inlet system, an idle system and a main running system.

The inlet system consists of the fuel bowl, float and needle valve (or needle and seat). The fuel, before passing to the metering systems, is stored in the fuel bowl, and it is maintained at the correct level by the float and needle valve.

If the fuel is not at the correct level in the fuel bowl, the fuel metering systems will

TABLE 5.1   Fuel/air requirements

Running condition	Mixing ratio (by weight) Fuel : Air
Starting	1 : 1-3
Idling	1 : 8-10
Low speed running	1 : 10-13
Light load ordinary running	1 : 14-16
Heavy load running	1 : 12-14

not be able to mix the fuel and air in the correct proportions, particularly when accelerating, cornering and braking. A high fuel level will richen the mixture, causing excessive fuel consumption and poor running. On the other hand, a low fuel level can be even more serious due to the leaning effect it has. This may result in flat spots when accelerating out of turns, or, in extreme cases, the engine could overheat and seize.

A high fuel level may be due to an incorrectly adjusted float, or a needle and seat which is not seating properly and shutting off the fuel when the float rises to the correct level. This can be caused by excessive wear to the needle and/or seat, or by a speck of dirt which may prevent the needle closing fully.

A low fuel level condition may also be the result of an improperly adjusted float, but it could be due to the fuel lines or the needle and seat being too small to flow sufficient fuel to keep the fuel bowl full.

The fuel bowl is always vented so that the fuel is being mixed according to the outside air pressure. Without a vent, accurate metering would not be possible, as fuel vapours would build up pressure in the bowl and displace fuel out through the main and idle metering circuits.

The float is usually made of brass stampings soldered together into an airtight assembly, but it may also be formed from plastic or a closed cellular material. Brass floats are resistant to all types of fuel except nitromethane, and generally plastic or cellular floats are not damaged by most common fuels. However, if you intend to use a fuel other than petrol or methanol, it is wise to check with the carburettor manufacturer regarding possible float damage.

The needle and seat is usually made of steel, although some needles may have a Viton coating on the tip. The Viton promotes excellent sealing and acts as a shock damper, but it should not be used with fuels containing any alcohol or nitro.

The needle valve controls the flow of fuel into the bowl, so some thought must be given to increasing its flow capabilities if an alcohol fuel is being used. Generally, it is not possible to obtain larger needle and seat assemblies for this purpose, so it will be necessary to modify the seat by very carefully drilling the fuel discharge holes oversize. I would recommend you use a pin vice to hold the drill when you do this.

The idle system provides a rich mixture at idle and low speeds when not enough air is being drawn through the carburettor to cause the main system to operate. (FIGURE 5.1).

When the throttle slide is nearly closed, the restriction to air flow causes a high vacuum on the engine side of the throttle slide. This high vacuum provides the pressure differential necessary for the idle system to operate. The normal air pressure (14.7 psi) acts on the fuel in the float bowl, forcing it up through the idle jet and into the air stream.

To emulsify the fuel as it passes through the idle jet (pilot jet), and to provide a fine adjustment of the idle mixture strength, an air bleed circuit and an air adjustment screw is incorporated in the idle system. Turning the air screw out (anti-clockwise) decreases the air bleed restriction and leans the idle mixture. Conversely, turning the screw clockwise richens the mixture by reducing the amount of air passing through the air bleed circuit.

Many carburettors have the two hole type idle system illustrated in FIGURE 5.1, which gives better low speed and mid-range throttle response than the simpler one hole type. At very small throttle openings, the by-pass hole, and not the pilot hole, actually

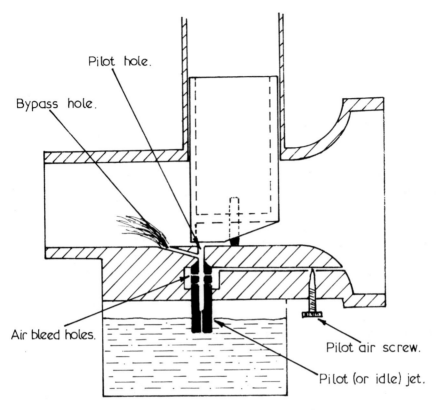

Pilot hole.

Bypass hole.

Air bleed holes.

Pilot air screw.

Pilot (or idle) jet.

Fig. 5.1   Idle system operation.

provides the engine with fuel. Instead, the pilot hole acts as a supplementary air bleed to further atomise the fuel after it passes through the idle jet. Then as the throttle opens wider the pilot hole, too, begins to spray fuel. This serves to supply the engine with additional fuel until the air speed through the carburettor increases sufficiently to start the main system flowing fuel into the air stream.

As the throttle is opened wider and engine speed rises, so the air speed through the carburettor increases, bringing the main fuel delivery system into operation (FIGURE 5.2). If a carburettor of the correct size has been selected, this should happen at about quarter throttle as the idle circuit reaches the limit of its fuel flow capability at that time. A serious flat spot would result if the main system was not operational and supplying the additional fuel required to prevent a lean mixture.

In the two-stroke engine, a partial vacuum is created in the crankcase by the upward movement of the piston. Because atmospheric pressure is higher than the pressure in the crankcase, air rushes in through the carburettor to equalise the pressure difference. On its way into the crankcase, the air has to speed up as it passes through the carburettor bore. This speeding up of the air reduces the pressure below atmospheric inside the carburettor bore, allowing normal atmospheric pressure (14.7 psi) to force fuel up through the main jet and past the needle into the air stream. The pressure differential existing here is often referred to as the 'signal' of the main metering system, because it starts and stops fuel flow.

95

No fuel discharges from the main metering system until air flow through the carburettor produces a pressure drop or signal of sufficient intensity for the atmospheric pressure, acting on the fuel in the fuel bowl, to push fuel up through the main jet and past the metering needle to be discharged into the air stream. Pressure drop (or vacuum) within the carburettor varies with the engine speed and throttle opening. Wide open throttle and peak rpm give the highest air flow, and consequently the highest pressure difference between the fuel bowl and the needle jet's discharge orifice. This, in turn, produces the highest rate of fuel flow into the engine.

To compensate for various engine displacements and engine operational speeds, a range of carburettors with a variety of bore diameters are available to create the pressure drop necessary to bring the main fuel circuit into operation. A small carburettor will provide a higher pressure difference, at any given rpm and throttle opening, than a larger carburettor, assuming engine size is the same. This is a very important aspect of carburation, which partly explains why the biggest is seldom the best. If the signal being applied is too weak (due to the bore diameter being excessively large), this could delay fuel discharge in the main system, causing a flat spot due to excessive mixture leanness. Also, fuel atomisation will not be good at any engine speed. Poor atomisation spells poor combustion and reduced horsepower, so, if you must err when selecting a carburettor, err on the small side, as the effect on performance will be far less devastating.

In the main fuel system, metering is controlled by the main jet, the needle jet and the needle.

The main jet controls fuel flow from the fuel bowl into the needle jet. An increase in the main jet diameter richens the mixture, but there are other aspects worthy of consideration. The shape of the jet entry and exit, as well as the bore finish, also affect fuel flow. Carburettor manufacturers measure the flow of every jet, and then number the jet according to its flow characteristics, not according to the nominal bore diameter. For this reason, jets used to meter petrol should not be drilled to increase their size if you desire accurate fuel metering. An engine burning alcohol does not require such accurate metering, unless fuel consumption is a consideration, so jet drilling may be in order when large jets are not available.

In the case of Mikuni carburettors in particular, there is another problem. Due to its popularity, outsiders are manufacturing main jets to suit these carburettors but, unfortunately, many of the jets fall far below the level of quality and flow parity of the genuine Mikuni item. I have seen many jets improperly drilled. Some had deep spiral grooves in the bore, others had steps and tapers in the bore. When jets like that pass through quality control undetected, then obviously their flow checking must be either non-existent or at best haphazard, so I would suggest that you use only genuine jets from the carburettor manufacturer.

At most throttle openings, the volume of fuel introduced into the air stream is controlled primarily by the taper of the needle and the diameter of the needle jet. As illustrated in FIGURE 5.2, it is the clearance between the needle and needle jet which regulates fuel flow between quarter and three quarters throttle, although the main jet does have some influence. Above three quarter throttle the main jet mainly controls fuel metering, but the needle/needle jet does exercise partial control.

To assist in atomisation and high speed fuel flow metering, many carburettors also incorporate an air bleed circuit in the main metering system. The air bleed aids fuel

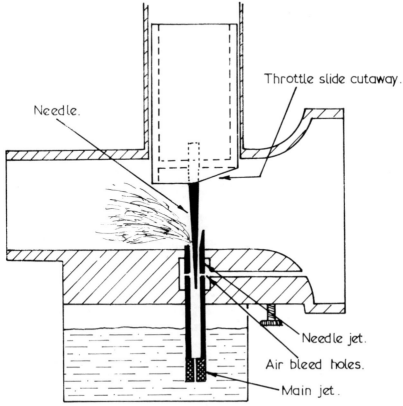

Fig. 5.2 Main metering system operation.

vaporisation by introducing air into the fuel before it enters the air stream. When the fuel is thus broken down into smaller particles, combustion speeds up because there is more fuel surface area exposed to the combustion flame.

The air bleed also acts as a compensator or air corrector in adjusting high speed fuel flow requirements. Uncorrected, the carburettor would deliver a fuel/air mixture which would become richer as air speed through the carburettor increased. The reason for this is that the pressure drop in the carburettor is in direct proportion to the air speed through its bore and, in turn, fuel flow is in direct proportion to the pressure drop thus created. However, the actual mass of air passing into the engine does not remain in proportion with air speed, so the mixture strength would become excessively rich with increases in air speed through the carburettor if uncorrected.

Fuel flow, in both the idle and main circuits, is also influenced by the throttle slide cutaway size at throttle openings between one eighth and half throttle (FIGURE 5.3). Increasing the cutaway size reduces airflow resistance and leans the mixture. This occurs because air flow into the engine is greater (due to reduced air flow resistance) but fuel flow does not increase proportionately, as the larger cutaway reduces the pressure drop within the carburettor bore.

The Mikuni Powerjet carburettor is still rather new to road racing motorcycles (although Yamaha have been using them since 1976), being originally designed for snowmobile racing engines. These carburettors have, in addition to the normal 97

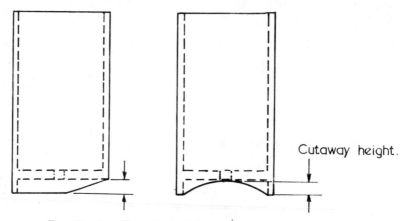

Fig. 5 . 3   Throttle slide cutaway size.

metering systems, another separate system with its own power jet and delivery tube, hence the name Powerjet. The delivery tube hangs in the air intake, in front of the throttle slide, and is connected through a metering orifice to the float bowl. Up to almost full throttle, the Powerjet carb operates just like any other Mikuni but, as full throttle is approached, the air moving past the tip of the Powerjet delivery tube creates a depression great enough to allow atmospheric pressure to push fuel through the power metering jet and up the delivery tube into the airstream.

The Powerjet therefore has the effect of enriching the mixture at full, and close to full throttle, and then only when air velocity is high enough to create a vacuum of sufficient intensity to discharge fuel. It is, in effect, a load sensitive enrichment system which allows for more accurate (i.e., leaner) fuel metering at part-throttle operation. This ensures clean acceleration and smooth running out of turns, yet gives proper full throttle mixture richness for high power and effective engine cooling. The effect is an improvement in part-throttle performance and reduced fuel consumption. Additionally, some two-strokes have a tendency to lean out as they pass beyond full power rpm with conventional carburettors, but the Powerjet Mikuni is able to cure this. Normally, when a Powerjet carburettor is used, the main jet size will be around 70-100 smaller, depending on the size of the power jet fitted to the carburettor. (TABLES 5.2a & 5.2b).

Having discussed the way a carburettor works, it should be obvious that not all carburettors are suitable for high performance applications. Some are just too small; others do not have jets and needles that are readily obtainable; some have metering systems which allow acceptable performance on stock machines, but are too crude to provide the correct fuel/air mixture in a racing engine; and others have totally inadequate float/needle valve systems, so that flooding, hard starting and poor running is always a problem. For these reasons I limit myself to the use of Mikuni carburettors. Of course there are other good carburettors around, but I have found Mikunis to be the most easily obtainable, and there is no problem finding suitable needles and jets etc. There is no point in using a carburettor that can't be properly tuned due to the non-availability of alternative needles and jets.

Obviously the choice is yours when it comes to selecting a carburettor, but do give heed to my advice regarding the size to use. Always remember that the carburettor

TABLE 5.2a   Mikuni powerjet jetting comparison for Yamaha IT175

	Yamaha IT175F	Yamaha IT175G
Carburettor	34mm	32mm Powerjet
Main jet	360	210
Power jet		82.5
Needle	6F21	6F21
Needle jet	P-8	P-8
Cutaway	2.0	2.0
Pilot jet	70	60

TABLE 5.2b   Mikuni powerjet jetting comparison for Yamaha TZ250

	Yamaha TZ250D/E	Yamaha TZ250G
Carburettor	34mm	34mm Powerjet
Main jet	320 to 360	230 to 270
Power jet		60 to 80
Needle	6F9	6DH3
Needle jet	0-2	N-8
Cutaway	2.5	2.0
Pilot jet	70	60

meters the fuel according to the signal being received in the fuel bowl. A carburettor too large for the engine produces a weak signal, consequently the metering system cannot function correctly.

To illustrate this, you might like to try a simple experiment. Fill a container with water and draw the water up through a drinking straw and then through a piece of ¼in hose. Did you notice how much more sucking you had to do to get the water flowing up the piece of hose? That very same principle applies to fuel flow through a carburettor's metering system. The small carburettor being sucked on by the engine (like you sucking on the straw) gets the fuel responding quickly to the requirements of the engine.

The other advantage of using a carburettor of the right size is this: a high air velocity through the bore lowers the air pressure (i.e., creates a partial vacuum), which makes the fuel more volatile and easily vaporised. You probably already know that water will change from liquid to gas (steam) at a lower temperature on the top of a mountain than at sea level, because the air pressure is lower. Likewise, with petrol, vaporisation improves with a decrease in air pressure. Additionally, the high air speed in itself assists in breaking up the fuel and vaporising it. Properly atomised fuel blends more evenly with air filling the cylinder and power goes up due to the improved combustion which results.

In TABLE 5.3, you can see what size Mikuni carburettors are recommended for various applications. If you are using another brand of carburettor then you will have to do some experimenting, generally with carburettors a couple of millimetres smaller. Many carburettors, size for size, flow more air than a Mikuni, but their metering circuits are not so sophisticated, hence the need for a smaller size.

Generally speaking, less experienced riders and all those operating moderately modified engines would use the smaller size carburettors listed for each engine size and 99

TABLE 5.3   Recommended Mikuni carburettor sizes

| Cylinder size (cc) | Carburettor size (mm) | | |
	Enduro	*Motocross*	*Road race*
50-62			27-29
80		27-29	29-32
100		30-32	32-34
125	30-32	33-36	35-38
175	33-35		35-38
250	36	37-40	40-42
350-500	36-38	38-42	40-44

application. Rotary valve engines, radically modified engines, and more experienced riders, could use the larger size carburettors. The increase in maximum power will not be very great (maybe 1 hp), but the engine will rev perhaps 500-800 rpm harder with the larger carburettor before falling off the power band.

Looking through the table, you will note some odd carburettor sizes. You cannot buy a 35mm Mikuni for instance; but you can bore a 34mm carburettor out to 35mm. In fact, you can save yourself quite a lot of money if you do this, rather than buy a new carburettor to improve performance. Actually a 32 or 34mm Mikuni bored out to 35mm will flow very close to the same amount of air as a 36mm carb because the bored carburettor is more streamlined inside. This occurs because the smaller carburettor finishes up with a bore diameter very close to the throttle slide chamber size, so there is less disruption to the air as the carburettor bore cross-sectional size changes less.

When a carburettor is being bored, the utmost accuracy is required, otherwise the carburettor will be ruined. If the new bore is offset to the left or right of centre, then the engine may refuse to idle due to air leaking past the side of the throttle slide. Likewise, if more than 0.25-0.35mm is removed from the floor of the bore, the engine will also not idle as it will be impossible to adjust the slide down low enough to restrict air flow into the engine. Therefore, if you are boring a 34mm Mikuni to 35.3mm, which is the maximum oversize by the way, I would suggest that the new bore be offset by 1mm so that the boring tool removes very little from the carburettor floor. A 32mm Mikuni can be bored to 33 or 34mm in a similar way.

A 32mm Mikuni may also be machined to 35mm, but this is much more difficult and the finished carburettor is really only suitable for a road race bike or superkart. In this instance the bore is offset 2.5mm, which means that 0.5mm is removed from the floor of the bore. Some engines will idle with a carb modified like this, others won't. If the engine refuses to idle, there are a couple of ways out. Often changing the idle jet and air screw adjustment will cure the problem, even if it means you have to lean the mixture excessively to slow the engine down. Alternatively, the floor under the throttle slide can be grooved 0.5mm deeper to allow the slide to seat lower and reduce air flow into the engine.

When the 32mm Mikuni is bored to either 34 or 35mm, it is necessary to machine the top of the throttle slide to reduce its height. If this isn't done, the slide will run out of travel before the throttle is fully opened.

Mikunis use two types of main jets. The hex head jets are flow rated in cc per

minute. Jets from size 50 to 195 are available in steps of 5, and sizes 200 to 500 are in

TABLE 5.4   Mikuni needle jet application chart

Series No.	Type	Main jet	Sizes available	Carb type
159	P	Hex	O-0 to R-8	30-36mm spigot
166	P	Hex	O-0 to R-8	38mm spigot
171	P	Hex	O-0 to Q-8	30mm flange
176	B	Hex	N-0 to Q-8	30-36mm spigot
183	B	Hex	N-0 to Q-8	38mm spigot
188	P	Hex	O-0 to Q-8	32mm flange
193	P	Hex	N-0 to Q-8	24mm flange
196	P	Round	O-0 to Q-8	30-36mm spigot
205	P	Hex	O-0 to Q-8	34mm flange
211	P	Hex	N-0 to Q-8	30-36mm spigot
249	P	Hex	N-0 to Q-8	24-28mm spigot
224	P	Hex	Z-0 to CC-5	40-44mm spigot

Note: 'P' type needle jets are intended for use primarily in 2-stroke piston port engines.
'B' type needle jets have bleed holes and are normally used in 4-stroke and rotary valve 2-stroke engines.

steps of 10. The round head main jets are aperture sized. The largest jet available is a 250, which has an aperture size of 2.50mm.

The needle jet has a code to identify its size. For example, a 159 P-8 needle jet is a 159 series jet which fits 30-36mm spigot mount Mikuni carburettors (TABLE 5.4). The letter-number combination shows the fuel hole size. The letter denotes the size in increments of 0.05mm, and the numbers signify size increments of 0.01mm. Therefore a P-8 jet would have a hole size of 2.690mm. There is one exception to this: the −5 needle jet is 0.005mm larger than a −4 jet (TABLE 5.5).

In TABLE 5.4 you will note there are two types of needle jets available: the 'P' type and the 'B' type. The 'P' type have a single air bleed hole (FIGURE 5.2) and are used in most piston-ported two-stroke engines. The 'B' type have several air bleed holes. They are for use in rotary valve two-strokes and four-stroke engines. In the case

TABLE 5.5   Mikuni needle jet sizes

Size	Dia.(mm)	Size	Dia.(mm)	Size	Dia.(mm)
N-0	2.550	P-2	2.660	R-4	2.770
N-2	2.560	P-4	2.670	R-5	2.775
N-4	2.570	P-5	2.675	R-6	2.780
N-5	2.575	P-6	2.680	R-8	2.790
N-6	2.580	P-8	2.690	Z-0	3.150
N-8	2.590	Q-0	2.700	Z-5	3.175
O-0	2.600	Q-2	2.710	AA-0	3.200
O-2	2.610	Q-4	2.720	AA-5	3.225
O-4	2.620	Q-5	2.725	BB-0	3.250
O-5	2.625	Q-6	2.730	BB-5	3.275
O-6	2.630	Q-8	2.740	CC-0	3.300
O-8	2.640	R-0	2.750	CC-5	3.325
P-0	2.650	R-2	2.760		

of the primary ('P') type, air that comes from the air bleed orifice is mixed with fuel which has already been metered by the needle and needle jet. The bleed ('B') type, on the other hand, is designed to hold air in the body section of the needle jet, so in this case fuel and air (actually a frothy fuel/air mixture) is metered by the needle and needle jet.

The metering needles are identified by a code such as 6DH2. The first number indicates the needle series. The following letter/s indicate the needle taper. If there is one letter, the taper is uniform along the length of the needle, but if there are two letters, this indicates that the taper changes midway along the tapered section. The first letter indicates the upper taper and the second letter the lower taper.

Starting with letter A, which has a meaning of 15 minutes of arc, each letter in sequence denotes an additional 15 minutes to the angle between the two sides of the needle. Therefore a DH taper has an angle of 1°0' on the top, and 2°0' on the bottom taper (TABLE 5.6).

TABLE 5.6   Mikuni needle tapers

Letter	Taper	Letter	Taper	Letter	Taper
A	0°15'	J	2°30'	S	4°45'
B	0°30'	K	2°45'	T	5°0'
C	0°45'	L	3°0'	U	5°15'
D	1°0'	M	3°15'	V	5°30'
E	1°15'	N	3°30'	W	5°45'
F	1°30'	O	3°45'	X	6°0'
G	1°45'	P	4°0'	Y	6°15'
H	2°0'	Q	4°15'	Z	6°30'
I	2°15'	R	4°30'		

TABLE 5.7a   Mikuni series 4 needles
To fit some 26mm carburettors and 22 & 24mm flange mount carburettors

Needle	X	Y	10	20	30	40	50
4D3	50.3	25.3	2.511	2.511	2.421	2.253	2.100
4D8	50.3	22.8	2.519	2.519	2.381	2.211	2.000
4E1	50.3	28.0	2.515	2.515	2.345	2.127	1.924
4DG6	50.3	24.0	2.518	2.518	2.405	2.119	1.850
4DH7	50.3	23.0	2.518	2.518	2.386	2.098	1.790
4F15	50.3	26.5	2.512	2.512	2.400	2.120	1.881
4J13	50.2	24.0	2.513	2.513	2.230	1.800	1.400
4L6	50.3	24.5	2.515	2.515	2.178	1.660	1.190
4F6	50.5	25.3	2.514	2.514	2.406	2.145	1.876
4L13	45.1	25.0	2.518	2.516	2.339	1.842	
4F10	50.2	24.5	2.513	2.513	2.385	2.135	1.877
4J11	41.5	21.3	2.512	2.506	2.188	1.776	
4P3	50.5	25.0	2.510	2.506	2.436	2.284	2.122

Note: X is the overall length of the needle in mm.
Y is the dimension from the top of the needle to the start of the taper.
The numbers 10, 20, 30 etc., indicate the needle diameter in mm at a point 10, 20, 30 etc. mm from the top of the needle.

The number after the letters is a manufacturing code which indicates how far down the needle the taper starts, eg: needles marked 6DH2 and 6DH3 have the same taper, but 6DH3 is the richer needle as the taper starts 22.0mm from the top of the needle, whereas the taper begins 28.0mm down with the 6DH2. TABLES 5.7 indicate the dimensions of the more common Mikuni needles.

If the needle is identified as a 6DP5-3 in the bike owner's handbook, this would indicate that the needle is a 6DP5 and that it is fitted standard with the circlip in the third groove, counting the top groove as number one.

The throttle slide cutaway size is indicated by a number stamped under the slide, eg: a 2.0 signifies a 2.0mm cutaway. Smaller engines usually need a 1.5, 2.0 or 2.5 cutaway, and larger engines a 2.5 or 3.0.

The idle jet (pilot jet) is available in sizes 15 to 80, in steps of 5. Fine adjustment of the idle mixture is by means of the idle air screw which richens the idle mixture when turned in (clockwise).

The float level is adjusted with the fuel bowl removed and the carburettor inverted

TABLE 5.7b   Mikuni series 5 needles
To fit 26-32mm spigot mount & 28-34mm flange mount carburettors

Needle	X	Y	10	20	30	40	50	60
5D6	59.3	27.5	2.515	2.515	2.460	2.290	2.120	
5FJ9	59.2	35.0	2.517	2.517	2.517	2.364	2.021	
5D120	59.1	28.2	2.520	2.520	2.479	2.311	1.980	
5F3	58.0	27.4	2.519	2.519	2.419	2.135	1.863	
5EH7	57.6	28.5	2.517	2.517	2.473	2.210	1.848	
5E13	57.5	29.5	2.515	2.515	2.484	2.197	1.803	
5EJ13	57.8	26.5	2.519	2.519	2.431	2.210	1.766	
5DL13	60.2	32.0	2.515	2.515	2.515	2.362	1.922	1.463
5EJ11	60.3	28.5	2.515	2.515	2.515	2.241	1.839	1.420
5EL9	60.3	27.0	2.517	2.517	2.441	2.221	1.780	1.248
5FL11	60.3	28.2	2.518	2.518	2.438	2.175	1.740	1.256
5EP8	60.2	33.0	2.513	2.513	2.513	2.245	1.780	1.120
5FL14	58.0	28.0	2.520	2.520	2.440	2.170	1.735	
5FL7	58.0	28.0	2.518	2.518	2.440	2.170	1.735	
5DP7	57.6	26.4	2.512	2.512	2.440	2.259	1.580	
5J6	58.0	27.5	2.518	2.518	2.340	1.890	1.450	
5L1	58.0	27.0	2.518	2.518	2.330	1.811	1.297	
5C4	55.1	24.0	2.516	2.516	2.448	2.310	2.179	
5F18	58.0	27.0	2.521	2.521	2.515	2.257	2.006	
5J9	58.0	27.0	2.522	2.520	1.432	1.996	1.505	
5F12	51.5	23.3	2.021	2.021	1.882	1.631	1.375	
5D1	53.5	27.6	2.510	2.510	2.496	2.338	2.169	
5DP2	60.3	32.4	2.515	2.514	2.513	2.418	2.067	1.418
514	60.0	27.0	2.514	2.509	2.442	2.071	1.690	1.332
5D5	57.6	30.0	2.513	2.513	2.510	2.366	2.205	

Note: X is the overall length of the needle in mm.
   Y is the dimension from the top of the needle to the start of the taper.
   The numbers 10, 20, 30 etc., indicate the needle diameter in mm at a point 10, 20, 30 etc.
   mm from the top of the needle.

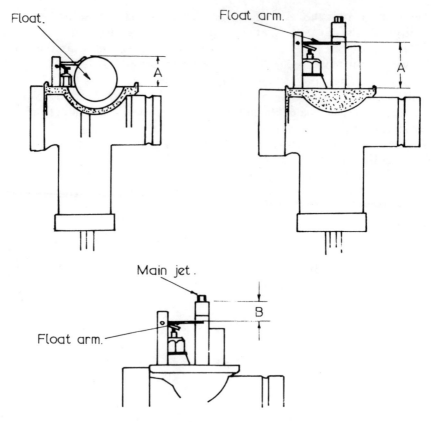

Fig. 5 . 4   Mikuni float levelling.

(FIGURE 5.4). With the float tongue contacting the needle valve, the distance 'A' should be equal to the specified float level. Usually, this will be 20 to 35mm depending on the carburettor type. This measurement is made with the fuel bowl gasket removed.

Some Mikuni carburettors have the float level adjusted to dimension 'B'. In this instance the level is usually around 9 to 10mm; again this varies from model to model.

Many tuners begin tuning carburettors by trying to determine the correct main jet size. This procedure is correct if the engine has not been extensively modified and the standard carburettor is still being used. However, if you find large changes in the size of the main jet do not seem to be having very much influence on the half to full throttle mixture strength, then you can be fairly certain that a larger needle jet is required.

When an engine has been extensively modified, I prefer to begin testing (after ensuring that the float level is correct) with the main jet removed. If the engine will just run at part throttle, but floods as the throttle is opened, then the needle jet is large enough. However, if you find that the engine keeps going at three quarter to full throttle you can be sure a larger needle jet is needed. Note that this test should be done with the needle lowered to the No.1 (i.e., lean) clip position.

After you have determined a needle and needle jet combination that is too rich, you can then try various size main jets until you find one that allows the engine to run
104 reasonably well at full throttle. Don't worry about throttle response or acceleration for

the time being. Carry out this test with the needle raised to the middle clip position.

Next we have to find what size idle jet (pilot jet) is required. Start these adjustments by backing out the idle speed screw until the throttle slide is completely closed, and then turn the screw back in until the slide just barely breaks open. Having done that, close the idle air screw completely and back it out 1 to 1½ turns. Start the engine and attempt to obtain a smooth 1000-1500rpm idle, by juggling the air screw and the idle speed screw in turn.

TABLE 5.7ci   Mikuni series 6 needles
To fit 30-38mm spigot mount carburettors

Needle	X	Y	10	20	30	40	50	60
6H1	62.3	37.5	2.510	2.510	2.510	2.412	2.041	1.696
6DH2	62.3	28.0	2.511	2.511	2.466	2.295	2.000	1.660
6F9	62.3	28.9	2.516	2.516	2.475	2.210	1.949	1.678
6CF1	61.5	29.5	2.512	2.512	2.429	2.240	1.974	1.710
6FJ6	62.3	35.2	2.505	2.505	2.505	2.376	2.040	1.606
6DH3	62.3	22.0	2.512	2.512	2.458	2.286	1.948	1.607
6J3	62.3	36.7	2.515	2.515	2.515	2.359	1.912	1.456
6L1	62.3	37.0	2.512	2.512	2.512	2.335	1.826	1.313
6DP5	62.3	32.1	2.518	2.518	2.518	2.372	1.834	1.141
6N1	62.3	37.0	2.514	2.514	2.514	2.278	1.672	1.058
6DP1	62.3	28.9	2.511	2.511	2.476	2.312	1.748	1.075
6F3	60.5	34.2	2.512	2.512	2.512	2.313	2.050	
6DH4	62.3	25.5	2.520	2.520	2.440	2.258	1.915	1.575
6J1	64.0	36.2	2.517	2.517	2.517	2.339	1.919	1.495
6DH7	62.2	28.5	2.516	2.516	2.505	2.316	2.009	1.688

Note: X is the overall length of the needle in mm.
Y is the dimension from the top of the needle to the start of the taper.
The numbers 10, 20, 30 etc., indicate the needle diameter in mm at a point 10, 20, 30 etc. mm from the top of the needle.

TABLE 5.7cii   Mikuni series 6 needles
To fit 30-38mm spigot mount carburettors

Needle	X	Y	Z	10	20	30	40	50	60
6F5	62.3	38.1	19.0	2.515	2.456	2.454	2.364	2.098	1.840
6F4	62.3	32.0	19.4	2.515	2.442	2.436	2.206	1.939	1.678
6F8	62.3	34.0	21.5	2.512	2.512	2.386	2.214	1.945	1.688
6FJ11	62.3	36.0	18.7	2.519	2.481	2.481	2.367	2.030	1.610
6F16	59.1	36.7	18.5	2.519	2.489	2.489	2.372	2.104	
6DH21	52.3	30.1	16.5	2.515	2.470	2.465	2.328	2.024	
6F16	64.6	31.2	18.4	2.520	2.404	2.400	2.201	1.941	1.679

Note: X is the overall length of the needle in mm.
Y is the dimension from the top of the needle to the start of the taper.
Z is the dimension in mm from the top of the needle to the pronounced taper point.
The numbers 10, 20, 30 etc., indicate the needle diameter in mm at a point 10, 20, 30 etc. mm from the top of the needle.

TABLE 5.7d   Mikuni series 7 needles
To fit 40-44mm spigot mount carburettors

Needle	X	Y	10	20	30	40	50	60	70
7FO6	72.3	29.0	3.005	3.005	2.951	2.680	2.415	2.140	1.876
7H2	72.3	28.9	3.005	3.005	2.928	2.575	2.230	1.868	1.507
7J2	72.3	28.8	3.005	3.005	2.904	2.460	2.010	1.569	1.125
7F2	73.0	43.5	2.515	2.515	2.515	2.515	2.312	2.040	1.703

Note: X is the overall length of the needle in mm.
Y is the dimension from the top of the needle to the start of the taper.
The numbers 10, 20, 30 etc., indicate the needle diameter in mm at a point 10, 20, 30 etc.
mm from the top of the needle.

If you are tuning a multi-cylinder engine and you can get the engine to settle down to a good idle at this point, you should then synchronise the throttle slides so that they open and close together. The easiest way to do this is to remove the needle and needle jet and then open the throttle just wide enough for a length of ⅛ in bronze welding wire to be slipped down a carburettor throat for the throttle slide to seat on. Then, holding the throttle open just wide enough to keep the welding wire trapped, adjust the throttle cable length on the other carburettor/s so that another piece of ⅛ in welding rod can just slip under the throttle slides.

If the engine will not idle, it is probable that the idle jets are wrong. Jets that are too small are indicated by an increasing idle speed as the air screws are turned in. Turning the screws in should cause the engine to run rich at some point (usually ½ to 1 turns from being fully closed) when the idle jets are of the correct size. An idle jet that is too large is indicated by an ever-increasing idle speed, as the air screws are backed further and further out. Note that the air screws must not be opened more than 3 turns, otherwise they will vibrate out.

Once the idle has been adjusted, you can test that the slide cutaway is of the correct height. The cutaway influences the mixture between ⅛ and ½ throttle, and especially in the range of ⅛ and ¼ throttle opening. Therefore, if the engine tends to cough and die when the throttle is cracked open, but gains revs as the throttle is closed, change to slides with less cutaway (i.e., richer). (At times minor leanness at this point can be corrected by raising the needle one or more notches).

If you find it necessary to change the slides, recheck throttle synchronisation and determine that the idle jet is still of the correct size. A change in idle jet size is generally only required when a large change in cutaway height has been made.

Now take the bike for a run and check that the main jet is approximately correct by testing how it runs at ¾ to full throttle. If the engine runs well and the plug reads a good colour then the main jet is close enough to begin searching out the correct needle profile and/or needle position.

The needle taper and position controls the fuel/air mixture between ¼ and ¾ throttle. To determine if a change is required, test the bike on a smooth and level road for at least half a mile at ¼ throttle, and then at ½ and finally ¾ throttle. If the engine 'four strokes' and misses at a steady throttle opening, the mixture is too rich, so lower the needle one groove at a time until smooth running is realised. On the other hand, an engine that snatches and surges is running lean, so the needle will require raising.

TABLE 5.8   Mikuni metering guide

	1/8	1/4	3/8	1/2	3/4	full
Throttle opening position						
Slide cutaway	A	A	B	B	C	D
Pilot or idle jet	A	A	B	C	D	D
Pilot air screw	A	A	B	C	D	D
Needle jet	B	A	A	C	C	D
Needle size	C	B	A ·	A	B	C
Needle position	B	B	A	A	B	D
Main jet	D	D	C	C	B	A
Power jet	D	D	D	D	C	A

These letters indicate metering effectiveness at various slide openings.
A — most effective
B — fairly effective
C — small influence
D — no influence

Next, try steady accelerations from 1/4 to 1/2 throttle and from 1/2 to 3/4 throttle and note whether the engine appears to be lean or rich. Then repeat the test but snap the throttle open each time. You may find that the mixture is lean at 1/4 throttle and changes to rich between 1/2 and 3/4 throttle. This would indicate that the needle is too thin between those points, so a change to a needle with a thicker profile, generally at the 30 and 40mm points (see TABLES 5.7) would be required. After fitting the new needle you may find it necessary to change the clip position either up or down, depending on the needle thickness at the 10 and 20mm points, to cure the 1/4 throttle leanness originally experienced.

Once the correct needle and needle position has been determined, the bike should be tested at three quarter to full throttle to find the right main jet diameter. What we want is a mixture rich enough to avoid piston and engine overheating, but not so rich that the engine is losing power due to poor combustion.

When trying to find the optimum size main jet, it is always preferable to begin testing with a main jet way too large and work down from there, otherwise if you start out testing with a jet too small the engine could easily overheat and seize. As you come down closer and closer to the size required, the engine will perform progressively better. When you reach the point where the engine feels to be running at its best, you should do some careful and serious spark plug reading to ensure that the mixture is, in actual fact, correct.

It takes practice and a proper magnifier of 4X or 6X power to pinpoint correct mixture strength. The things to look for that indicate certain operating conditions are indicated in TABLE 5.9. You will note that all of the plug end actually exposed to the combustion flame is examined and read, not just the insulator nose as some so mistakenly believe.

For the plug reading to be accurate, it will be necessary to run the engine at full throttle and maximum speed for at least 6 miles, and then immediately cut the engine dead. If you allow the engine to slow down as you bring the bike to a stop, and then slowly trickle through the pits, the plug reading will be meaningless.

TABLE 5.9   Checking mixture strength by spark plug reading

Spark plug/mixture condition	Indications
Normal — correct mixture	Insulator nose light tan to rust brown. Little or no cement boil where the centre electrode protrudes through the insulator nose. The electrodes are not discoloured or eroded.
Fuel fouled — rich mixture	Insulator nose black and possibly wet. Steel plug shell end covered with a black soot deposit.
Overheated — lean mixture	Insulator nose chalky white or may have a satin sheen. Excessive cement boil where centre electrode protrudes through insulator nose. Cement may be milk white or meringue-like. Centre electrode may be 'blue' and rounded off at the edges. Earth electrode may be badly eroded or have a molten appearance.
Detonation — lean mixture	Insulator nose covered in tiny pepper specks or maybe tiny beads of aluminium leaving the piston crown. Excessive cement boil where centre electrode protrudes through insulator nose. Specks on the steel plug shell end.

When you find a main jet which gives a good plug colour then, by way of a double check, make a piston crown and combustion chamber reading. If the top of the piston and combustion chamber is dry and coloured very dark brown to black with hard carbon, then the mixture is correct. A wet and black sooty appearance indicates an over-rich mixture, and grayish deposits are a sure sign of dangerous leanness.

Having found the correct main jet size don't be fooled into thinking that you will not have to change it again. Two-stroke engines are very fussy about mixture strength and engine overheating, therefore you will find it necessary to jet the engine to suit different tracks and compensate for changes in atmospheric conditions. Even your ability as a rider comes into consideration. As your skill develops and you are able to hold the throttle wide open for longer distances around a track, you will have to jet richer to cool the engine. Fast tracks with long straights demand larger jets than short, low speed twisty circuits. High altitude running requires leaner jetting, and so forth.

Since the temperature, humidity and barometric pressure all affect air density, it is obvious that the mixture strength, the ratio of fuel to air being introduced into the engine, will vary from day to day and from place to place (because of altitude difference). Under normal circumstances the change in air density is of little or no consequence to the average road rider, but the racing engine tuner, seeking as much power as possible and desiring to avoid engine and piston overheating, has to take the air density into consideration before each and every race, or even during an enduro where large changes in altitude are experienced.

When the air density decreases, this reduces the amount of oxygen inducted into the cylinder, therefore the mixture becomes richer. Conversely, an increase in air density increases the quantity of oxygen entering the motor, so there is a corresponding leaning of the fuel/air mixture. To compensate, it will be necessary to fit richer or leaner main jets.

Remember, when compensating for a change in air density, that the change in density also affects the pressure exerted on the fuel in the float bowl. Therefore a decrease in relative air density (RAD) will automatically lean the fuel/air mixture to a degree, because of the lower air pressure. This means that you don't fit 5% smaller jets when the RAD falls by 5%. I usually reckon that a change in RAD of 12 to 15% requires a 5% change in fuel jet size. Remember, too, that a decrease in RAD is usually due to hot or high altitude conditions, conditions which in themselves reduce the engine's cooling efficiency. To compensate for possible engine overheating it is good to keep the mixture slightly rich when the RAD is low.

If you intend to tune your carburettor taking RAD changes into consideration, you must have a reference point and work from there. After you have tuned your carburettor as outlined on previous pages, you should make a record of the RAD and then experiment with jet sizes at other RADs, according to the percentage difference between the baseline RAD and the RAD on the day you are retuning the carb.

The relative air density can be worked out from FIGURE 5.5, providing you know the air temperature and the uncorrected barometric pressure. RAD meters are available and these give a direct percentage density reading.

There is another factor involved and, unfortunately, this cannot be read off the RAD graph or meter but, as the humidity affects true air density, we have to take it into account to be completely accurate. The effect of the humidity is quite small, except when both the temperature and relative humidity are high. Water vapour has weight and, as such, combines with the weight of the air to distort the true 'weight', or density, of the air. Think of it in this way: you are the air and your clothing is water vapour, wearing clothes you are going to exert more pressure (weight) on the bathroom scales than your true undressed weight. To find your true weight, you have to subtract the pressure exerted by your clothes. Similarly, when we want to find the true air density, we have to subtract the pressure exerted by water vapour in the atmosphere.

If you take a look at TABLE 5.10, you can see that the pressure exerted by water vapour at 100°F is 1.93in Hg. If the barometric pressure at the time is 30in Hg the true air pressure is only $30.0 - 1.93 = 28.07$in Hg, a decrease of 6.4%. Therefore, in this instance, the mixture could have ended up 6.4% rich if the relative humidity was not taken into account.

Usually the amount of water vapour is less than the amount indicated in the column headed 'Saturation Pressure', as this assumes a relative humidity of 100%. (Relative humidity compares the amount of water vapour present with what the atmosphere is capable of holding.)

To find the true air pressure, use the formula:-

$$CAP = UBP - \left(SP \times \frac{RH}{100}\right) \text{ inches mercury}$$

CAP = corrected air pressure
UBP = uncorrected barometric pressure. i.e., read straight off the barometer
SP = saturation pressure from TABLE 5.10
RH = relative humidity

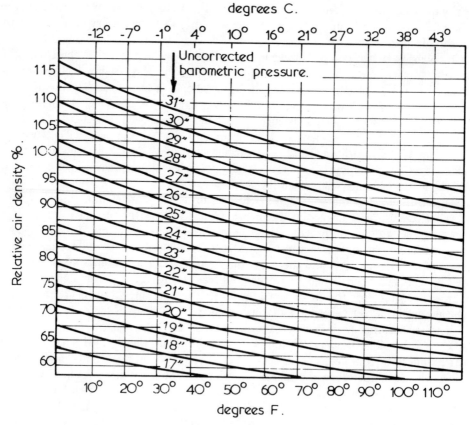

degrees C.

Note- standard sea level pressure at 59°F = 29.92″ mercury.

(14.706 lb./sq. inch or 1013 millibars.)

Fig. 5.5 Relative air density chart.

Once the corrected air pressure has been calculated, the true relative air density can be read straight off the relative air density graph.

If you are using a RAD meter the percentage reading must be corrected using the formula:-

$$\text{Corrected RAD} = \text{RAD reading} - \left(S\% \times \frac{\text{RH}}{100}\right)$$

$S\% =$ saturation percentage of water from
    TABLE 5.10
$\text{RH} =$ relative humidity

The one thing you must be sure to do, if you wish to be successful in tuning your engine according to the relative air density, is to keep complete and accurate notes. If you find that your engine works best with 270 main jets with a 90% RAD, be sure that

TABLE 5.10   Humidity saturation pressure and percentage

| Temperature | | Saturation pressure | | Saturation percentage of water |
°F	°C	in Hg	Millibars	
40	4.4	0.247	8	0.83
60	15.6	0.521	18	1.7
70	21.1	0.739	25	2.5
80	26.7	1.03	35	3.3
90	32.2	1.42	48	4.7
100	37.8	1.93	65	6.5

you make a note of the fact in your tuning diary. Then, on each occasion the air density is again 90%, you will know exactly what size jets to use, providing the tracks are of a similar layout. If the track is a faster one with larger straights, you may have to jet richer. At another location the RAD might be 98%, so armed with the information in your diary you know that you should try a 280 main jet. May be it will be the correct size, but then it may not be. There are no hard and fast rules here, no two engines respond to RAD changes exactly alike. Usually small displacement, high rpm road race engines and liquid cooled engines in a high state of tune are most affected by a change in air density.

The mixture ratio is also affected if there are any air leaks, so you must be very careful to seal the manifold to the barrel, and the carburettor to the manifold, using the correct gasket and the right type of gasket cement. This may seem a rather small thing, but you would be amazed at the number of tuners who use Silastic to seal the manifold/carburettor. Silastic is excellent as an oil sealant, but it is not petrol resistant, therefore it should not be used anywhere in the induction tract. I recommend the use of Permatex No.3 for this purpose.

An air filter also reduces the air density (particularly if it is clogged full of dirt), but in this instance by restricting air flow into the cylinders. Obviously the restriction can be done away with by removing the filter. This may be acceptable for some road racing bikes, but all other types, including road race karts, should be fitted with effective filters.

Long engine life and effective air filtration are very closely related and, contrary to popular opinion, a clean air filter of good design (such as K & N) does not reduce engine power output by very much at all. On road bikes such as the Yamaha RD400, however, the air filtration system does have a devastating effect on performance. This is due to the use of a tiny air filter and a very restrictive air box, designed to cut down induction roar and reduce noise pollution.

Many enthusiasts are fooled into thinking that they have gained many horsepower by fitting 32 and 34mm Mikunis to their otherwise standard RD250s and RD400s. Usually, the improvement in power is more the result of the removal of the air box and filter than from the larger carburettors. Carburettors of the size indicated work very well on hot street RDs and also production racers, but they are too large for standard engines. TABLE 5.11 indicates the performance increase realised from removing the air box and filter off an RD400 and fitting a pair of K & N filters to the standard 28mm carbs, which have been jetted richer. Compared to what a pair of 34mm Mikunis will do, you can see that the smaller carbs come out on top. If you don't want to fit K & N 111

TABLE 5.11   Yamaha RD400E dyno test
(Standard European engine)

rpm	Test 1 (hp)	Test 2 (hp)	Test 3 (hp)
2000	6.4		5.7
2500	8.2		7.7
3000	9.6		9.3
3500	13.5	8.3	13.1
4000	15.4	12.8	15.6
4500	18.2	16.6	18.0
5000	24.5	20.6	24.7
5500	26.3	24.2	26.9
6000	30.3	28.7	31.1
6500	33.9	33.5	35.5
7000	36.8	35.9	38.5
7500	36.1	39.3	38.9
8000	30.0	33.1	32.7
8500	22.3	25.4	24.8
9000	17.8	22.2	20.2

Test 1 —   *Standard 28mm carburettors with standard air box and filter connected.*
Test 2 —   *34mm Mikuni carburettors with K & N filters.*
Test 3 —   *Standard 28mm carburettors with air box and filter removed and K & N filters fitted.*

Note: Dyno would not hold a steady load below 3500rpm with the 34mm carburettors, so these figures have been omitted.

filters to your street bike, but prefer the standard setup, do cut the muffling ribs and baffles out of the air box and drill lots of holes in it so as to allow a free flow of air into the engine. With richer jetting, this alone will give a 7-10% power increase.

If you are an off-road rider, you should take a good, careful look at your bike's filtering system. I would estimate that the majority of dirt bikes suffer considerably more wear from inducting dust, mud and water into their internals than they do from very hard, high speed competition riding. We don't want any dust or mud going into the engine at all. This material is very abrasive, prematurely wearing the piston, rings, cylinder and bearings. Also, we must keep water out of the engine. A few specks of water on the plug will stop the engine dead. If the engine takes a good gulp of water, the piston and head could crack because of the sudden temperature decrease.

The first thing you need is a good air filter, properly oiled. For dry events, I think the K & N range of cotton filters are tops. If there is a lot of mud and water around, I prefer the Uni foam filter as it does a better job of keeping water out. Whatever type of filter you use it must be oiled, but be sure to use a water-resistant oil, not engine oil. Waterproof oils will not stop water getting into the engine, that is the task of the filter, but they will not break down into a soapy mess like engine oils, and most gear oils, when they contact water. When an oil breaks down like this, the air filter operates in a similar way to an unoiled filter: very poorly. Bel-Ray filter oil is good, but expensive. If you are worried by the price, try Castrol ST90. It is a 90 weight waterproof gear oil, about one third the price of Bel-Ray filter oil.

A good, well oiled filter is totally useless if it isn't correctly fitted. Unfortunately many bike manufacturers make it very difficult to do just that and this adds to the problem, as it is often impossible to see or feel if the filter is properly in place or not. About the only thing to do is give the sealing edge of the filter a coat of waterproof grease, and then take your time fitting it, being as careful as possible.

The design and location of the air box has a large bearing on just how much dust, mud and water the air filter is going to have to cope with. By paying special attention to sealing the air box you can reduce the load on the filter considerably. Often there are gaps between the rear mudguard, the side covers and the air box, which let in whatever is being thrown off the back tyre. If you seal up these gaps with duct tape or with rubber strips glued into place, you will be contributing much to longer engine life.

Remember, when you go about sealing off the air box from the mudguard and side covers, that you have to let air into the motor or it won't go. The dryest, most dust-free place from which to draw air is from under the fuel tank, so direct your efforts towards getting air into the air box from that area, if possible.

Another point to remember when you seal the air box is that, if water does get in, it has no way of getting out unless you put a reed valve in the bottom of the air box, like Suzuki does on their RMs. If you cut a simple hole in the bottom of the air box to let water out it will also allow water in, and in huge quantities. A reed valve type drain allows flow in one direction only, so if your bike doesn't have this style of drain, do fit one.

Don't be fooled into thinking that, now the air box is taken care of, there is no way water will ever again get into your engine and cause it to stop part way through an enduro. Water can, and does, get into carburettors in many different ways. The most obvious way is in the fuel itself. Leaving your fuel drums standing upright in the rain is inviting trouble, and so is leaving the funnel stuck in the bike's fuel tank while you run through the rain to fetch a drum of fuel, which you have been so careful to place inside a nice dry service tent.

Another way water can enter the carburettor is via the float bowl overflow tube. Some enduro riders plug the overflow outlet — in fact, Bing have been leaving overflows off some of their carburettors for a couple of years now, relying on excess fuel to drain off past the tickler. I still believe in leaving the overflow tube in place, and running down-hill from the outlet, so as to allow excess fuel to spill out of the fuel bowl. The overflow tube should drain into a catch tank of about 150cc. It will require emptying at each fuel stop.

Ridding the Bing of an overflow hasn't been the answer to keeping water out of this carburettor, as water can still find its way in past the tickler. What you must do, if you have a bike fitted with a Bing, is remove the tickler and cover the hole with a plastic tube terminating high up under the fuel tank. If you need a rich mixture to get the bike started in freezing weather, you will have to lay the bike on its side and let it flood for a couple of seconds.

Water can also get into the carburettor by running down the throttle cable, so make sure that the adjusters at both ends of the cable are taped up. Tape the top of the carburettor too; remember that a vacuum exists within the throat and slide chamber, so water can enter the engine by being drawn through the thread on the top of the slide chamber.

Some tuners wonder if 'pumper' diaphragm-type carburettors offer any advantages over the more normal slide throttle and float bowl carburettor. In 113 motorcycle applications, I would say a definite 'No', but they do have a place on go-kart engines which otherwise require the extra burden of a fuel pump to lift fuel from the fuel tank up to the carburettor. The majority of kart engines are fitted with this type of carburettor which employs engine crankcase pulses to both pump and meter fuel.

Karts with fixed gearing (i.e., no gearbox) require a carburettor capable of accurate fuel metering over the greatest possible rpm range, and the pulse carburettor fills this need. The 100cc McCulloch engine, for example, utilises a large 35mm bore carburettor for good high speed air flow, yet the pulse metering enables the engine to run well and accelerate cleanly out of tight turns where engine speed drops to 5000rpm.

The main difficulty with pulse carburettors is that they work well only on the engine for which have been specifically made. Their air passages, which bleed crankcase pressure into and away from the chamber behind the metering diaphragm, have orifices calibrated to be sensitive to the crankcase compression ratio and the cylinder displacement. Any change in either of these factors will upset fuel metering.

The other problem with pulse carburettors concerns the tuning of them. I have seen many engines seize because their tuners didn't understand very basic tuning procedure. Maybe it is because these carburettors are so simple to tune that some have been caught out. There are just two screws to adjust: one controls the low speed mixture and the other the high speed mixture. There is an overlap of functions at medium speed, and herein lies the problem. If the low speed mixture is adjusted too rich, then the high speed screw will have to be leaned right off to allow clean acceleration out of tight corners. This then causes an excessive lean condition at high speed, so that the engine overheats and locks up.

What you have to do is adjust both the low and the high speed screw to the setting recommended by the manufacturer, and then do your fine tuning out on the circuit. McCulloch recommend 1½-2 turns open for the high speed screw and 1-1¼ turns open for the low speed screw. I have found it preferable to set the screws a little closer than this. Usually ¾ turn open for the low speed and 1½ turns open for the high speed is a good place to begin testing on short tight sprint tracks.

After you have allowed the engine to warm up to normal operating temperature, you can fine tune the mixture adjustment. Turn the high speed screw out until the engine 'four strokes' and then lean it off a little at a time ($\frac{1}{16}$turn) until the engine runs correctly at full throttle and maximum rpm on the main straight. Next adjust the low speed mixture for good acceleration out of tight turns. If the engine runs rough and smokes badly when accelerating, turn the low speed screw in to lean the mixture. If the engine falters and misses coming out of turns, open the low speed screw a little to attain smooth acceleration. When you are happy with the way the engine pulls out of corners, you should check the high speed adjustment again to ensure that the mixture is still correct.

It is very important that you adjust the mixture in the way outlined, otherwise you will soon run into trouble. I would say that of the seized kart motors I have worked on 80% have been caused by improper carburettor tuning. Usually, I find the low speed screw is anywhere from 4 to 7 turns open, and the high speed screw closed up to about ¼ to ½ turn open.

Many go-kart classes are Box Stock categories which do not permit carburettor
modifications. However, if you read the regulations you will generally find a maximum

size listed for the carburettor bore, for example, also the rules usually state that all fixing devices (i.e., nuts, bolts, screws, etc.) are free. To get the best out of your engine you will have to use these rules to advantage, for you can be sure other tuners will. The 100cc Box Stock McCulloch class rules give the maximum carburettor size as 35.66mm for the throttle bore, and 29.08mm for the venturi diameter. Many carburettors have a venturi closer to 28.3mm, so you should enlarge and polish it, using a hand scraper and emery paper. The screw fixing the butterfly to the throttle shaft should also be modified to reduce air flow restrictions. Remove the star washer from under the head of the screw and file the screw down until there is a groove just deep enough to turn the screw back into the shaft. Put Loctite on the screw to prevent it vibrating back out of the throttle shaft. Next file the protruding thread of the screw flush with throttle shaft.

If the carburettor regulations are free, performance can be improved by heliarc welding the butterfly to the throttle shaft, and then filing the shaft down to a thickness of 1.5mm. When this is done, be sure to adjust your throttle pedal stop so that you can just get full throttle, otherwise you will twist the end off the throttle shaft.

The fuel discharge nozzle causes quite a loss of flow, so this should be filed to reduce its width to a minimum. You will also note a small plug protruding into the airstream of the McCulloch carburettor just in front of the venturi. This can be removed entirely and the hole filled with epoxy, or the plug can be shortened and refitted.

Karts raced on faster circuits may have the venturi diameter increased up to a maximum of 32mm, but do be careful to richen the mixture as this modification can give rise to a dangerous high speed lean-out.

All McCulloch carburettors benefit from an air horn to smooth air flow into the carburettor bore. An air horn, with a nicely rolled radius similar to that illustrated in FIGURE 5.6, should be fabricated. Without the air horn, flow is reduced by up to 8%.

Most road race karts use motorcycle engines equipped with conventional float chamber carburettors, which of course means that some type of fuel pump must be installed. The pump which I recommend is a pulse type unit manufactured in America by Outboard Marine Corporation. The type 'AY' pump (Part No. 385784), designed for 60-100 hp outboard motors, is the most readily available and easily capable of supplying the required fuel volume for even the hottest TZ250 engines.

To ensure a good strong pulse, the pulse tube connecting the crankcase with the pump must be short (i.e., no longer than 4in) and of small internal diameter. (Most fittings require ¼in bore tube.). If you find the pump will not supply sufficient fuel (this usually only occurs when pulse tubes longer than recommended, and very wild inlet port timings approaching 200° duration, are used), you can fit a small 150cc auxiliary fuel tank to gravity feed straight into the carburettor fuel inlet. The auxiliary tank fills at low rpm and keeps the carburettor full at high speeds when pump pulses are weak. Common plastic tubing is best for the pulse line as it is much stiffer than neoprene tube, hence it conveys a stronger pulse to the pump.

Unlike automobile carburettors, motorcycle carburettors will not tolerate even very low fuel pressure before they give way to flooding. Being designed for gravity feed operation, their float system is not capable of shutting off fuel flow through the needle and seat at a pressure as low as 1 psi. Therefore, when a pulse pump is fitted, you will have to incorporate a fuel by-pass line, and also perhaps a pressure regulator, in your fuel system. (FIGURE 5.7). The by-pass line should be of the same internal diameter as 115

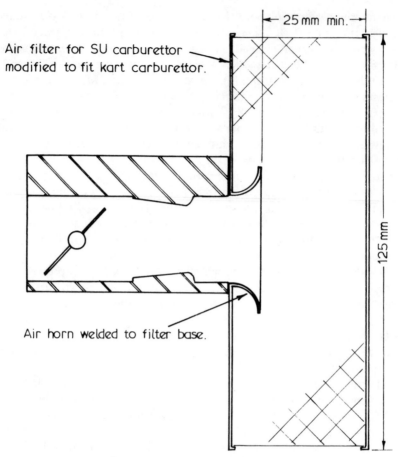

Air filter for SU carburettor
modified to fit kart carburettor.

25 mm min.

125 mm

Air horn welded to filter base.

Fig 5.6 McCulloch carburettor air horn & filter.

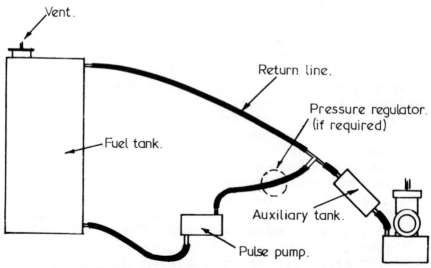

Vent.

Return line.

Pressure regulator.
(if required)

Fuel tank.

Auxiliary tank.

Pulse pump.

Fig. 5.7 Road race kart fuel supply arrangement.

the fuel line, and installed such that it is at a level approximately 6-12 inches higher than the carburettor fuel inlet. It must tee-off within one or two inches of the fuel inlet and discharge excess fuel in the top of the fuel tank. These precautions will ensure the fuel will not take a path of low resistance and return to the fuel tank, starving the engine.

When a carburettor is being installed, there are a few things you need to watch. The first point you must check is that you are actually getting full throttle. Inexperienced tuners are often fooled to believe the slide is opening fully when they see it disappear from the bore of the carburettor, forgetting that the cutaway is perhaps 2-3mm higher than the back of the throttle slide. What you must do is look right down the bore of the carburettor, using a mirror if necessary, and see if the back of the slide is hanging in the airstream. Alternatively, you can remove the needle and feel with your finger if the slide is opening fully.

Also check that the carburettor, manifold and inlet port are correctly aligned, as misalignment will disrupt air flow. Most inlet manifolds are a loose fit on their retaining bolts, so if care is not exercised the manifold can quite easily be mounted out of line with the inlet port. When you test the alignment of the carburettor and inlet manifold, ensure that the retaining clamp is fully tightened as this tends to distort the neoprene material of which the manifold is made. Without the clamp tensioned, the carburettor and manifold often appear to mate perfectly, but once tightened the neck of the manifold may protrude into the air stream. Any offending material should be cut away with a very sharp knife or razor blade. Then dress the surface with a high speed grinder or a chainsaw file.

Each time the carburettor is refitted to the engine, ensure that it is not tilted off centre. Some manufacturers have a locating notch moulded in the inlet manifold to facilitate correct carburettor positioning, but most leave it up to the tuner to sight through and line up. A carburettor, when tilted off vertical, will be leaned-out, as this lowers the fuel level in the float bowl.

The type of fuel that you are permitted to use in your engine will be laid down by the body governing your particular branch of competition. Generally, fuel of a much higher octane rating than that which is available at the local service station pumps can be used. In nearly all forms of racing, 100 octane aviation petrol (100/130 Avgas) is allowed and, at times, 115 octane aviation fuel (115/145 Avgas) or even alcohol fuels are permitted.

In most brands the higher octane rating is obtained by adding tetra-ethyl-lead and ethylene dibromide. The decomposition products from these additives may cause trouble in two-stroke engines, therefore I recommend the use of racing fuels that contain very little t.e.l. Instead, the higher octane should be obtained by the fuel company blending additives such as acetone, toluol (methyl benzine), benzole, ethanol or methanol. Fuels using these additives will not cause any problems in two-stroke engines, but usually they are considerably more expensive than those with an octane rating boosted purely by the addition of t.e.l.

One problem with t.e.l. is that it builds up on the spark plug insulator and, being electrically conductive, will cause the engine to misfire. I have found some fuels so loaded with t.e.l. that the plug has shorted out completely and stopped the engine after only a short period of running.

Alcohol fuel is permitted in most categories of speedway and dirt flat-track racing. 117

Both methanol (methyl alcohol) and ethanol (ethyl alcohol) have an octane rating by the Research method of 140 – 160, depending on mixture richness. Therefore these fuels can be used with very high compression ratios.

Methanol and ethanol have a very high latent heat of vaporisation, i.e., it takes a lot of heat to convert them from liquid form into vapour. Petrol has a latent heat of evaporation of 135 Btu/lb., methanol 472 Btu/lb. and ethanol 410 Btu/lb. This heat, required for proper atomisation, is removed from the piston crown, combustion chamber and the cylinder, resulting in an internally cooler engine.

An engine burning methanol will usually show a 6-8% power increase over one running on Avgas 100/130 (i.e., Racing Fuel 100), without any change in compression ratio. With the compression ratio increased to its maximum, power can rise as much as 15-17%. Where does the power increase come from?

The two cycle engine is a type of heat engine, i.e., one that burns fuel to cause the expansion of gas, and the subsequent movement of the piston. The more heat produced by the combustion fire, the more pressure there will be exerted on the piston, which gives us a power increase.

Using petrol, the fuel/air ratio for best power (i.e., the strongest force on the piston) is 1:12.5. With methanol, for example, we can increase the fuel/air ratio to 1:4.5, although I usually prefer a ratio of 1:5.5; less than 1:7 is too lean.

One pound of petrol has the energy potential of about 19,000 Btu (one British Thermal Unit is the amount of energy required to raise the temperature of one pound of water one degree Fahrenheit.). In comparison, methanol delivers around 9,800 Btu/lb., which means that it produces less than 52% of the heat energy of 1lb of petrol. However, because we are mixing more methanol with each pound of air (1:5.5) than petrol (1:12.5), we are actually producing more heat energy by burning methanol.

To work out how much more heat energy is produced, we have to divide 12.5 by 5.5, which equals 2.27. Next we multiply 9800 by 2.27, which gives us 22,246. This indicates that methanol, in the correct fuel/air proportions, will produce 17% more heat energy than petrol at the correct fuel/air ratio.

$$\left(\frac{22,246}{19,000} \times 100 \right) - 100 = \quad 17\%$$

By comparison, the maximum increase we can obtain using ethanol is about 10%, although it does have anti-knock and cooling properties very nearly the same as methanol. In coming years, I expect we will see a marked increase in the useage of ethanol in both racing and road engines. As the world's oil supply dries up, more racing organisations and governments will encourage the production and use of ethanol derived from grain and sugar producing plants. Strong public opinion against all forms of motor sport using valuable reserves of crude based fuels will, I expect, soon force many sanctioning bodies to ban the use of petrol in motor racing, with the obvious alternatives being ethanol or ethanol/toluol, ethanol/acetone blends.

From the above calculation, you can see that an engine running on straight methanol will burn more than twice as much fuel (1.8 times as much for ethanol) as one burning petrol. Therefore you must be careful to ensure that the fuel tap, fuel lines and needle valve will flow the required amount of fuel.

This can present some problems, as many carburettors will not flow the required amount of fuel through the standard needle and seat. Often a larger replacement is not available, so you will have to enlarge the discharge holes to increase flow by the amount necessary. At times you will find it impossible to get main jets large enough, so again you will have to resort to some drilling.

Most Mikuni carburettor jets (the hex head type) are classified with regard to their fuel flow rate, the number stamped on the jet standing for the ccs of fuel the jet is capable of flowing in a certain time. If you are changing from petrol to methanol, then you should start testing with jets at least 2.3 times as large, eg: change 210 jet to a 480.

The round head Mikuni jets are rated according to their nominal bore diameter in millimetres, eg: a round head 250 jet has a nominal aperture of 2.5mm. Again, when changing from petrol to methanol you will have to begin with jets with an aperture area 2.3 times as large. (Aperture area $= \pi r^2$).

Keep in mind also when you convert to an alcohol fuel, either neat or blended, that the fuel/oil ratio may have need of adjustment. Straight methanol would require only 80% as much oil, or a 25:1 ratio in many applications, although some engines will require a 16:1 mix. It is always best to start testing at 20:1 and work from there.

There are other problems involved in the change to alcohol, some of which will affect you and some your engine. Since your life is the most important, we will deal with you first. Methanol is extremely poisonous and, as it is an accumulative poison, it can build up over a period of time and oxidise to form formaldehyde, eventually causing blindness or even insanity. It is absorbed through the skin and lungs, either by direct contact or from the vapours. Inhalation of the exhaust gas can also be dangerous as vaporised methanol is usually present, especially when rich mixtures are being used.

Alcohols are a very effective paint stripper, and they may attack some fibreglass resins. They have a scouring effect on fuel tanks and lines so these should be soaked in alcohol and then drained so that the residue does not find its way into the carburettor when you switch from petrol to alcohol.

Methanol and ethanol will absorb huge amounts of water out of the air, so they must always be kept in an air-tight container. The fuel will also have to be completely drained from the tank and the carburettor to prevent the formation of water-induced corrosion and oxidization. This can be particularly damaging to a carburettor and usually results in blocked metering passages.

After burning alcohol in a two-stroke engine it is most important to run a petrol/oil mix rich in oil through the engine each time you put your machine away after a day's running. If this is not done, you will soon find corrosion and etching of the cylinder wall, crank and piston pin, needle and ball bearings that will lead to premature failure. To prevent this occurrence, I would suggest that you run a half pint of 16:1 petrol/oil mixture through the engine.

In colder climates, starting difficulties may be encountered when pure alcohol is being burned. Some use other more volatile fuels blended in, to help overcome this problem. Usually 5% acetone or a maximum of 3% ether is used. I do not recommend starting aerosols containing ether, due to the possibility of engine damage being caused by detonation. Personally I feel the best method is to remove the spark plug and pour about a half teaspoon of either petrol or neat acetone into the cylinder before you attempt to start the engine.

Alcohol burners demand a good ignition system. Not only does the ignition have to cope with much higher compression pressures, it may also be called on to fire plugs 119 wetted by the very rich mixture being inducted. Alcohol fuels burn much more slowly than petrol, so it will be necessary to experiment with more ignition advance. It is not possible to predict just how much additional advance will be required as there are so many variables involved, but you should begin testing with about an extra 3-5° advance.

Before you advance the spark lead, do make sure that the carburation is fully sorted out. If the engine runs just slightly lean, with added spark lead you could very easily hole a piston. As well as a much larger main jet, it is probable that a different needle profile and a larger needle jet will be required. To correct off idle leanness, a bigger pilot jet and a small 1.0 to 1.5mm slide cutaway may be needed.

Nitromethane, as such, isn't really a good fuel but it can give two-stroke engines a power boost if used sensibly. Nitro's only virtue is that it contains approximately 53% by weight oxygen, so in effect it is a chemical super-charger. In drag car engines it is blended 80-90% nitro to 10-20% methanol, but there is no way a two-stroke engine can hold together with more than a 20% nitro-80% methanol blend. Even then, I would only use nitro in small and rugged single cylinder dirt track engines. To deter detonation, or other engine damage, it is always necessary to lower the compression ratio. If your engine runs reliably at a 17:1 compression ratio on methanol, then you should be able to use a 14:1 ratio with a 20% nitro-80% methanol fuel mix.

As with methanol, nitromethane demands a rich fuel/air mixture. Using a 20% nitro blend, the mixture would be approximately one part fuel to three or four parts air, i.e., 1:3-4. This means that you will have to increase the main jet size by about 22-25% above that required for pure methanol with a 20% nitro-80% methanol mixture. A 12-15% jet increase will be close for a 10% nitro blend.

The safest way to avoid error when mixing nitro with other fuels is to mix according to volume, eg: for a 20% nitro blend you will use one gallon of nitro to four gallons of methanol.

Care is in order when handling nitromethane, as it may become explosive. Normally nitro is quite safe, but it may be made shock sensitive by any of the following practices:-

a)   the addition of hydrazine in fuel blending
b)   the use of caustic soda or any other alkaline for cleaning the mixing drum
c)   the use of 'unpickled' anodised aluminium fuel tanks. After anodising, the tank must be allowed to stand for a few days filled with a solution 10% vinegar—90% water.

TABLE 5.12 indicates the basic fuels available to the racer. Some may be used neat or blended, others are combustion accelerators and, as such, are blended in very small quantities with alcohol fuels only.

When methanol or ethanol is the base fuel, propylene oxide may be added to increase the combustion flame speed. If you decide to use propylene oxide, be very careful to blend in not more than 3-5% by volume and ensure a rich fuel/air mixture of 1:4.5-5.0 is maintained, otherwise mechanical damage may result. Propylene oxide can become explosive if allowed to come in contact with rust particles or copper and its alloys. Therefore it must be stored in plastic or aluminium containers. Once blended with other fuels it is relatively stable.

Acetone is often blended with alcohol to accelerate combustion flame speed, and
120   also to reduce its tendency to pre-ignite when lean mixtures are used. Usually a 10%

TABLE 5.12   Fuel characteristics

Fuel	Specific gravity	Fuel/air ratio (lb/lb)	Heat energy (Btu/lb)	Latent heat of evaporation (Btu/lb)
Acetone	0.791	1:9.5, 1:10.5	12500	225
Benzole	0.879	1:11.0, 1:11.5	17300	169
Ethanol	0.796	1:6.5, 1:7.5	12500	410
Ether	0.714		15000	153
Methanol	0.796	1:4.5, 1:6.5	9800	472
Nitromethane	1.13		5000	258
Petrol	0.743	1:12.5, 1:13.5	19000	135
Propylene Oxide	0.83		14000	220

acetone/90% alcohol blend is all that is required for this purpose, although much higher percentages of acetone may be blended if desired.

If you are concerned about the high fuel consumption when an alcohol fuel is burned, you may be interested in a fuel commercially blended by BP, called BP-K. It is a mix comprising 50% methanol, 35% petrol (97 octane), 10% benzole and 5% acetone. The fuel jet size required is approximately 50%-60% larger than for straight petrol. BP-K is very similar to 115/145 Avgas in respect to its anti-knock and engine 'refrigeration' qualities.

Another alcohol mix which can substitute for 115/145 Avgas is a blend of 30% alcohol (either ethyl or methyl), 60% 100/130 Avgas, 10% acetone. A fuel jet increase of 20-30% will be needed.

In areas where 100/130 and 115/145 Avgas is not available, you can blend pump petrol with certain additives to boost its octane rating, and still remain legal if alcohol blends are not permitted in the rule book. These days, the highest grade petrol has a Research rating of about 97/98 octane, but this can be raised to equal, or even exceed, the performance level of 100 octane five star petrol. Toluol, benzole and acetone are the most readily obtainable and simple to blend fuels available.

Toluol, marketed under the name Methyl Benzine, by Shell, may be blended in proportions up to 1:2 with petrol (33⅓%) to produce a fuel of 102-103 octane. More than 33⅓% toluol is not recommended, as starting difficulties may be encountered. 20% toluol/80% petrol will give an octane number of 99 to 100, and a 25% toluol/75% petrol mix results in a 100 to 101 octane fuel. A change in carburettor fuel jet sizes is not necessary.

Benzole, also marketed as 'industrial solvent' in some countries, is generally most easily obtained from BP outlets. It will mix with petrol in all proportions, but care is required as benzole is toxic. A 50% benzole blend raises 97/98 octane petrol to approximately 102-103 octane. In this proportion a jet increase of around 5% will be needed.

As with benzole, acetone can be mixed with petrol in all proportions, but it is more usual to use a 10% or 15% acetone blend to produce a fuel of 100 and 103 octane respectively. A change in fuel jet size is not necessary when blending in these proportions. Acetone can be obtained from Shell Chemical Co.

At the present time in America and England, there are a large number of concentrated octane booster additives coming onto the market. All are designed to convert premium pump petrol into racing fuel. When blended in the correct 121 proportions, boosters which work raise the octane rating of 97/98 octane fuel to between 100 and 102 octane maximum. Some companies claim that in high concentrations their boosters will produce 108-110 octane fuel (i.e., equal to 100/130 Avgas), but I have not found this to be true. In fact quite a number of boosters will give only a 0.7 to 1.5 octane increase.

When using these concentrated additives, there are two things you must keep in mind. The first is that American concentrates are marketed in US quarts, which equal 946cc as opposed to the Imperial quart of 1136.5cc. Therefore, if you live outside the US, don't pour a one quart can of octane booster into 24.5 gallons of petrol and expect a 1% booster to 99% petrol mix. For a 1% concentration you would blend a 1 quart can in 20.4 Imperial gallons of petrol (92.7 litres).

The other point is with regard to mixing technique. Don't just pour a can of octane booster into a drum of fuel and expect it to blend properly. What is preferable is to mix the concentrate with about 2-3 gallons of petrol, give the drum a good shake, and then add this mixture to the remaining petrol.

Since much confusion exists as to what octane ratings are all about, we will have a look into the subject. Most people realise that we can get more power with a high octane fuel because we can use a higher compression ratio, and perhaps more spark advance, without running the engine into detonation. However, did you know that a change from, say, 97 octane pump petrol to 110 octane racing fuel (100/130 Avgas) would not give a power rise for most motocross bikes? In fact, you could possibly lose power, if the engine was not changed in any way to take advantage of the octane increase.

To understand why this is so, we have to delve back into history a little to see why a numbering system was introduced to grade fuels, and discover exactly to what the octane numbers refer. Back about the time of World War I, aircraft engines would suddenly self-destruct, through detonation. An engine might run just fine on one batch of fuel, but punch holes in the pistons on the next batch. The fuels seemed to be the same, weigh the same, and may perhaps have come from the same refinery.

The fuel companies tried chemical analysis in an endeavour to achieve parity from one load of petrol to the next, but, in spite of an intensive programme, they were not able to weed out the batches which were prone to produce knock (detonation). Therefore special fuel research engines, with a variable compression feature, were constructed to evaluate and grade fuels. Such a standard test engine (a single cylinder, heavy duty unit) would be warmed up to standard test temperature, run at standard rpm and load, and then have the compression ratio increased until the fuel being tested just produced engine knock. Its anti-knock quality would then be specified as its Highest Useable Compression Ratio (HUCR).

Even with every fuel lab supplied with the same type of test engine, and using the same standard test procedure, it was discovered that the same fuel could test out with differing HUCR numbers in different test laboratories. It was decided that some unvarying standard was needed by which to calibrate the lab engines. Two pure substances were chosen as reference fuels. The high reference fuel chosen was iso-octane, while the low reference fuel was normal heptane (n-heptane).

Now it was decided that a fuel under test would be run in the variable compression engine and its HUCR determined. Then a series of runs would be made with various mixtures of iso-octane and n-heptane until a blend was found which produced knock behaviour identical to the fuel being tested. At this point the quality of the test fuel would be rated in relation to the percentage of iso-octane in the reference fuel mixture which gave identical test results. For example, a test fuel which behaved the same as a mixture of 75% iso-octane/25% n-heptane would be called 75 octane fuel. Using this standard test procedure, fuel of constant quality could be refined and supplied for a variety of applications.

Since that time a number of test procedures have come into use to simulate a variety of engine operating conditions. Motor spirit is usually rated according to the Research or Motor test methods. Both measuring techniques use the same single cylinder, variable compression test engine, but the Motor method employs a greater engine speed and a higher inlet mixture temperature than the Research test. Hence the Motor method is a more severe test, and generally yields octane numbers 6 to 12 less than the Research test. (TABLE 5.13). This distinction is important, as it informs us that the Motor Octane Number (MON) is more relevant to a racing engine than is the Research Octane Number (RON).

Another common number seen on American service station pumps is the Pump Octane Number (PON). This is the average of the RON and MON:

$$\frac{RON + MON}{2}$$

and yields a very creditable rating of a fuel's performance under actual road conditions.

The Supercharge test is applied to aircraft fuels which exceed 100 octane numbers, as the other tests become meaningless at just over 100. The SON (Supercharge Octane Numbers) are significant from 100 to well over 300. Two tests are involved, the F3 and F4 tests, which explains why aircraft fuels have a dual rating such as 100/130. The first number refers to the F3 test, which simulates a supercharged engine running on a chemically-correct fuel/air mixture, as when cruising. The F4 number gives an indication of the fuel's performance rating with an enriched mixture and increased supercharge boost, as would be supplied during aircraft take-off or during combat conditions.

Numbers over 100 cannot refer to percentages of iso-octane. They are, in fact, performance numbers devised to extend the scale of anti-knock measurement past that possible with pure iso-octane. As such, they give a rough estimate of the power potential of the fuel when a heavy supercharge boost is applied to a suitable engine. For example, 115/145 Avgas has the potential of increasing an aircraft engine's power by 45% over that possible using pure iso-octane fuel.

TABLE 5.13   Octane test comparison

Research octane number	Motor octane number	Pump octane number
92	85.7	88.8
97	89	93
100	91.6	95.8
103	92.5	97.75
105	94.2	99.6
108	97	102.5
110	99	104.5

The anti-knock properties of hydrocarbon fuels are related to their molecular structures. The paraffins (such as normal heptane and kerosene) are long chains of carbon and hydrogen held together by weak molecular bonds which are easily broken by heat. Iso-octane is a member of the iso-paraffin family. These have a branched-chain structure that form stronger bonds to resist detonation better. The cyclo-paraffins (or napthenes) also have good anti-detonation properties with their hydrogen and carbon atoms well bonded in a ring shape molecule. The aromatic fuels, such as toluol, also have a ring-shaped structure with very strong bonds. This explains why they have such good anti-knock characteristics.

The chemical composition of the fuel determines just how rapidly the fuel will burn and whether it will be resistant to detonation at high compression pressures and temperatures. The fuels with weak molecular bonds break up and burn spontaneously (i.e., without being ignited by the combustion flame initiated by the firing of the spark plug) at lower temperatures and pressure than fuels with strongly bonded structures. Some fuel additives, such as the aromatics, make excellent anti-detonants because they burn slowly and don't oxidise or burn completely until combustion chamber temperature and pressure is very high. Aromatic fuels therefore inhibit, or slow down, combustion. For this reason a high octane fuel will not increase engine power unless the engine actually needs a fuel which is chemically stable at high temperature and pressure. Obviously, if the engine does not have a compression ratio and spark advance great enough to produce high combustion pressure and temperature, then the high octane racing fuel will not burn completely, resulting in loss of power.

Chapter 6
Ignition

TWO-STROKE engines of the type being considered in this book rely on an electric spark to initiate combustion of the fuel/air charge which has been inducted into the cylinder. For the engine to operate efficiently, the spark must be delivered at precisely the right moment in relation to the position of the piston in the cylinder and the rotational speed of the crankshaft. Additionally, the spark must be of sufficient intensity to fire the fuel mixture, even at high compression pressure and high rpm.

Today, very few two-stroke engines use a coil and battery ignition system. However, we will consider the operation of this type of ignition first as this will enhance your understanding of the workings of magneto, magneto-type capacitor discharge, and battery-type capacitor discharge systems.

The battery and coil type system relies on a battery, either 6 or 12 volt, to supply the initial electrical energy; a set of points to time the spark, and a coil to intensify the voltage of the electrical energy supplied by the battery so that it is capable of jumping the spark plug gap and firing the fuel mixture (FIGURE 6.1).

When the points are closed, electric current flows through the coil's low voltage primary winding, and then through the points to earth. The current in the low tension winding produces a magnetic field which surrounds the coil's secondary or high tension winding. As soon as the points open, current flow through the primary stops, and the magnetic field collapses, causing an electric current to be inducted in the secondary winding. This creates a high voltage spark (up to 25,000 volts) capable of jumping across the spark plug electrodes to fire the fuel/air mixture.

In FIGURE 6.1, you will note that a condenser is also included in the primary ignition circuit. Many have the idea that the condenser stops the points from burning, but this is secondary to its main function, which is to drain off electrical energy quickly from the coil's primary winding. This speeds up the collapse of the magnetic field when the points open and increases the high voltage spark intensity. Without a condenser, the electrical energy inducted in the coil's high voltage winding would be too feeble to produce a spark.

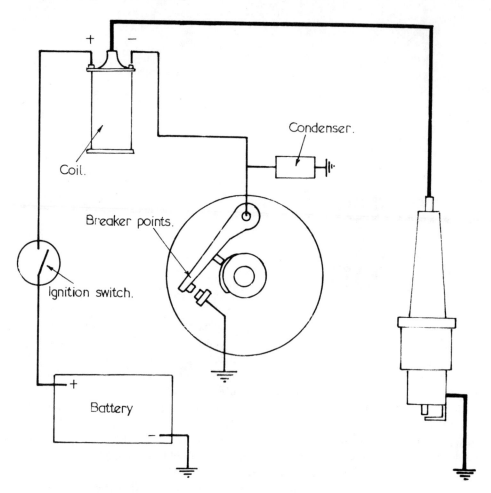

Fig. 6.1   Conventional negative earth ignition system.

The coil and battery system works very reliably and efficiently, even in high speed four-stroke racing engines. However, due to ignition problems peculiar to two-stroke engines, this type of ignition has largely been replaced by ignition systems which produce a high voltage spark more quickly. The rise time (i.e., the time from 10% of maximum output voltage to 90% of maximum output voltage) is between 75 and 125 microseconds with a conventional coil and battery system. In that interval a spark plug, surrounded by a conductive petrol/oil mist, will have time to bleed off voltage across the insulator nose, causing a misfire, or at best result in a spark of low intensity. Capacitor discharge and magneto systems both overcome this problem, having a rise time of 20 microseconds and 45 microseconds respectively.

The magneto systems fitted to two-stroke engines have, over the years, often gained a bad reputation. True, in a few instances this reputation was well founded but, generally, a magneto system will give reliable and efficient service if correctly maintained. The most common causes of trouble are burned out and pitted points due to a lack of regular maintenance, and electrical collapse of the condenser. This is usually as a result of the condenser being mounted in a very hot area. For good service, the condenser must be mounted away from extreme engine heat in a relatively cool location, preferably close to the ignition coil. When this is done, it is a simple matter to connect the condenser to the coil's input terminal rather than run a long wire back to the points. Only when the condenser is collapsing the coil's primary magnetic field quickly will an intense spark result.

With a magneto, the primary current is produced in a similar way as for an alternator, hence there is no need of a battery. The alternating current (a.c.) is not rectified to direct current (d.c.), but passes through the magneto's points as is. This contributes to good point life, as there is little possibility of pitting if the point gap is correct and the points are kept free of oil and grease.

When the points are closed, the primary current passes through the coil's primary winding, producing a strong magnetic field that surrounds the secondary high voltage windings. This magnetic field collapses when the points open, inducing a high voltage current in the secondary which fires the spark plug. In this respect the magneto is very similar in operation to the coil and battery system (FIGURE 6.2).

Because the magneto primary voltage is not regulated to 6 or 12 volts as with a

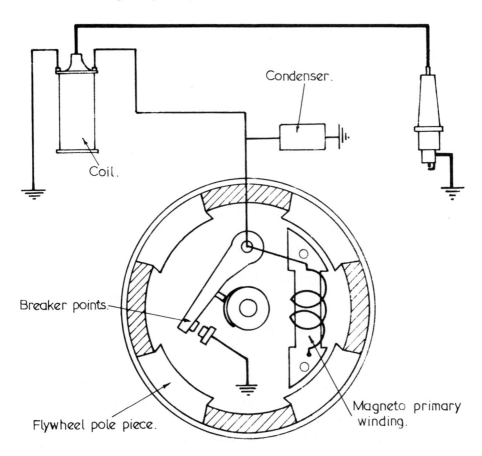

Fig. 6.2 Flywheel magneto ignition system.

battery ignition system, the primary voltage increases proportionately with the engine speed. This feature of the magneto ensures that the coil is fully energised (saturated) between each plug firing, regardless of how fast the engine is spinning. Also, because the primary voltage increases with an increase in rpm, the secondary voltage does likewise, producing a proportionately bigger spark. For example, if a primary voltage of 8 volts induces 10,000 volts in the secondary, then a primary voltage of 24 volts will result in a secondary voltage of 30,000 volts.

At this time, the majority of two-stroke engines come from the manufacturers with capacitor discharge ignition (CDI). There are two types of CDI systems, the battery type and the magneto type. The battery type requires a battery to supply the system's primary current, while the magneto type generates its own primary current. In all other respects both types function in a similar way.

Without a good understanding of electronic circuitry and switching, it is quite difficult to comprehend exactly how CDI systems work. My knowledge in this field is limited, but I will endeavour to explain simply how CDI operates.

Basically, the system utilises electronic devices to step-up the output voltage from the battery or magneto to something like 375-400 volts. The primary current, after being boosted to this voltage, is then stored in the storage capacitor. An electro-magnetic trigger (usually located in the rotor attached to the end of the crankshaft), on passing close by the trigger coil, induces a pulse which closes an electronic switch called an SCR (silicon controlled rectifier). This allows the storage capacitor to send a surge of power through the ignition coil's primary windings, which induces a high voltage in the secondary to fire the spark plug.

CDI systems will generally give good service if a few basic precautions are taken. Most problems result from poor electrical connections or poor earth connections. To avoid bad connections, clean all the terminals with solvent and, when pushing the connectors together, ensure that they are a good tight fit. Then tape the connectors together so that they cannot vibrate apart. Earth connections are just as important as any other electrical connection. Usually, the connection between the 'black box', for example, and the bike's frame, is quite good. As the earth has to go back to the engine, test to see that the engine is earthed to the frame, using a continuity tester.

When mounting the 'black box' and coils on a sidecar outfit or go-kart, keep them away from engine or exhaust heat. Heat is a killer of electronic components, which is why they are often mounted on a heat sink. Remember that, as well as dissipating heat, a heat sink can also absorb huge amounts of heat if mounted in a hot environment.

With capacitor discharge ignition it is very important to ensure that a spark plug wire will not jump off or be in a position where it could be pulled off accidentally. If this occurs when the engine is running, it is quite probable that the electrical insulation of certain components will break down and cause the system to burn out. Also, keep in mind that you should ensure the plug wires are grounded if you ever flood the engine and it becomes necessary to turn it over vigorously with the plugs removed.

Unfortunately, CDI systems do, at times, fail. Total failure in itself is quite serious, especially if you are in the lead! But more difficult to detect is the type of problem more usual with CDI. Generally, the spark-producing system functions very reliably, but the automatic advance/retard station, which is made up of electronic components, does give trouble. When this occurs, the engine will continue to run, as strong sparks are still being supplied. But if the system is 'locked' in the full advance mode, detonation and engine seizure are a likely result. Less serious is a system functioning fully retarded, as this will cause sluggish performance at lower engine speeds.

There is nothing that you can do to prevent advance/retard system failure, but you can save yourself a good deal of expense and worry if you realise such a problem can exist. Some racers chase their tails for a whole season trying to find lost horsepower, unaware that the CDI is the cause of the trouble. Others spend hundreds of dollars replacing seized pistons and barrels for several successive meetings when all along the trouble has been the CDI stuck on full advance.

If your bike has a CDI with an advance/retard system (check with the manufacturer) you can avoid this sort of unnecessary expense and frustration by regularly checking the timing with a strobe light. Usually you will have to connect the strobe to a 12 volt battery as most bikes do not have a suitable power source. If the advance/retard system is working properly, you will note that the timing marks line up at certain engine speeds and move apart at others. When the system is malfunctioning, the timing marks will not line up at any speed, or in the case of a system which employs a high rpm retard mechanism which has locked on full advance, they will remain aligned at all engine speeds.

To get some idea of how seriously over-advanced an engine can be when a high-speed retard station fails to function correctly, we should examine the Motoplat ignition unit fitted by Rotax to their type 124 air-cooled and liquid-cooled kart engines. Prior to mid-1980, the ignition provided steady ignition timing (i.e., without any advance/retard). With this Motoplat unit the timing was set at 1.0mm before TDC (14° advance). Later model engines were fitted with an ignition unit incorporating a high-speed retard function. With this type of Motoplat the advance is set at 3.76mm before TDC (27.5° advance). After 5000rpm the automatic retard gradually reduces the ignition advance with rising engine speed, so that at 11,000rpm the timing has decreased to 1.2mm or 15.5° before TDC. Obviously if the automatic spark retard failed, and the engine was operated with the Motoplat locked on full advance, the engine would quickly fail.

Regardless of the ignition system employed, the spark plug must fire at the correct time if good power is to be made and engine damage avoided. Some two-strokes are timed to spark at 2mm before TDC, others at anywhere from 0.4mm to 4mm. Probably you are wondering why the difference? Well, first, the length of the engine's stroke will affect the amount of advance required. A short stroke engine with 2mm advance will have considerably more advance measured in degrees of crankshaft rotation than a long stroke engine with spark timing of 2mm before TDC. For example, a 125cc engine with a stroke of 60mm and 2mm ignition advance has 18.8° advance, the same as a 125 engine with a 50mm stroke and 1.65mm advance. The advance angle can be calcuated using the formula:-

$$A = \operatorname{Cos} \frac{P^2 + R^2 - L^2}{2 \times P \times R}$$

where A = ignition advance in degrees
       R = engine stroke divided by 2 in mm
       L = con-rod length (usually stroke multiplied by 2) in mm
       T = ingition timing in mm
       P = R + L − T

As mentioned in the previous chapter, the burn rate of individual fuels differs. Methanol burns slowly, therefore more advance is required as the combustion flame must have progressed just as far by the time the piston passes TDC as it would if the fuel were petrol. To compensate for the slower rate of burning, the flame must be started earlier.

Beside the type of fuel being burnt, there are other factors which influence flame speed. Very rich and very lean mixtures both burn slowly, hence more spark advance will be needed. A mixture close to full power lean burns the hottest and requires the least advance.

An increase in the compression ratio increases the density and temperature of the compressed fuel/air charge. This increases the rate of combustion. Likewise, an improvement in the volumetric efficiency of the engine will have a similar effect. Therefore a change in porting, a new expansion chamber, or a carburettor which allows the engine to breathe better, may require that the spark lead is reduced.

As the engine speed increases, fuel atomisation improves, which means that the fuel will be broken up into smaller particles. Small fuel particles have a proportionately larger surface area, therefore they burn more rapidly, which means less advance is necessary. This is why an engine which required, say, 1.8mm advance running at 10,000rpm may require only 1.0mm advance operating at 11,500rpm.

The size of the combustion space and the position of the spark plug in that space also influences the advance required. Obviously the further the flame has to travel, the longer it will take to completely burn the mixture. Consequently an engine with a squishless (quiescent) combustion chamber or a large bore diameter will usually require more advance. Also an engine in which the spark plug is offset from the centre of the combustion chamber will increase the distance the flame must travel, hence the need for additional advance.

Any modification which significantly raises the peak hp output of a two-stroke usually results in higher piston crown and cylinder head temperatures. A hot fuel charge burns more quickly, so the advance must be reduced.

With four-stroke engines it is usual for the modified engine to require considerably more advance than standard. However, from the foregoing you can see that this does not apply in the case of two-strokes. In fact, it is quite unusual for a two-stroke engine to need more advance than that specified by the manufacturer. It is difficult to say just how much advance a modified engine will require, but as they can be easily damaged because of too much ignition advance, I would suggest that you reduce the recommended timing by 20% to begin with. Therefore, if the standard timing is 2.5mm before TDC, start testing with 2mm advance and then increase it in steps of 0.1mm to find if more advance improves the performance. Many enthusiasts have a tendency to over-advance the timing in an effort to pick up every last fraction of performance. My advice is to use the least amount of advance conducive to peak performance. For this reason, I think it is a good idea to back-track to make sure that more advance is better. In this example, if the engine seemed to run better with each 0.1mm increase until you arrived at the standard timing of 2.5mm, drop back to 2.2mm just to make sure that the engine is really performing at its best with 2.5mm advance.

Obviously, to do any timing changes you are going to need a timing dial gauge. It is one of the most important tools in a two-stroke tuner's kit, so purchase a good one, after all they are only the price of a couple of new pistons. Some enthusiasts think that they can adjust the timing using an automotive strobe timing light, but this is not so. A strobe light will only indicate if the electronic advance/retard mechanism (in the case of CDI systems) is working correctly. The timing marks will always line up at lower engine speeds if the electronic components are functioning correctly, regardless of how far the ignition timing is under or over-advanced.

Some manufacturers quote their timing figures in degrees and suggest the use of a protractor or degree wheel to adjust the ignition to the correct advance. This is a very slow way. I feel that it is far better to convert their figures to mm before TDC using this formula:-

$$T = L + R \times (1 - \text{Cos A}) - \sqrt{L^2 - (R \times \text{Sin A})^2}$$

where T = timing in mm
A = timing in degrees
L = engine stroke in mm divided by 2
R = con-rod length in mm (usually stroke multiplied by 2)

For example, McCulloch quote the timing for their 100cc go-kart engine as 26° before TDC. In mm before TDC this would be as follows:-

A = 26°
L = 63.7mm
R = 20.765mm

$$T = L + R \times (1 - \text{Cos A}) - \sqrt{L^2 - (R \times \text{Sin A})^2}$$

$$= 63.7 + 20.765 \times (1 - .8988) - \sqrt{63.7^2 + (20.765 \times .4384)^2}$$

$$= 63.7 + 2.1 - 63.05$$
$$= 2.75\text{mm}$$

To adjust the timing on CDI systems using a timing dial gauge is quite easy, but you can waste a lot of time setting the dial gauge up if you go about it the wrong way. Assuming that the timing is to be adjusted to 2.5mm before TDC, this is the procedure to use. Insert a pencil in the spark plug hole and turn the crankshaft until the pencil rises to the highest point. In this position the piston will be approximately at TDC. Screw the timing gauge fixture into the plug hole and, after zeroing the gauge, insert it into the mounting fixture. Push the gauge down until it reads 3.0mm (i.e., about 0.5mm more than the timing figure) and lock it into position. Now gently rock the crankshaft backwards and forwards to find true TDC. When you have found TDC, hold the crankshaft in this position and turn the face of the gauge around until the zero mark aligns with the pointer. With that done, again rock the crank to ensure that the pointer does actually indicate zero when the piston is at TDC. When you are sure that the dial gauge is reading zero at TDC, rotate the crankshaft to align the timing marks, at the same time noting how many mm the pointer moves through. If the pointer has made two revolutions of the dial and is now indicating 0.5, then the timing is correct.

Using this method you must be very careful to note the movement of the pointer, 131 as most timing gauges are graduated 0-50-0 not 0-100. Therefore 0.3mm, for example, would be either to the left or right of zero, the same as 0.7mm. Because of this drawback some prefer to set the dial gauge up this way: rotate the crankshaft to align the timing marks; insert the dial gauge into the mounting fixture and lock it into position; zero the gauge, being very careful to note that the timing marks remain aligned; rock the crank backwards and forwards, then ensure the timing marks align when the pointer indicates zero; rotate the crank to TDC and read the timing advance straight off the dial. It sounds easy, but you will find that it is quite difficult to check the timing this way. The problem is that the crank usually moves when you attempt to zero the dial, throwing the timing marks out of alignment.

With a points-type ignition system (either magneto or battery and coil) you will find it even more difficult to achieve accurate timing using the latter method. Points-type ignition is a little different to adjust than CDI, as you don't have any useful timing marks. Instead a continuity test light (or a buzz box) is connected across the points (FIGURE 6.3). When the light goes out, indicating that the points have just opened, the dial gauge reading will show whether the timing is correct. If the timing is incorrect then the points will have to be adjusted. Some manufacturers mount the points on a moveable base plate, which can be rotated to achieve the desired ignition advance. Some, however, do not have this facility, so what you must do is increase or decrease the points gap to change the timing.

Perhaps the greatest obstacle to achieving accurate ignition timing is the inadequate timing marks which many manufacturers provide. Generally, I have found

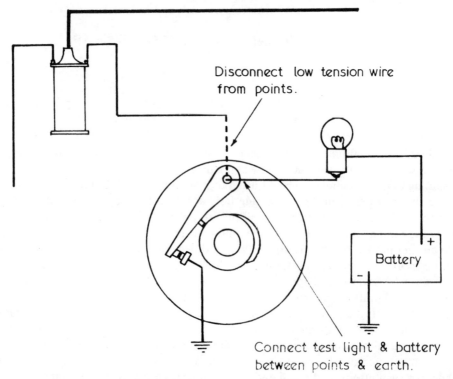

Disconnect low tension wire from points.

Battery

Connect test light & battery between points & earth.

Fig. 6.3 Using a test light to check when points open.

it impossible to adjust the timing to an accuracy of better than ±0.15mm of the desired figure, using the naked eye and the manufacturer's standard timing marks. To make the timing marks easier to see, they should be painted black and the surrounding area left unpainted, or else the entire area should be painted black and the marks painted white or silver. Often, you will find that the rotor face stands proud of the stator by anything up to 5mm, which means that it will be very difficult, if not impossible, to adjust the timing accurately because of parallax error, even if the timing marks are clearly visible. In this situation you have two options. Either you can make a fixture with a sight slot, like a gun sight, to sight through onto the timing marks, or you can pull the rotor off the end of the crank and very accurately extend the timing mark onto the rotor's periphery, using a three corner file or a scriber. Anything which you can do to improve the accuracy and repeatability of ignition timing adjustments will lessen the possibility of detonation and allow the engine to perform at its best.

If your machine has a points-type ignition system, don't attempt to adjust the timing using the stock timing marks. Instead, always set the advance with a dial gauge and a light connected across the points. Many of the piston failures experienced by engines like the early Yamaha RD twins can be traced back to inaccurate ignition timing as a result of the tuner relying on the stock timing marks.

Detonation, and to a lesser extent pre-ignition, both damage many two-stroke engines. Detonation occurs when a portion of the fuel/air mixture, usually the 'end gases', begin to burn spontaneously after normal ignition takes place. The flame front created by this condition eventually collides with the flame initiated by the spark plug. This causes a rapid and violent burning of any remaining fuel (almost an explosion) which hammers the engine's internal components with such force that the cylinder wall and piston crown actually vibrate. This vibration makes the pinging sound which an alert ear can pick up. Pre-ignition is ignition of the fuel/air charge by a 'hot spot' before the spark plug fires to initiate normal combustion. Typically, this leads to a loss in performance much like excessive ignition advance in its early stages. If allowed to continue it can destroy an engine.

When engine damage results from either type of abnormal combustion, the culprit can usually be identified after an examination of the piston and spark plug. Pre-ignition damage is caused by the extreme combustion temperature which results, melting the piston crown and also, possibly, the ring lands. If a hole is present in the piston, it will appear to have been burned through with a welding torch. The metal around the hole will be fused and have a melted appearance. The spark plug may have the centre electrode melted away and, in extreme cases, the insulator nose and earth electrode will also be fused.

A piston damaged by detonation will show signs of pitting on the crown. The edge will be gray and eroded, as if sandblasted. In the very early stages, gray ash-like deposits form on the exhaust-side edge of the piston crown. In extreme examples, the piston will be holed. The hole will appear to have been punched through, with radial cracks and a depressed area around the hole. A spark plug subjected to fairly severe detonation will usually show signs of cracking at the insulator nose. Engines with plated aluminium cylinders will exhibit a sand-blasted effect around the top lip of the bore.

Pre-ignition can frequently be traced to deposits in the combustion chamber or on the piston crown becoming incandescent. Since these deposits do not conduct heat well, 133 very high temperatures can be reached within such accumulations. Spark plug heat ranges can also affect pre-ignition. If the electrodes retain too much heat from previous combustion cycles, they will glow and pre-ignite the fuel.

The conditions which lead to detonation are high fuel/air mixture density, high compression ratio, high inlet charge temperature, best power fuel/air ratio (i.e., 1:12.5), and excessive spark advance. A piston crown or combustion chamber overheated by pre-ignition can initiate detonation by excessively heating the 'end gases'. Go-kart engines with fixed gearing may also suffer from detonation when pulling out of low speed corners, if geared too high. Except in the latter two cases, detonation is eliminated by reducing the ignition advance and possibly by jetting richer (TABLES 6.1 and 6.2).

TABLE 6.1   Effect of ignition advance on combustion temperature

Ignition timing (mm)	Spark plug electrode temp. (°C)
2.0	853
2.25	876
2.5	908
2.75	962

TABLE 6.2   Effect of fuel flow on combustion temperature

Fuel flow (litre/hr)	Spark plug electrode temp. (°C)
3.0	904
3.25	880
3.5	857
3.75	832
4.0	800
4.25	766

Due to increased combustion temperatures in a modified engine, consideration must be given to finding a spark plug with the correct heat range. A hot plug transfers combustion heat slowly and is used to avoid fouling in engines with relatively low combustion temperatures. A cold plug, on the other hand, transfers heat rapidly from the firing end. It is used to avoid overheating where temperatures are high, as in a racing engine (TABLE 6.3).

TABLE 6.3   Effect of spark plug heat range on plug temperature

Plug type	Under-plug temperature (°C)
Champion L4G	264
Champion L3G	252
Champion L2G	243

The length of the insulator nose and the composition of the electrode alloy are the primary factors in establishing the heat rating of a particular plug. Hot plugs have long insulator noses, and hence a long heat transfer path. Cold plugs have shorter nose lengths to transfer heat more rapidly from the insulator tip to the cylinder head fins (or water jacket), via the metal spark plug body (FIGURE 6.4).

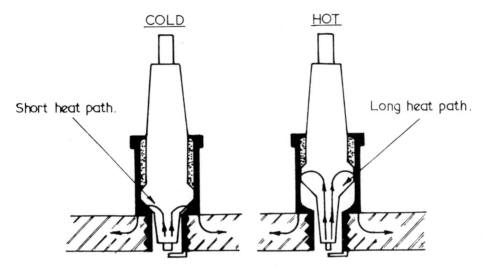

Fig. 6.4 Spark plug heat range.

Generally, two-stroke engines do not require a plug more than one or two grades colder than standard, even when extensively modified for very high power outputs. Providing the engine is in good condition, and the carburettor is correctly tuned, reading the nose of the plug will indicate if one with the correct heat range has been chosen. So that you do not end up with engine damage it is advisable to begin testing with a plug which is too cold, or else test the machine at moderate load and speed, and then check the plug before you engage in any full power running.

For the plug reading to be accurate, it will be necessary to run the engine at full throttle and maximum speed and then cut the engine dead. If you allow the engine to keep running as you bring the bike to a stop, the plug reading will be meaningless.

The signs to look for when reading a plug are indicated in TABLE 6.4. You will note that it is not just the colour of the insulator nose in which we are interested. The entire firing end of the plug exposed to the combustion flame must be examined and read.

Of course, spark plug heat range must be tailored to each race circuit. Tracks with a long, fast straight may require a plug one grade colder. Conversely, a tight, wet track may require a plug one grade hotter than normal.

Once you have determined the correct plug heat range, don't swap over to another brand with an 'equivalent' heat range. Heat range conversion charts should be used as a guide only, when you swap from one plug brand to another, as individual plug manufacturers use different methods of determining the heat range of their plugs. If you cross-reference the conversion charts from all the plug manufacturers you will find that they disagree with each other, due to varying test procedures.

As well as the heat range, the gap style of the plug must also be considered to 135

TABLE 6.4   Spark plug reading for heat range and other conditions

Spark plug condition	Indications
Normal — correct heat range	Insulator nose white or very light tan to rust brown. Little or no cement boil where the centre electrode protrudes through the insulator nose. The electrodes are not discoloured or eroded.
Too cold — use hotter plug	Insulator nose dark grey or black. Steel plug shell end covered with tar-like deposit.
Too hot — use colder plug	Insulator nose chalky white or may have satin sheen. Excessive cement boil where centre electrode protrudes through the insulator nose. Cement may be milk white or meringue-liké. Centre electrode may 'blue' and be rounded off at the edges. Earth electrode may be badly eroded or have a molten appearance.
Pre-ignition — use a colder plug and remove piston and combustion chamber deposits	Insulator nose blistered or fused. Centre electrode and side electrode burned or melted away.
Detonation — retard ignition and richen mixture	Fractured insulator nose in sustained or extreme cases. Insulator nose covered in tiny pepper specks or even tiny beads of aluminium leaving the piston. Excessive cement boil where centre electrode protrudes through insulator nose. Specks on plug shell end.

obtain the best performance, and in a few instances to avoid engine damage (FIGURE 6.5). The spark plug which I recommend for all two-stroke applications, with a few exceptions, is the fine wire type Champion Gold Palladium. This type of plug has a very wide heat range to resist both fouling and pre-ignition. It can be supplied with the standard Gold Palladium centre electrode or, for special applications, with a platinum centre electrode (TABLE 6.5). The small diameter centre electrode requires less voltage to fire than a regular electrode. This feature allows easier starting of all engines employing magneto type ignitions (either points or CDI) as the voltage available at lower cranking speeds is diminished. The insulator nose is a special 'open' design which allows more clearance within the firing end of the plug for better scavenging of deposits.

The conventional regular gap plug is my next choice after the fine wire type. It does not have such a good heat range and anti-fouling properties as the Gold Palladium, but it is cheaper. However, it has a heat range far superior to the retracted gap style. Really, the retracted gap plug should only be used when absolutely necessary. This type of plug has little resistance to fouling and it generates a poor combustion flame front, due to the way in which the plug masks the spark within its nose in a pocket of stagnant air. Combustion efficiency and speed depends to a large extent on

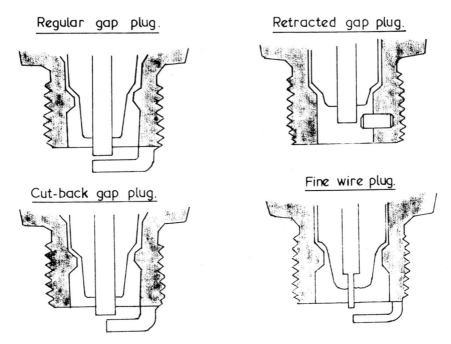

Fig. 6.5 Spark plug gap styles.

TABLE 6.5 **Champion spark plug heat range chart**
(courtesy of Champion Sparking Plug Co.)

	Regular	Gold Palladium	Gold Palladium	Fine Wire	Retracted
14mm thread — ¾in reach : N series					
Hot	N4	N4G			
	N3	N3G	*N87G	N87	
					N62R
	N2	N2G	*N86G	N86	
	N60				
					N60R
		N59G	*N84G	N84	
	N1				
	N57	N57G	*N82G	N82	N57R
		N55G	*N80G	N80	
					N54R
Cold					†N52R

* special plug for high compression engines
†Silver electrode

14mm thread — ½ in. reach : L series

	Regular	Gold Palladium	Retracted	Retracted
Hot	*L82			
		*L6G		
	L4J			
	*L78	*L4G	L62R	
	*L77J	*L3G	L60R	
		*L2G	L57R	†L87R
		*L55G	L54R	†L84R
Cold				†L82R

* .472 in. reach
† special methanol plug

14mm thread — ⅜ in. reach : J series

	Regular	Gold Palladium	Gold Palladium	Retracted
Hot	J5			
		J64G	*UJ7G	
	J4J			J62R
	J2J	J60G		J60R
	J79			
				†J57R
Cold				†J54R

* plug has auxiliary gap
† not suitable for methanol — use L series methanol plug and N677 gasket

turbulence within the combustion chamber causing the compressed fuel/air charge to rush through the plug electrode gap and propagate the combustion flame throughout the combustion chamber. When the spark generates a combustion flame in an area of relative calm, as in the end of a retracted gap plug, some time elapses before the flame radiates out into the turbulence of the combustion chamber. The fact that the insulator nose is in an area of such calm also means that fuel and ash deposits collect very easily to foul the plug.

A variation of the regular gap plug is the cut-back gap. This type has a shorter earth electrode which extends midway across the centre electrode. The main benefit of this design is that it requires less voltage to fire at high rpm than the regular gap plug. Champion plugs of this type have a 'J' suffix (eg: L4J, L77J). Of course, regular gap plugs can be modified by filing the earth electrode back when cut-back plugs are not available in the heat range required. This modification will, however, make the plug's heat range just a little cooler.

In some heat ranges the only spark plugs available have an auxiliary gap ('booster gap') to help resist low speed fouling. Since the booster gap increases the voltage requirement to fire the plug quite considerably, they can cause problems in competition engines. A booster gap plug can be identified visually by a small hole in the stud of the plug which ventilates the interior booster gap. In the case of Champion plugs, they can be recognised easily by a 'U' prefix (eg: UL81J, UJ7G). It is recommended that booster gap plugs be 'pinned' when installed in high-speed engines, by inserting a straightened paper clip down the vent hole. Whey you have pushed the wire in as far as it will go, cut it off level with the top of the plug terminal.

Another point worthy of consideration is the reach of the plug. A plug which is too short and does not extend the full threaded length of the spark plug boss in the head will reduce performance by masking the ignition flame. Additonally, it can invite a hot spot in the form of carbon building up in the unused portion of thread. A plug that is too long will have threads exposed in the combustion chamber. The threads fill up with carbon which damages or strips the threads in the head when the plug is removed. Also, the exposed threads, or the carbon deposited in them, may become a hot spot precipitating pre-ignition.

On any engine the spark plug reach should be checked, all the more so if the combustion chamber has been modified or if a temperature gauge thermocouple washer is fitted under the plug. In some instances a change to another plug reach may be in order, but in most cases the use of a single solid copper gasket will ensure the proper depth fit. The range of Champion gaskets for 14mm plugs is listed in TABLE 6.6. It should be noted that it is quite in order to use a solid gasket and the standard folded gasket together. This is necessary, for example, when ¾in reach Gold Palladium plugs are used in applications where ⅝in reach plugs are normally fitted.

TABLE 6.6   Champion gaskets for 14mm spark plugs

Gasket thickness (in)	Part No
0.057	N675
0.080	N673X1
0.096	N673X2
0.135	N677
0.070/0.052	N678

Note: Part No N678 is a thread-on gasket, the others are solid.

The width of the spark plug gap for best performance depends primarily on the compression pressure of the fuel/air charge, the engine rpm, the spark plug gap style and the high speed voltage output of the coil. Increasing the first two factors without an increase in the latter calls for a decrease in the gap width. Therefore, it is fairly safe to say that all radically-modified engines will require a gap narrower than that recommended by the manufacturer.

Manufacturers generally stipulate a relatively wide gap (0.6 to 0.7mm) as this improves performance at lower rpm and reduces the risk of the gap being bridged by whiskers of carbon, or beads of lead, oil or petrol. As there is much less turbulence in the combustion chamber at low engine speeds, it is very easy for a blob of carbon or fuel to settle between the plug electrodes, shorting it out. With a wider gap the odds are better because the speck of carbon or the bead of fuel may not be large enough to bridge the gap. Later, when the engine is given a high-speed burst, the increased turbulence will 'blow' the electrodes clean. Also, because the spark generated in a wide gap is larger than that in a narrow gap, a more sizeable initial combustion flame is produced. This improves flame propagation through the fuel charge and allows for a more complete burn of the compressed mixture. Hence hp at lower revs goes up.

As the engine speed and compression pressures increase, the coil is not able to supply electrical energy of sufficient voltage to jump a wide spark gap and keep the air between the electrodes ionised for a period long enough to initiate combustion. What happens is that the coil has enough energy reserve to electrically bridge the spark plug electrodes but, before the spark generated can get a combustion flame started, turbulence within the combustion chamber will actually blow out the spark. This was a big problem with the early CDI systems, as the spark was produced for only a very short duration. Current CDIs have a shunt incorporated to lengthen spark duration, allowing marginally wider plug gaps. When a narrow gap is used, the magnetic field within the gap is much more intense, as it is confined to a much smaller space. Hence the spark 'holds together' for long enough to effect ignition, in spite of receiving severe buffeting from the turbulent gases within the combustion chamber.

From experience I would recommend that any competition engine with an operating speed in excess of 9000rpm would use a plug gap of 0.5mm if fitted with a fine wire plug, fired by a CDI system. With a coil and battery, or magneto system, the gap may have to be reduced to 0.4mm. When retracted gap plugs are used, the gap will be 0.4 to 0.45mm with CDI and 0.35 to 0.4mm for other systems.

Engines operating at speeds of around 7500 to 8500rpm will require a gap of 0.55 to 0.6mm with a fine wire plug and CDI. If retracted gap plugs are fitted, the gap will be 0.4 to 0.45mm.

If the ignition system has been modified, or if a special ignition has been fitted, check to see that coil polarity is correct before you try experimenting to determine what plug gap gives the best performance in your engine. A coil with reversed polarity loses the equivalent of 40% energy as the spark has to jump from what would normally be the earth electrode (the side electrode) to the centre electrode. Because the side electrode is many hundreds of degrees cooler than the centre electrode, there is much more restrained electron activity on the metal surface. This considerably increases the voltage required to cause the electrons to leave one electrode and jump to the other, thus ionising the gap and creating a spark. Cold engines are more difficult to get started for this very reason. The plug electrodes are cold, therefore a very high voltage is necessary to tear the electrons from one surface and have them jump the gap to the other electrode.

With a coil and battery type ignition system the polarity is correct when the wire from the coil to the points is connected to the coil terminal with the same polarity as the earth terminal of the battery, i.e., if the negative (−) battery terminal is earthed, then

the wire running between the coil and the points should be connected to the negative

(−) coil terminal. With other ignition systems the polarity is seldom marked, so it is a matter of following the manufacturer's wiring diagram precisely, otherwise the ignition may still function but the polarity could be wrong. Also take care that you do not fit mis-matched components, using a rotor/stator assembly from one bike, and a coil/electronic control unit from another. Even if the bikes are basically identical, but one is a year or two older than the other, it is quite possible to run into trouble.

A dished spark plug side electrode indicates incorrect polarity (FIGURE 6.6). The dish is caused by metal leaving the electrode each time a spark jumps across to the centre electrode. Normally, this would only be visible in road bikes where the plug has a service life of 3000 to 5000 miles.

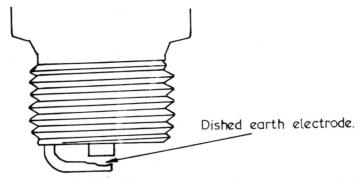

Dished earth electrode.

Fig. 6.6   Dished earth electrode indicates wrong polarity.

The life of a spark plug in a two-stroke racing engine is not as short as many would suppose. Many have the idea that a new plug is required for each race, but this is just not so. With proper care, a plug should last at least 300 miles, and up to 500 miles. An exception would be in the case of engines using nitro, or if the engine blows, coating the insulator with metallic deposits.

A road machine should have the plugs filed, gapped and tested every 1,800-2,000 miles, and a race machine after each meeting. Bend the earth electrode back far enough to permit filing of the sparking surfaces shown in FIGURE 6.7. A points file should be used to file a flat surface with sharp edges on both the centre and side electrode. This lowers the voltage required to fire the plug, firstly because electricity prefers to jump across sharp edges, and secondly because the electrical conductivity of the electrodes is improved. Combustion heat and pressure tends to break up and oxidise electrode firing surfaces, increasing the electrical resistance. Filing removes this 'dead' material and exposes new, highly-conductive metal.

Retracted gap plugs, naturally enough, cannot be filed. Also the centre electrode of fine wire plugs should not be filed, otherwise it will be damaged.

Spark plugs should never be cleaned with a wire brush, as metallic deposits will impregnate the insulator and short out the plug. I also do not recommend cleaning in an abrasive plug cleaner, as some abrasive material always seems to become wedged between the insulator and plug shell. If this cannot be probed out with a scriber, it will drop into the cylinder and possibly cause damage. However, if you choose to have your plugs abrasive blasted, be sure to remove all abrasive grit inside the plug nose and from the threads and gasket.

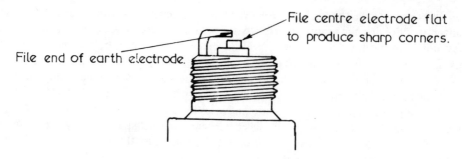

File end of earth electrode.

File centre electrode flat to produce sharp corners.

Fig. 6.7 Spark plug electrode filing.

Personally, I prefer to leave plugs uncleaned. If they are fuel or oil-fouled, I clean them with a tooth brush and ether. Trichloroethylene or chlorothene are also excellent. Be sure to blow the insulator dry before refitting the plug. If the insulation is breaking down due to leaded fuel deposits, or other metallic deposits, I throw the plug away. Do not use carbon tetrachloride to clean plugs as this will leave a conductive deposit. Carbon tetrachloride will remove oil and fuel, but it leaves behind the makings of a fine carbon deposit that could short the plug.

The spark plug lead provides the high voltage electrical connection between the coil and plug. It also forms an effective insulating barrier to prevent the ignition current tracking to earth. If the insulation is damaged by coming in contact with hot metal, or by abrasion, a short circuit could result. Therefore, plug leads must be carefully routed to avoid such damage.

Apart from the plug lead, the spark plug cap can also be a source of high voltage leakage, or flashover. The cap must be free of dust, moisture, cracks and carbon tracks, both inside and out, to ensure that full voltage is reaching the plug. If it's raining or wet, the spark plug cap will be wet on the outside, but if it is of good design, like the KLG cap and some Japanese, it should remain free of moisture inside.

While a high voltage leak is the most common cause of ignition failure in wet weather, the low voltage system can also give trouble if not correctly waterproofed. Regardless of whether your bike employs a points or CDI system, the crankcase cover should be carefully sealed with Silastic, and don't forget to seal around both the inside and the outside of the rubber grommet which protects the wires entering through the cover. Condensation within the sealed cover is usually not a problem, but it is a good idea to give everything a light spray with WD-40 to prevent any trouble from moisture in the air. Be careful that not too much WD-40 is applied, otherwise it will run over the surfaces to be sealed and prevent the Silastic from adhering.

If, after this, you still have a problem with water entering the ignition cover, a vent hose will have to be fitted to run from the cover to high up under the seat or the fuel tank. What can happen is that the engine heats and expands the air within the ignition cover, building up pressure which ruptures the Silastic seal. Then when you ride through a water hole the sudden drop in temperature cools the air, causing it to contract and suck in water.

The kill button can also give trouble, so be sure to fit a good, sealed Japanese button. Then seal it with Silastic to further enhance its water resistance.

Chapter 7
The Bottom End

THE BOTTOM END is certainly the least glamorous part of the two-stroke engine, and if you are like me it is also the part you would prefer to forget about until something actually goes wrong. Because the two-stroke is so easy to dismantle, the bottom end seems difficult to get at by comparison.

Fortunately the modern day engine has a crankshaft-rod-bearing assembly that in normal service is very reliable and requires little attention. But this is not to say there is nothing that can be done to improve the crankshaft assembly. Your careful attention in this area will not only pick up power and reduce fatigue induced by vibration, it will also decrease the number of crank rebuilds required and lower the cost of being competitive.

Most two-stroke crankshafts are a pressed together affair. During assembly at the factory, or from useage, the crank can get out of alignment. This sets up vibration in the engine which soaks up power, wrecks the bearings and fatigues you. The only way to overcome the problem is to blueprint the crank assembly. If you have a single cylinder engine this can wait until the bearings or crankpin are due for replacement. However, if your machine is a twin cylinder road racer, I would encourage you to set up properly even brand new crankshafts. When you do this you can be assured of 700 miles trouble free from TZ250 and TZ350 crankshafts.

If you don't have a press, dial gauge and centres, you should take your crankshaft to a reputable firm to have the work done. However, don't assume every motorcycle or engineering shop will do the crankshaft work to the accuracy required. Before you hand your crank over, have a talk with the shop foreman, tell him what you require and why you insist on accuracy. If he wants your job, he will probably show you other crankshafts he has done and prove their accuracy.

The first step is to press the crankpin out and separate the crankwheels. Then have the wheels magnaflux crack tested. Next, check each crankwheel for concentricity. A crankwheel is concentric when the axle is exactly in the centre of the flywheel. Generally, the shafts are not exactly in the centre of the flywheels, which produces an 143 imbalance and vibration. For example, the radius from the shaft's centre to the top of the flywheel might be 2.498ins. The radius to the bottom of the flywheel might be 2.502ins, indicating that the shaft is 0.002in off centre. The dial gauge would show the runout to be 0.004in. What we want is not more than 0.001in runout, so the crankwheel will require very light machining in the lathe to bring the radius of the flywheel to within 0.0005in of centre.

After the wheels are true, the crankpin holes and crankpin diameter must be checked to ensure an interference fit of 0.002-0.003in per inch of diameter. If the fit is too loose, the crankshaft will not stay in alignment.

When a suitable crankpin is found, fit a new big end bearing on the pin, slip the con-rod on and measure the small end side shake. The amount the small end moves from side to side indicates the big end radial clearance. Unfortunately, even all new parts at times indicate up to 0.055in small end movement, which is very close to what I consider to be the serviceable limit, 0.065in. A bearing, rod, pin combination with 0.030-0.040in play should be sought. This will ensure relatively good big end life (FIGURE 7.1).

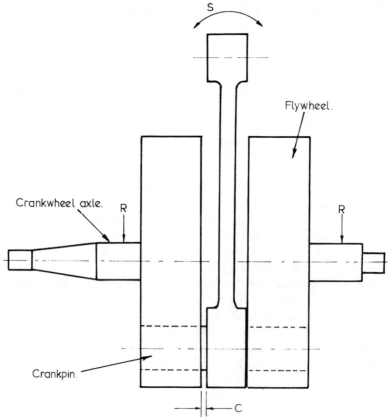

C - big-end side clearance (0.5mm to 0.6mm)
R - crankshaft runout (0.04mm maximum)
S - little-end side shake (0.8mm to 1.3mm)

Fig. 7.1 Critical crankshaft measurements.

For the ultimate in big end bearing reliability, a lot of painstaking work is required. Basically, the big end assembly will give the best service if the bearing rollers do not skid on the pin or con rod eye. To achieve this ideal situation you will have to work the big end assembly to several very close tolerances.

Looking at TABLES 7.1 and 7.2 you will note the dimensions in which we are interested. Naturally, we have to select components which not only fall into either of the two selective fit categories dimensionally but which also exhibit true parallelism. If the pin or big end eye, or any of the individual rollers, are not parallel, the rollers will still skid no matter how carefully we match these parts for fit.

TABLE 7.1   Typical big-end bearing radial clearance

Crankpin diameter (mm)	Radial clearance (mm)	
	Minimum	*Maximum*
18	0.023	0.035
20	0.025	0.037
22	0.028	0.040
25	0.031	0.043
27	0.034	0.046
30	0.038	0.050

Note: the above clearances are for high speed racing engines. Low speed road and play bike engines could use clearances 25% less.

TABLE 7.2   Typical big-end assembly tolerances

	Crankpin	Big-end eye	Bearing rollers
Nominal dimension (mm)	20	26	3
Tolerance	-0.006 -0.010	$+0.010$ $+0.020$	-0.002 -0.006
Selective fit A	$20\begin{array}{l}-0.008\\-0.010\end{array}$	$26\begin{array}{l}+0.010\\+0.015\end{array}$	$3\begin{array}{l}-0.004\\-0.006\end{array}$
Selective fit B	$20\begin{array}{l}-0.006\\-0.008\end{array}$	$26\begin{array}{l}+0.015\\+0.020\end{array}$	$3\begin{array}{l}-0.002\\-0.004\end{array}$

Also, if we are to avoid skidding rollers, we must ensure that the connecting rod has been machined true. To determine this you will have to make a pair of dummy pins about 100mm long to fit the little end and big end eyes. Measuring between both ends of the dummy pins will determine if the rod is bent or has the eyes machined out of parallel (FIGURE 7.2). Next check that the eyes have been machined in the same plane (i.e., not twisted). To do this set the big end of the rod up with a dummy pin fitted, on a pair of parallel V-blocks. Then, with a dial gauge, measure to see that both ends of the pin fitted in the little end are the same dimension from the surface plate.

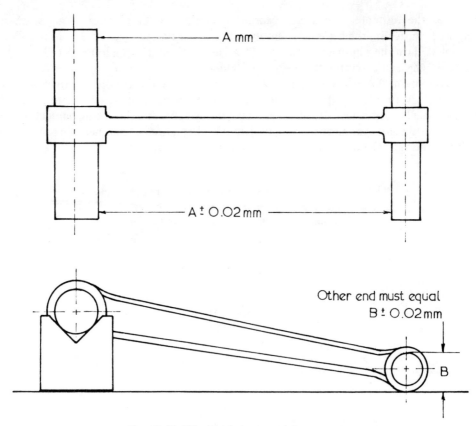

Fig. 7.2 Checking con rod trueness.

In multi-cylinder engines crankshaft balance must be maintained to avoid vibration damage to the crankshaft and bearings. This means that the weight of each big end assembly must be equal, and the weight of each little end assembly must be equal. The big end assembly is made up of the crankpin, big end bearing and thrust washers, and the rod big end. The little end assembly comprises the rod little end, the little end bearing and thrust washers, and piston pin. Unfortunately, few tuners have the equipment to do this balancing themselves, so this usually means that all these components must be sent to some automotive firm for balancing. If this is true in your case, be sure to pack each con rod assembly in a separate plastic bag and instruct the firm doing the balancing that under no circumstances are parts to be swapped from one assembly to another, otherwise all the time spent on obtaining proper big end tolerances will have been wasted.

The pistons, of course, will also have to be balanced, using either an accurate pair of laboratory scales or a simple beam balance. When the lightest piston is found, remove metal from inside the piston skirt and around the pin bosses to reduce the weight of the other pistons to within 1 gram of the lightest piston.

Whenever the big end or main bearings are replaced, don't just use any bearing which will fit. The loads experienced by the bearings in two-stroke engines demand the use of high quality parts if reliability is to be maintained. Therefore only those bearings equivalent to, or superior to the original components, should be utilised.

If you wish to use bearings better than those fitted as standard, you may be able to obtain a suitable replacement from the German INA bearing company. Their two-stroke bearings are the best available. Try to get main bearings with fatigue resistant plastic or fibre cages rather than riveted steel cages which seem prone to cracking up.

Main bearings with plastic cages demand plenty of lubrication to enable cool running. If the bearing overheats the plastic cage will distort or melt, causing bearing failure. To improve lubrication you may have to drill an oil feed hole in the crankcase to each bearing, similar to that illustrated in FIGURE 7.3. The hole should be about $\frac{5}{32}$in diameter, drilled from the transfer slot or the barrel spigot recess to the main bearing housing.

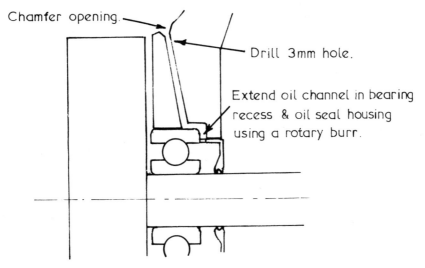

Chamfer opening.

Drill 3mm hole.

Extend oil channel in bearing recess & oil seal housing using a rotary burr.

Fig. 7.3 Main bearing oil feed.

The big end bearing must be as light as possible, otherwise the inertia generated by the swinging of the con rod as it passes top and bottom dead centre will cause the rollers to skid and over-heat the bearing and rod big end. A lightweight bearing can be accelerated and decelerated quickly, but a heavy bearing will continue to rotate at a more constant speed, rather than staying synchronised with the relative rotational speed of the crankpin.

Most people are surprised to know just how much influence the angular swing of the con rod has on the rotational speed of the big end bearing. Normally, the bearing should rotate at half the relative crankshaft rpm. On the surface it would appear that a big end bearing in a motor spinning at 11,000rpm would be rotating at 5,500rpm. However, when you look at FIGURE 7.4 you can see that this is not so. At TDC the angular swing of the rod is in the opposite direction to rotation, but in the same direction at BDC. With a 2 to 1 rod length to stroke ratio (eg: engine stroke 54mm; rod length centre to centre 108mm) the instantaneous rotational speed of the rod in relation to the crankpin is 25% greater or less than the crank speed. Thus, at an engine speed of 11,000rpm the relative rotational speed will be 13,750rpm at TDC, and 8,250rpm at BDC. Remembering that the bearing rotates at half these speeds, we can see that its 147

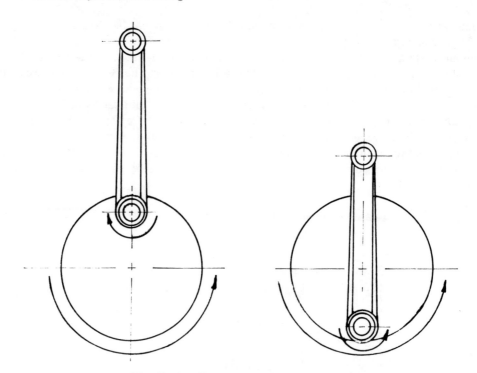

Fig. 7.4 Big-end bearing speed oscillates.

revolution rate must drop from 6,875rpm to 4,125rpm, and increase back again to 6,875rpm twice per crankshaft revolution. If the bearing has enough weight, it will resist this rapid oscillation, forcing the rollers to skid.

Most modern two-strokes have steel big end bearing cages plated with tin or copper, to provide a low friction surface. These can be beneficially replaced by very light INA bearings with a special lightweight silver plated cage. Such a move could raise the red line speed of a street engine modified for road racing by 2000rpm. The Yamaha RD400 is very popular for road racing, but its standard bearings are not up to the task. The simple solution is to substitute big end bearings out of Yamaha's TZ250 road racer. With these bearings, the RD400 will run reliably for hours at 10,000rpm.

From time to time a few tuners get hooked on the fad to lighten the crankshaft. They feel the flywheels should be machined to a 'T' or 'V' shape to reduce their weight and increase engine acceleration. Acceleration will increase, but you will have to change gears so much more that the machine will be slower around the track.

This is not to say all crankshaft lightening is a no no, as a very small number of engines will benefit from a moderate reduction in rotating mass. Generally, we can forget about the majority of Japanese engines, as these already have very light flywheels. The only exceptions would be some single cylinder 250cc motocross engines and also the Yamaha RD400 when these are modified for road racing. The amount of metal removed is quite small, usually not more than 6oz from the inside of each flywheel. This reduces the weight of the RD400 crank, for example, by 1.5lbs.

Before the crank is reassembled, the rods (even if new) must be crack tested. If the engine has a history of rod failures, the rods should be polished along the beams and then shot peened. Also polish and radius any corners formed by the oiling slots in the big-end (FIGURE 7.5).

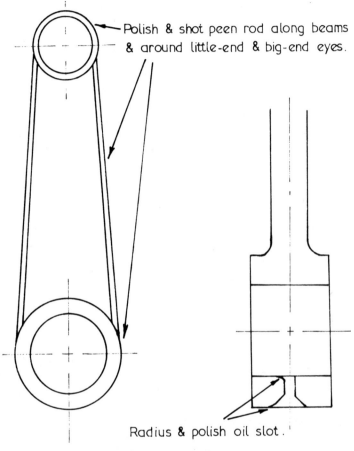

Polish & shot peen rod along beams & around little-end & big-end eyes.

Radius & polish oil slot.

Fig. 7.5 Con rod modification.

The tough skin formed on the con rod by forging gives it much of its strength and fatigue resistance. Therefore the rod should never be polished unless you intend to follow up with shot peening to create another work toughened skin. I consider it a waste of time polishing the entire rod.

If you have a look at a rod you will see, along its edges, a rough band where metal appears to have been sawn away. That is where the excess metal called flash was squeezed out from between the forging dies when the rod was being made. Later, most of the flash is trimmed off, but a bead is left, as you can see. Of course, there is no hard skin along this ridge, in fact its roughness is a stress raiser, so the ridge should be removed with a sanding belt. Give the entire beam a polish with fine emery cloth and then follow up with buffing and shot peening.

After the rods have been prepared and the crankpins and bearings matched, the crankwheels can be reassembled. Scrupulous cleanliness is essential, and care should be taken to ensure the wheels are started on the pin as accurately as possible. Use a 149 straight edge across the wheels to check this. If the pin is shouldered, the wheels are pressed hard home, but if a straight pin is used, the necessary rod side clearance must be maintained by inserting two feeler strips of the appropriate thickness, usually 0.25-0.3mm, on either side of the big-end and pressing until the strips are just ensnared.

The alignment should be checked between centres, using a dial gauge in contact with the bearing seat of a crankwheel axle. Any runout is eliminated by holding one wheel and striking the other with a copper or lead hammer. Runout must be kept to a maximum of 0.0015in, but 0.001in is preferable (FIGURE 7.1).

Some people weld cranks to keep them in alignment but I do not agree with this practice. Welding hardens steel and makes it prone to fatigue fractures. Therefore, I use Loctite on the fit between the crankpin and crankwheels. Apply a small amount of Loctite to the pin, and a larger amount in the crankwheel holes, before pressing the shaft together. Take care that you do not allow Loctite into the bearing.

Before the crankshaft is refitted, the crankcase will require some reworking to reduce friction in the engine and increase piston and ring life. At all times the piston should be perpendicular to the crankshaft, but production tolerances being what they are, this is seldom the case. For the piston to be 90° to the crankshaft the con rod must be straight, the cylinder bore axis must be at 90° to the base of the barrel, and the top of the crankcases must be parallel with the crankshaft centre.

To check the parallelism of the crankcase first loosely bolt the two halves together. Then fit the cylinder and evenly tension the cylinder retaining bolts to align the case halves. Next tension the crankcase bolts. With this done, the cylinder can be removed and the cases measured for trueness. The simplest way to effect this with accuracy is to fit a mandrel in the main bearings and take a measurement from the mandrel to a straight edge laid across the top of the crankcase (FIGURE 7.6). The dimension between the mandrel and straight edge must not differ by more than 0.001in from one side of the crankcase to the other. Usually, it will be found necessary to machine the top of the cases to bring them into line with the crank.

When the crankcase has been trued, the crank, together with new main bearings and seals, can be fitted. Take the time to lubricate the seals and bearings before fitting the crankshaft. A dry start will quickly wreck any engine.

Engines with horizontally-split crankcases can experience problems with the main bearings attempting to spin in their housings. The TZ250 Yamaha is particularly prone to this. The outer races do have little pips on them that fit into a small cavity where the case halves join, but this hasn't stopped the trouble. About the best move is to go over all the holes in the case faces and chamfer them. Studs tend to pull metal up around their threads and this can stop the cases mating tightly. When the shaft is fitted apply some Loctite to retain the bearings in the case.

Possibly the part of a two-stroke that takes unequalled abuse and gives the tuner the most trouble is the piston. Fortunately piston technology is constantly moving ahead, and piston related unreliability can, to a large degree, be eliminated by regular piston replacement and correct installation of the part in the first instance.

The largest improvement to be made to pistons came when the means were discovered for adding large quantities of silicon to the aluminium alloy. This has drastically reduced the piston expansion rate, minimising the incidence of seizure. Silicon also imparts more strength to aluminium at high temperatures and increases

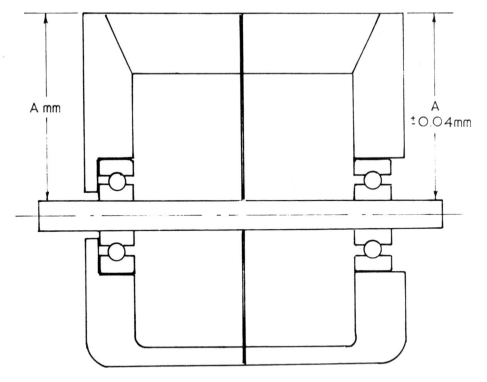

A mm

A
±0.04mm

Fig. 7.6 Checking crankcase parallelism.

wear resistance.

Quality pistons for competition use generally contain around 18-22% silicon. Unfortunately, there are pistons being sold that do not contain very much silicon at all, even though the manufacturers claim they are racing pistons. This occurs because high silicon content pistons are difficult to manufacture and expensive to machine. Consequently, I stick with the manufacturer's original pistons if the engine was designed for road racing, enduro, motocross etc. in the first place. I have usually found original pistons to be of good quality. This particularly applies to Japanese pistons; they seem to be able to produce a very good product.

There is one area for concern with standard replacement pistons which must always be checked; a large percentage are cracked from new. The best insurance against this is to have all your new pistons Zy-Glo crack tested. If you can't find an engineering shop with Zy-Glo equipment, check out aircraft repair workshops in your area.

Another problem with standard replacement pistons is that many do not have any circlip extractor slots. This means that only tail-type wire circlips can be used and unfortunately this type of circlip wrecks engines. The constant rubbing of the gudgeon pin against the circlip wears through the tail, allowing it to drop into the cylinder, scoring the bore and possibly seizing the motor. If tail-type circlips are replaced regularly, say after every second race meeting, this kind of damage can be avoided.

A better solution is to machine extractor slots into the piston so that tailless 151 circlips (or tail-type circlips with the tail cut off) can be fitted (FIGURE 7.7). The slot need only be ⅛in. wide to allow a small electrical screwdriver or the point of a scriber to fit under the circlip so that it can be flicked out. It should be cut in the position shown, using a small round key file or a ⅛in. dia. mounted grinding tip. Do not use a hacksaw blade or three cornered file to make the extractor slot, as the abrupt corner will form a stress point and eventually cause the piston to crack.

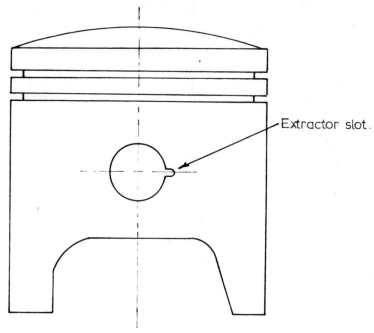

Fig. 7.7 Circlip extractor slot.

If you have an early model Yamaha you will not have to worry about machining extractor slots into the pistons. From the G model on, Yamaha pistons have been made with these slots, so when piston replacement is necessary substitute late model pistons.

We tend to think of pistons as being round, but actually the skirt is cam ground an oval shape. The piston also tapers from top to bottom (FIGURE 7.8). Both ovality and taper are necessary to prevent seizure. The top of the piston gets twice as hot as the bottom of the skirt, therefore it expands more and, due to the extra material around the pin bosses, more heat is directed to this area, elongating the piston across the piston pin axis. To compensate for this, the piston is also ground oval. Therefore you must be careful to measure piston clearance only on the thrust faces, and at the bottom of the skirt.

Before the piston is fitted, there are several clearance checks to be made. The first of these is the fit of the piston pin. It should be an easy slide fit, slipping through the piston under its own weight. A tight pin is to be avoided as this will overload the sides of the piston when the engine is running. At high engine speeds the crankshaft tends to whip and, if the pin is tight, this load will be transferred to the side of the piston, possibly distorting it and causing seizure.

A tight pin may also change the expansion characteristics of the piston and cause

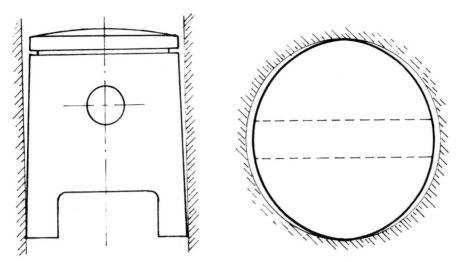

Fig. 7.8   Pistons are ground tapered & oval.

scuffing or seizure on the piston thrust faces. When the piston is unable to expand correctly along the pin axis it will expand at 90° to the pin and force the thrust faces of the piston hard against the cylinder wall.

When you are handling pistons take care not to drop them, as this can distort the piston skirt and lead to engine seizure. Also keep in mind that you must never bang a piston pin out using a hammer and drift. Beside the risk of bending the rod if it is not properly supported, you may easily push the piston out of shape. If the pin will not push or tap out easily, heat the piston in boiling water or oil and then gently tap the pin out. Often you will find that the pin will not budge because the piston pin holes are slightly closed over by metal frazes. After the ends of the pin holes are cleaned out with a sharp knife or bearing scraper, the pin will push out effortlessly.

The clearance of the piston in the cylinder is most important. A piston without enough clearance will seize. A piston with too much clearance wears quickly, can't maintain a good ring seal, and overheats because heat transfer to the cylinder wall is reduced.

Just how much clearance the piston should have, varies from engine to engine. Dissimilar piston and cylinder materials expand at different rates. Large diameter pistons expand more than smaller pistons. Most manufacturers using cast iron linered aluminium barrels specify a minimum clearance of 0.002-0.0025in. for cylinders up to 56mm, 0.0025in-0.003in. up to 72mm, and 0.0028-0.0033in. up to 85mm. Engines with plated aluminium cylinders typically run at clearances up to 0.001in. tighter.

Some engines do not have enough little end side clearance. If the clearance is tighter than 0.25-0.3mm the top of the con rod tends to overheat. This is indicated by blueing of the little end or by the presence of burnt oil in the eye of the rod. Engines fitted with thrust washers are easily cured by lapping the washers on 180 grit paper. If the engine doesn't use washers, either the rod or piston will have to be machined to increase the side clearance.

Because the two-stroke piston has to function with just the scantest amount of lubrication, some thought must be given to modifying the piston to encourage more oil up the cylinder walls. With the piston at TDC, only about 50% of the cylinder is   153 directly bathed with oil mist. Therefore we have to rely on the piston and rings collecting oil on the down stroke, and distributing it at the top of the cylinder on the compression stroke.

Unfortunately, this does not work out too well in practice, as the square edge of the piston skirt tends to scrape most of the oil off the cylinder wall as the piston descends (FIGURE 7.9). The way around the problem is to put a nice chamfer on the piston to extend about 2mm up the skirt. I do not advise a larger chamfer as many engines have a piston skirt barely long enough to cover and seal off the exhaust port when the piston is at TDC. A larger chamfer will encourage exhaust leakage into the crankcase during the induction cycle.

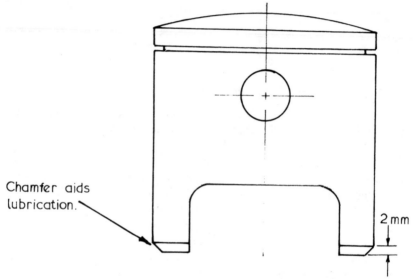

Chamfer aids lubrication.

2 mm

Fig. 7.9 Chamfer piston skirt.

When the piston skirt is chamfered, more oil will remain on the cylinder wall to lubricate the rings and the top of the piston, then on the compression stroke the rings will carry some lubricant to the upper cylinder area. Of course, oil does reach the top of the cylinder when the transfer ports are exposed to admit the fuel/air charge, but very little settles on the cylinder wall directly above the exhaust port.

Additional to improving lubrication, and hence engine life, an oil coating at the top of the cylinder and on the piston rings increases power by improving the seal between the rings and the bore wall. A decrease in compression leakage results in more power.

Leakage is a bigger problem at lower rpm, simply because there is more time for the gases to find their way through ring gaps and around the edges of the rings. This is why you will find that street bikes have two rings and high rpm road racers only one ring.

Many people mistakenly believe it is the ring's inherent radial tension that holds it against the bore wall to effect a seal, but this is not the case. Radial tension does help but it is gas pressure behind the back of the ring that forces the ring face against the cylinder wall (FIGURE 7.10).

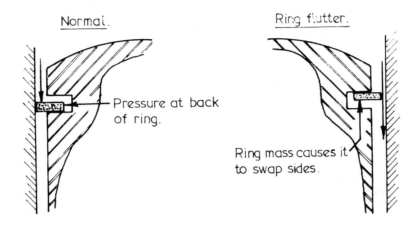

Fig. 7.10 Gas pressure seals piston ring against cylinder wall.

There is a detrimental phenomenon that can occur in high rpm engines, called ring float or ring flutter. As the piston approaches TDC it is slowed by the con rod, but the rings try to keep on moving. If they have enough weight they will leave contact with the lower side of the piston groove. When this happens, the ring seals off the gas pressure in the combustion chamber, preventing the gas getting behind the back of the ring to push it against the bore. Any gas pressure that may have been behind the ring quickly leaks into the crankcase, and combustion pressure forces the ring to collapse inward, causing it to break contact with the cylinder wall. This allows the combustion gases to blow by into the crankcase (FIGURE 7.10).

Radial tension in the ring is unable to prevent this type of blow-by caused by ring flutter. However, a certain degree of radial tension is necessary for good sealing, otherwise the pressure at the back of the ring would only equal the pressure trying to force the ring off the bore wall. This would allow blow-by, and it is this type we see occurring when the rings are badly worn and have lost their tension.

Ring flutter can also wreck engines due to an increase in piston temperature. When the ring loses contact with the cylinder it is unable to conduct heat away from the piston crown. This may lead to severe detonation and melted pistons.

The wider a ring for a given radial depth, the lower the engine speed at which ring flutter will occur. This is one of the reasons why thin rings are necessary in racing engines. Assuming the radial depth of the ring is 1/26th the cylinder diameter, then the maximum piston acceleration for a ring 1mm wide is approximately 127,000ft/sec/sec with other widths in proportion i.e., 84,700 for 1.5mm rings, 105,800 for 1.2mm rings, 158,750 for 0.8mm and 201,600 for 0.63mm rings.

Piston acceleration at TDC can be calculated using the formula:

$$G = 0.000457 \times N^2 \times S \times (1 + \frac{S}{2L}) \text{ft/sec/sec}$$

where $N =$ rpm
$S =$ stroke in inches
$L =$ con rod length

155

In a racing engine it may be found that the standard rings are too wide for operation at the engine speed at which we desire to run. This problem usually arises only when a street engine or motocross engine is modified for road racing. At times, the manufacturer makes a racing engine with the same size piston as the stock street motor. If this is the case it is a simple matter to substitute the racing piston in the modified motor. Some manufacturers have changed to thinner rings in later motors of basically the same design, and the later model piston and rings can be used.

Besides raising the speed at which flutter occurs, thin rings also reduce power loss due to friction. This is really only significant when engine speed is in excess of 9000rpm. The same can be said for single ring designs. Below about 8000rpm a two ring setup gives marginally more power, but above 9500rpm the situation reverses.

In this day of advanced metal technology, ring breakage is rare, and can usually be attributed to one of the following causes: excessive piston to cylinder clearance allowing the piston to rock and twist the rings as it passes TDC; worn piston ring grooves that let the rings jump about; excessive bore taper causing radial ring flutter; exhaust port widened excessively or ground an incorrect shape; sharp edges left in exhaust and/or transfer ports; insufficient ring gap; ring grooves not properly cleaned before fitting new rings.

Generally, a two-stroke engine should be set up with groove clearances between 0.04 and 0.1mm. Tighter than 0.04mm clearance will cause the ring to stick in the piston groove as carbon and varnish builds up. Before new rings are fitted, the piston grooves must be carefully cleaned to remove all traces of carbon. Then when the rings are fitted, measure the side clearance and ensure they are not jamming in the grooves. As a final check hold a straight edge along the side of the piston to confirm that the rings are seating correctly in their grooves (FIGURE 7.11). If the grooves have not been thoroughly cleaned, the rings will be flush or possibly even project past the ring lands.

When new rings are fitted they should be checked for end gap. Usually the ring gap is 0.1 to 0.12mm per inch of bore. This means an engine with a 54mm bore would need a gap of 0.2 to 0.25mm. Engines with 0.63mm rings require a much wider gap than this, as the rings are too narrow to lap over the ring locating pin. In this instance the required gap must be increased by the diameter of the locating pin. Therefore, an engine with a 54mm bore and a pin 1.2mm in diameter will need a ring gap of 0.2 to 0.25mm plus 1.2mm = 1.4 to 1.45mm.

The end gap of each ring should be measured with the ring fitted squarely into the top of the cylinder bore. To ensure an accurate measurement, all traces of carbon must be removed from the bore, using a scraper. Then fit the ring in the unworn part near the top of the cylinder. If the gap is insufficient, carefully file the ring ends, using a wet oilstone or a very fine file.

If an engine is assembled with ring gaps that are too narrow, damage may easily result. When heated, the rings will expand and cause the ends to butt together. This results in ring breakage or, if the pressure is not high enough to cause the rings to break, the cylinder wall will be scuffed.

It is always a sensible practice to dress the ring ends with an oilstone. Chamfering the outside edges reduces the chances of the sharp ends scuffing the bore. It is also a good idea to stone the inside corners of the ring ends too. The slight radius formed helps to stop any tendency the ring may have to pull the ring locating peg out of the piston (FIGURE 7.12).

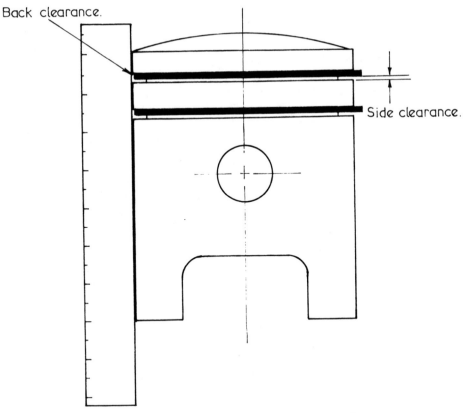

Fig. 7.11 Measuring piston ring groove clearance.

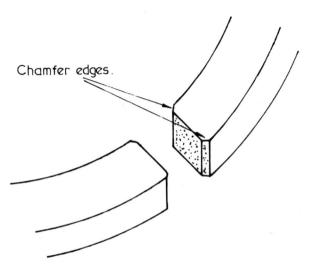

Fig. 7.12   Dress ring ends.

When rings are being fitted, care should be taken to avoid fitting them the wrong way up and to prevent damage by incorrect fitting technique. Piston rings can be twisted permanently if they are fitted in the groove at one end and then gradually screwed around until the entire ring is in place. Instead, they must be expanded sufficiently to fit over the piston and then allowed to drop into the groove. Special expander tools are available for this purpose but I prefer to use two 0.4mm feeler blades held between the ring and piston. The blades provide a bearing surface and stop the ring digging into the piston.

It is obvious that type 'A' rings in FIGURE 7.13 can be fitted only one way up. If the rings are upside down, the ends will foul on the locating pin, preventing the ring from seating in the groove.

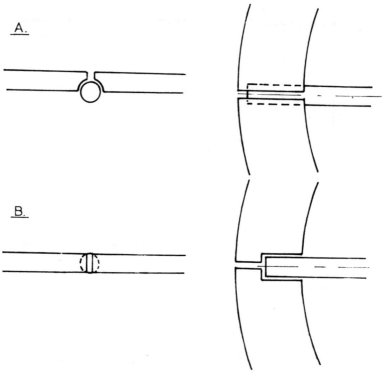

A.

B.

Fig. 7.13 Two methods of pinning piston rings.

On the other hand, type 'B' rings can be fitted incorrectly, so it is necessary to know something of the theory behind the various ring sectional shapes so that you may determine which way up the rings should be fitted.

The first ring, shown in FIGURE 7.14, is the type most commonly used in racing engines. It is called a rectangular section ring, for obvious reasons. The edges are usually chamfered equally so this type of ring can be fitted either side up.

Thinner rectangular section rings (i.e., 0.63-1.0mm) may be ground with a barrel face to reduce friction and improve the gas seal. Again, this ring may be installed any way up.

The keystone ring fitted in many motocross and road bikes is ground in the shape of a keystone. The idea behind this design is to reduce the incidence of ring sticking. As

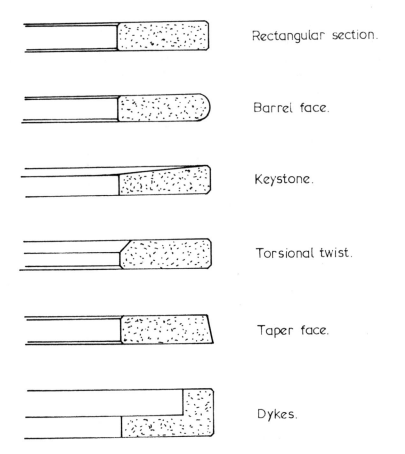

Rectangular section.

Barrel face.

Keystone.

Torsional twist.

Taper face.

Dykes.

Fig. 7.14 Common two stroke piston rings.

the ring moves in the groove it is supposed to scrape the groove clean. The cutaway section also provides a large space for the combustion gases to find their way into, to push the ring out against the bore wall. When fitting the keystone type ring, the chamfer should be uppermost. (Note — some keystone rings also have a slight taper on the lower edge of about 7°).

A few rectangular section rings have an exaggerated chamfer on one inner edge. This type is called an unbalanced section or torsional twist ring. The chamfer causes a slight dish in the ring face so that the lower edge makes high pressure contact with the cylinder wall. Some rings of this design have a step cut into the inner edge instead of the large chamfer, but, whatever method is used to create a high pressure area on the ring face, the ring must be fitted on the piston with the large chamfer or step to the top.

Taper face rings work in the same way as the previously mentioned rings, but in this instance the ring is made with a tapered face to exert a high pressure on the cylinder wall. These rings are always marked TOP, to identify the side that should be uppermost.

The other type of ring used in two-stroke engines is the 'L' section ring designed by Paul de K.Dykes. Obviously this type cannot be incorrectly fitted but, none-the-less, it is good to know why it is made in such a shape.

159

Dykes was involved in research into the problem of ring flutter and he came up with this design, which for many years was used in both four- and two-stroke racing engines. As piston ring technology has advanced, the Dykes ring has lost favour. Today it is used in a small number of two-stroke racing engines, and it is just being reintroduced into drag racing engines.

The main difficulty with the Dykes ring, as far as the two-stroke tuner is concerned, is ring sticking. I have never experienced this trouble but many two-stroke mechanics will not use it for this reason. Perhaps if the engine is not dismantled reasonably frequently (i.e., every 300 miles) sticking could occur.

If you take a look at FIGURE 7.15 you can see how Dykes designed his ring to be resistant to flutter. Note that the piston is also designed to complement the ring by having considerably more clearance above the vertical leg of the ring, as compared to the normal groove clearance for the horizontal leg. Therefore, even if piston acceleration is high enough to cause the ring to swap sides in the groove, it can not lift high enough to close the gap above the vertical leg. This feature ensures that gas pressure can always be maintained behind the ring to force it against the cylinder wall and prevent blow-by.

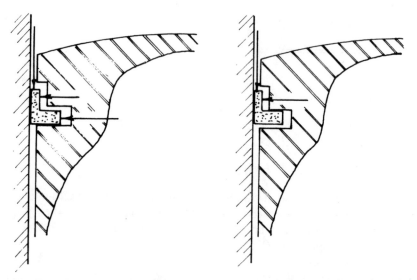

Fig. 7.15 Dykes ring resists high speed flutter.

To make life pleasant for the piston and rings, the cylinder must be faultless. There is only one type of bore which gives good performance. This is one that is perfectly round, parallel (i.e., no taper from top to bottom), and square to the cylinder base. Providing you have taken time correctly setting up the crankshaft and crankcases, a cylinder trued to these requirements will enhance performance and reduce wear to the piston, rings and bore.

When taking the barrel to a machine shop for reboring, have the base checked for trueness. If the cylinder is not square to the base it will be necessary to mount the cylinder on a mandrel and then skim the base in a lathe. You may find that such machining will render your barrel illegal in certain classes of kart racing, where a minimum cylinder height is specified in the regulations.

After squaring, the cylinder can be rebored. Make certain the machinist understands that the barrel base must be mounted directly on the boring jig's parallel bars. The barrel must never be shimmed to bring the cylinder in line with the boring bar. The bore should be taken to within 0.1mm of the required size and then honed to give the necessary piston clearance.

The cross-hatch pattern the hone leaves on the cylinder walls is critical if the rings are to bed-in quickly and last for a long life. Personally, I prefer a 45° crosshatch with a finish of 10-12 microinches. This type of finish makes it necessary to run the rings in, but they will wear well and not leak. A smoother finish does not retain enough oil and consequently allows a glaze to form on both the ring face and bore wall. Power is lost due to the poor ring seal, allowing gas leakage into the crankcase. A finish rougher than 12 microinches will greatly reduce the amount of time required to bed the rings, but ring life is shortened. Keep in mind that glazing can, again, be a real problem, but not due to a lack of lubrication. A rough finish acts like a file on the rings, the extra friction increases their temperature and causes glazing to form.

After being honed, the top lip of the cylinder should be chamfered to remove the sharp edge produced by boring. A smooth cut half round file is ideal for the job, but take care that you do not let it slip and nick the bore wall. If the sharp lip is not removed you will soon destroy the engine by pre-ignition or detonation.

Each time the engine is rebored, or even just honed, it is essential that all port openings be carefully filed and then dressed, otherwise the sharp edge formed will damage the rings and piston. To the naked eye the openings may appear smooth enough, but try running your finger around the edges and you will find just how razor sharp they are.

This problem of razor-edged ports exists with some new engines too. I have found the TZ Yamahas particularly bad, so if you own one of these be sure to dress the port openings before you run a new barrel. The idea is to smooth off the edges carefully with a cigarette size oilstone. The stone should be either 180 grit silicon carbide or hard grade Arkansas stone. The hard chrome in the bore of the TZ is not easy to dress, consequently this job can take up an entire day.

Barrels with iron cylinders are much easier to work with, even though it is equally difficult to get at the port openings in cylinders with a bore of less than 60mm. Initially, I like to shape the edges of the port using either a high speed grinder or a ¼in. chainsaw file. (Note — this step applies to cylinders with iron liners only, not those with any type of plating direct onto the aluminium.) This work with the grinder is done not only to deburr the sharp port edges, but also to make life easier for the rings in another way. If we put a chamfer around the port opening similar to that illustrated in FIGURE 7.16, the piston ring will be eased back into its groove as it closes over the port, reducing the possibility of ring bumping and/or breaking. The chamfer will be about 1.5-2mm wide and taper to a maximum depth of 0.5mm around the exhaust port. Because the other ports are much smaller, the chamfer can be reduced to 1.0-1.5mm wide and 0.3mm deep. After shaping the port edges, smooth them off with an oilstone.

When all the machining work is completed, the barrel must be thoroughly washed with hot, soapy water. Be sure to get all traces of honing grit scrubbed out of the cylinder, using a bristle scrubbing brush. Next spray the cylinder with a water 161

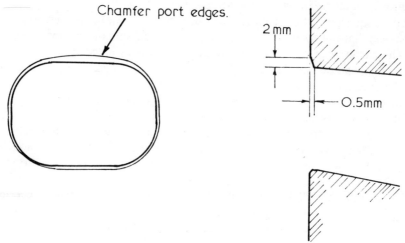

Fig. 7. 16   Port edges must be chamfered.

dispersant such as WD-40 and blow it dry with compressed air. Apply another coat of WD-40 to the bore.

As time passes, more racing engines are using barrels without any type of cylinder sleeve. Some people have suggested that factories are doing this to make their bikes lighter, since an iron sleeve weighs a kilogram or more. Actually, the real reason is associated with heat transfer.

Initially, manufacturers pressed the iron sleeve into the barrel, but the minute gap existing between the two formed an insulating barrier which seriously limited heat transfer to the cylinder's cooling fins. This reduced the power potential of all two-stroke engines.

Later, the aluminium cylinder was cast around the iron sleeve and bonded to it. This resulted in improved heat transfer and a corresponding increase in performance. However, no matter how effectively the two materials are bonded, there is always less than perfect heat conduction from the cast iron sleeve to the barrel.

The next development involved the total elimination of the iron sleeve. Because the piston rings would quickly wear and score a plain aluminium cylinder, the bore is plated with porous hard chrome by a special process. The chrome plating is usually 0.08-0.1mm thick and offers a reasonably long service life in racing engines. At times the chrome has been known to flake, and it is easily damaged by dirt inducted into the motor. Yamaha have been using chromed bores on their TZ range of motors for some time now, and Honda went the chrome cylinder route when they introduced their new CR250R motocrosser in 1978.

The German Mahle firm has been working with a superior electro-chemical plating called Nikasil. This plating was originally developed for Mercedes when they were building experimental Wankel rotary engines. Then Porsche began using Nikasil plated cylinders in the 630hp air cooled 917 model Le Mans racer. This engine later produced 1100hp in turbocharged form for the Can-Am series. Today, Nikasil cylinders are in use on tens of thousands of chain saws and other industrial two-strokes throughout
162 Europe. It has proved to be very successful in racing two-strokes' engines also; the

Morbidelli 125 and Rotax 125 and 250 production racer engines all exhibit excellent low wear characteristics for the cylinder, piston and piston ring.

The Nikasil coating is a nickel and silicon carbide matrix about 0.07mm thick. The nickel matrix is very hard, but it is comparatively ductile, whereas chrome is brittle. Dispersed through the nickel are particles of silicon carbide less than 4 microns in size. These extremely hard particles make up about 4% of the coating and form a multitude of adhesion spots on which oil can collect. So beside providing a very long wearing surface for the piston and rings to bear against, the silicon carbide particles also contribute to long engine life by ensuring good cylinder lubrication.

The latest advance in cylinder 'plating' was revealed to us at the release of the Kawasaki KX125 and 250 motocross bikes. Their patented electrofusion process involves the exploding of wire inside the cylinder in order to plate the bore. After a hone, the coating is about 0.065mm thick. Fifteen separate explosions plate the cylinder, first with three layers of pure molybdenum, followed by six alternate coatings of high carbon steel and molybdenum and then six layers of high carbon steel. When the cylinder is honed, the last three coats are removed.

The two types of wire are exploded in the centre of the cylinder by a 15,000 volt burst of electricity, which gasifies the wire. The gas expands out to the cylinder wall, burning up any oxygen in its path. This eliminates any risk of oxidation and ensures a good bond between the cylinder and the plating.

Originally, the electrofusion plating was applied only to the Kawasaki motocross engines, but now that the process has demonstrated its worth, Kawasaki are coating their road-going two-stroke engines as well.

In the future I expect we will see some process similar to that used by Chevrolet for their Vega engine introduced to the two-stroke engine fraternity. The Vega uses an aluminium cylinder block containing about 17% silicon. After being bored and honed, the aluminium bores are etched using a special technique. This removes enough aluminium to expose pure silicon and aluminium particles, to form a proper anti-wear bore surface.

When you have prepared the piston, rings and barrel as outlined, these parts may be fitted to the engine.

First, oil the little end bearing and the gudgeon pin, and then connect the piston to the con rod, taking care to install it the correct way round. After the gudgeon pin has been pushed in carefully fit the wire circlips. Always use new circlips and be sure to stuff a clean rag into the top of the crankcase. If you happen to drop a circlip, you don't want it falling down in there. Double check to ensure the circlips are properly seated in their grooves.

Before fitting the cylinder, give the piston and rings, and also the bore, a liberal coating of oil. Use straight oil and don't mix anything like STP with it, as piston rings are not designed to cut through goo like this.

An engine that has been properly prepared can be run-in in about 45-60 minutes. Start running at reasonably low speeds with a rich mixture and additional oil in the fuel. If you normally use a 20:1 mix, run-in on an 18:1 ratio. After about 15 minutes of operation at a fairly constant speed, try varying your speed and occasionally use up to about ¾ throttle. Continue changing your speed for another 15 minutes, but take care not to accelerate too briskly. Prolonged operation of a two-stroke at part throttle followed by a burst of full throttle may damage the engine. This occurs because only a 163 small amount of oil is present in the engine during constant light throttle running. Suddenly opening the throttle severely loads the engine but only a small quantity of oil is available to lubricate at slow speeds.

During the next 15 minutes gradually build up to racing speed, but do not use full throttle for more than two hundred yards on the main straight. Accelerate hard out of the corners for the last 15 minute segment, easing off after each burst to allow the rings and piston time to cool before the next blast. The hard acceleration is necessary to bed the rings into the bore. Do not hold full throttle for more than a few seconds or the rings and bore could overheat and glaze.

Some engines begin to 'lock up' during the run-in period and then seize under actual race conditions. As a safeguard against this, I would recommend that you remove the barrel after running-in and examine the piston for any sign of scuffing. If you find any high spots on the piston, remove it from the engine and, using a smooth cut millsaw file, gently file the high spots off the piston. This does not sound very scientific, but I can assure you that it works.

Not many engines require this treatment but there are a few that always seize where the piston bears against the exhaust port bridge, and there are others which lock up just under the bottom ring land at two points about 30° around from the gudgeon pin. Increasing the piston clearance usually doesn't help with either of these problems (FIGURE 7.17).

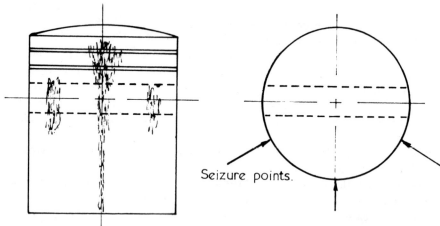

Seizure points.

Fig. 7.17 Possible seizure points on exhaust side of piston.

When a street engine is radically modified for racing, you may find it necessary to machine what we call a 'clearance band' around the top of the piston (FIGURE 7.18). This modification should be required only when the standard pistons are retained. The actual band can be machined in a lathe. It should be about 0.06-0.1mm deep and extend from the top of the piston to a point approximately 3mm below the bottom ring groove. Pistons in a racing engine operate at temperatures considerably higher than those experienced in street engines. The additional heat is concentrated in the piston crown and this results in abnormal expansion. The clearance band makes allowance for the crown to expand more without risking a lock up.

A bottom end assembled as outlined should prove relatively reliable in

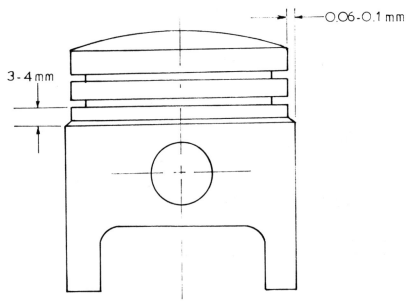

Fig. 7.18 Piston clearance band.

competition, providing you keep an eye on the tachometer red line. Deciding what the red line rpm should be can only be determined by actual experience with that particular make of engine.

You can not arbitrarily say, for example, that all single cylinder 125s can be safely run at 12,000rpm. As a starting point, run the engine initially at a speed equivalent to a mean piston speed of 3800 feet per minute and work up from there to a maximum of about 4500 feet per minute.

The mean piston speed is calculated using the formula:-

$$\text{Mean piston speed} = \frac{S \times 0.166 \times \text{rpm}}{25.4} \text{ ft/min}$$

$$S = \text{stroke in mm}$$

There is one point you must keep in mind that could save you from expensive engine damage. You already know how easy it is to over-rev the engine in first, second and possibly even third gear, but did you realise that the rate of engine acceleration is so brisk in the lower gears that the tacho doesn't even have sufficient time to keep pace? In fact, the readout on the tacho dial will be at least 500 and possibly up to 700rpm less than true engine speed. If you don't make an allowance for this, you could precipitate a blow up before you reach the first corner.

Chapter 8
Lubrication
and Cooling

THE RELIABILITY of any engine is closely related to adequate lubrication and efficient cooling. Unfortunately, it is in these areas that the two-stroke engine is most vulnerable. It has to rely on just the scantiest supply of lubricating oil to resist piston seizure in a cylinder badly distorted by the steep temperature gradient existing between the hot exhaust side and the much cooler inlet side of the barrel.

The lubricating oil must be able to prevent metal to metal contact of moving engine parts and at the same time assist in conducting heat away from the piston crown to the cylinder wall. Additionally, it must form a seal between the piston rings and cylinder wall to contain the pressure of combustion effectively. If the oil film is too thin, blow-by will result, reducing the amount of energy available to power the piston down.

There are basically three types of oil: mineral oil derived from crude stock; vegetable oil from the castor bean plant; and synthetic oil, which is man-made or man modified and used straight or blended with mineral or vegetable oil.

Most motorcycle oils are mineral-based, with a variety of additives used to improve them in certain functions. I would recommend mineral oils for all except competition two-stroke engines. My favourite mineral oil is Castrol Super TT. It will provide very good lubrication and wear resistance, better I believe than any other mineral oil available and better than most synthetic and castor oils. Like all mineral oils, Super TT will dirty the plug, and leave some carbon on the piston crown and in the combustion chamber.

In all of my competition engines, I specify Castrol R40 or R30 castor oil (R40 for air-cooled engines, R30 for water-cooled). This oil provides the best anti-wear protection of any oil that I know. The mere fact that my engines produce top horsepower testifies that it must be doing an excellent job of reducing friction by keeping moving parts separated. When you strip a 12,000rpm road racing motor after 300 racing miles and find the ring gaps opened up by only 0.007inch, and hone marks still visible on the cylinder walls, then you know the oil you are using is good.

Many tuners do not like castor oil or blended castor/synthetic because of some problems associated with the use of an oil of this type. Some claim that castor gums up the rings and causes ring sticking, but I have never found this problem, even on engines that are required to run 500 miles between rebuilds.

There is one area for concern, and this is the main reason why oil companies try to discourage the use of castor oil. Castor-based oils are hygroscopic, which means they will absorb moisture from the atmosphere. Therefore, once a container is opened, its entire contents should be used, or if oil is left over this should be poured into a smaller container so that no air space is left above the oil from which to absorb moisture. Remember, too, that castor oil will also absorb moisture after it has been mixed with fuel. Therefore, do not use fuel more than three days old, and don't forget to drain the fuel from the tank and carburettor bowl.

While we are on the subject of castor bean oil, don't think for a minute that all castor oils are as wear resistant as Castrol R. This all depends on how well the manufacturer de-gums the basic castor stock and on what additives are used. Some castors provide wear protection no better than average mineral and synthetic oils.

Today, more and more people are turning to and advocating the use of synthetic lubricant. There are several points in favour of synthetics, namely: less exhaust smoke, less incidence of plug fouling and less build-up on the piston crown and in the combustion chamber. Some also claim better wear protection and more power as a plus in favour of synthetic lubes, but in general my research has produced an opposite result. I have found some synthetic oils to have a wear factor twice as high as the better castor and mineral oils and I have never found a synthetic to allow an engine to produce as much power as Castrol R. For these reasons, I could not recommend the use of synthetic oil in highly stressed competition engines.

The manufacturers of synthetic oils claim their oils will give better power because the amount of oil in the fuel can be reduced (eg: Bel-Ray MC-1 is mixed 50:1 as compared to 20:1 for most mineral oils). But why should it ever be imagined that a smaller quantity of lubricant entering the engine will give a power increase? At the races it almost seems as if there is as much glory to be gained from running a fuel/oil ratio of 60:1 as there is in actually winning the race; by the pit bragging going on it would seem to be so!

My experience has shown that the more oil you pour into a two-stroke, the harder it runs. Just how much you should pour in depends on several factors, but it usually works out that the longer you hold the throttle wide open, the more oil you should use. This is due to the fact that the fuel/air ratio will be leaner at full throttle than at half and three-quarter. Therefore, with less fuel entering the engine at full throttle, proportionally less oil will be available for lubricating the piston at a time when it requires the most lubrication. Spelled out, it means that on a track with long straights you will have to use more oil than on a tight twisty track.

Keep in mind that your engine only needs enough oil to lubricate one stroke at a time and then the excess is burnt up. If your bike is dribbling oil out of the exhaust then you are running too much oil for its needs, or for your riding speed. A faster rider on the same machine may need more oil, because he is holding full throttle for longer periods.

When you start experimenting with oil ratios, always use the engine manufacturer's recommendation as a reference point and work from there. If you go 167 too rich, the spark plug will be coated with black soot and the exhaust pipe will be wet. If there is not enough oil, the plug could look white or grey, the pipe will be very dry, the piston crown will be white or light grey, possibly with 'death ash' forming under the crown. Any of these signs indicate that you are bordering on a seize up.

Generally, I would say that road racing engines will work best at a 16:1 to 20:1 fuel/oil ratio, depending on the nature of the course. Desert racers require 16:1 but, if plug fouling proves to be a problem, try 18:1 or 20:1. For enduro and motocross 20:1 or 22:1 is the best ratio. Go-karts with fixed gearing, without a clutch operating on short sprint tracks, will usually not tolerate more oil than 25:1 and, if you find that you are fouling plugs, you may have to drop as low as 30:1. Under no circumstances should you run leaner than 32:1.

All of the above fuel/oil ratios are for mineral and castor oils. Synthetic oils are an entirely different kettle of fish. If you choose to use this type of oil you will have to run it at the ratio the oil manufacturer recommends. This is because the oil people load the oil up with additives, in an attempt to give it acceptable scuff resistance when mixed at 50:1. Mixed at 25:1 there will be twice as much chemical additive and detergent being inducted into your engine and this could very easily cause carbon build-up and plug sooting, serious enough to stop or even damage the engine.

It seems that the trend towards leaner and leaner oil ratios has resulted from the desire of two-stroke engine manufacturers to eliminate plug fouling completely in two-stroke mower, outboard and chain saw engines. These engines are seldom serviced and the plug is probably only changed each time the rings are replaced. To cut down on spark plug deposits, the manufacturers decided on less oil and, unfortunately, this idea has carried over into competition two-stroke circles.

The results of my most recent oil testing are shown in TABLE 8.1. The engine was a fully worked Suzuki RM 125C motocross unit. As you can see, reducing the oil content from 20:1 to 27:1 (I wasn't brave enough to lower it any further) resulted in a power loss of about 8% at the top of the power range — a heavy price for the sake of a clean plug. On top of that the piston showed signs of scuffing bad enough to deter me from testing at 32:1 which, according to a lot of tuners, is the best mix when using R40.

When the fuel/oil mix ratio was raised to 16:1, power was marginally improved by about 2%, which is almost too small to measure on the dyno. However, the piston was much cleaner and the rings showed no sign of gumming up.

Accuracy is of utmost importance when blending oil and fuel. It is of no use mixing one and a half beer cans of oil to each drum of fuel, you have to be precise. For measuring the oil you need either a laboratory measuring cylinder or a graduated beaker. Fill the measuring container with the required quantity of oil, and be sure to allow the oil plenty of time to drain out when you pour it into your drum of fuel. Keep the measuring equipment clean, preferably in a dustproof plastic bag.

Determining how much fuel is in a drum is not easy. The drum may say that it contains 20 litres, but this can vary considerably, even when the drums are factory filled, as in the case of racing fuel. If you mix your own racing fuel the inaccuracy may be even worse, as a 20 litre drum will actually hold 22 litres filled nearly to the top. What I recommend is, assuming that you have brought your fuel in a drum that is supposed to contain 20 litres, drain the fuel from the drum and then refill it with precisely 20 litres measured with a suitable, accurate, 1 or 2 litre measure. Then take a rule and measure how many inches the fuel is from the top of the drum. Next make a gauge from light metal as shown in FIGURE 8.1, to fit in the neck of the drum and indicate the height of fuel for 20 litres. You can then use your gauge on any other 20 litre drum of fuel that you buy, assuming the drum style doesn't change.

TABLE 8.1   Suzuki RM125C horsepower/oil tests

rpm	Test 1 (hp)	Test 2 (hp)	Test 3 (hp)
8000	15.7	15.4	16.0
8500	18.8	18.7	18.7
9000	20.4	20.5	19.2
9500	21.3	21.7	19.6
10000	21.9	22.1	20.3
10500	22.6	22.9	20.7
11000	23.2	23.6	21.4
11500	17.3	17.6	15.8

Test 1 —   *Castrol R40 mixed at 20:1 with Shell 115 MB racing fuel. Champion N-57G plug — no sign of carbon. Light coat of 'varnish' on sides of piston.*

Test 2 —   *Castrol R40 mixed at 16:1 with Shell 115 MB racing fuel. Champion N-57G plug — slight trace of carbon on insulator, heavier deposits on plug shell and earth electrode. Less 'varnish' on piston than with 20:1 mix.*

Test 3 —   *Castrol R40 mixed at 27:1 with Shell 115 MB racing fuel. Champion N-57G plug — very clean — cleaner than plugs from 20:1 and 16:1 tests. Heavy 'varnish' coating right around ring lands and down exhaust side of piston.*

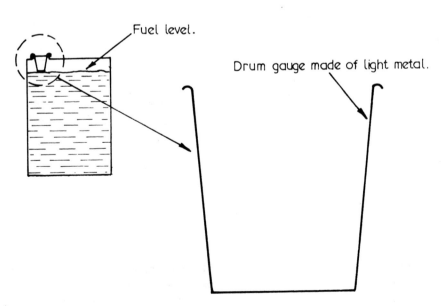

Fuel level.

Drum gauge made of light metal.

Fig. 8.1 Gauge for fuel mixing drum.

When blending oil and fuel you must be careful not to be confused by volumes which, on the surface, appear similar. In the Imperial system one pint is 20 fluid ounces, whereas in the US system one pint is 16 fluid ounces: considerably less. To assist you with mixing for various fuel/oil ratios refer to TABLE 8.2.

Incompatibility/insolubility of oil and fuel can mean big trouble, so don't take it for granted that all oils and fuels will mix properly. Mineral oils such as Castrol Super TT will blend with any of the leaded and unleaded fuels available out of the pump at the local garage, but it may not blend with some 100 or 115 octane racing fuels without the addition of 5-15% of benzol, toluol or methyl benzine.

Castrol R will blend with some regular pump fuels, depending on whether they contain a proportion of benzol or toluol. It will also blend with any 100 or 115 octane racing fuel containing 15% toluol, methyl benzine or benzol.

When methanol is used, it is necessary to mix it with a specially formulated oil. Castrol M castor oil and Shell Super M castor oil are both soluble in methanol.

To determine the compatibility of your fuel/oil mix, make up a small sample at the correct ratio in a clear glass bottle. Shake it well, as you should always do when blending oil and fuel. Leave it to stand for 24 hours, and check for separation. If there appears to be some insolubility, try mixing 5% toluol, benzol or methyl benzine. In

TABLE 8.2   Fuel/oil volume for fuel blending

Ratio	Imperial (per gallon)		US (per gallon)		Metric (per 5 litre)
	fl oz	*cc*	*fl oz*	*cc*	*cc*
12:1	13.3	379	10.7	317	417
14:1	11.4	325	9.1	269	357
16:1	10	284	8	237	313
18:1	8.9	253	7.1	210	278
20:1	8	227	6.4	189	250
22:1	7.3	207	5.8	172	227
25:1	6.4	182	5.1	151	200
27:1	5.9	168	4.7	139	185
30:1	5.3	152	4.3	127	167
32:1	5	142	4	118	156
40:1	4	114	3.2	95	125
50:1	3.2	91	2.6	77	100

Note:

1 Imperial fl oz = 28.4cc, 1 US fl oz = 29.6cc

extreme cases you may need up to 15% of these fuels added, to maintain solubility.

At times the oil may not completely separate out of the fuel, but, instead, may form in layers through it. When you find this problem, again try blending 5% methyl benzine, benzol or toluol with your mix.

No matter what type of oil you run, or how well it is blended, you will still end up with premature cylinder/piston wear and possibly even risk seizure if you don't allow the engine to warm up before working it hard. I recommend that you don't ride off until the barrel is getting reasonably warm. This will ensure that piston and bore wear is kept to a minimum. I have seen engines seized by being operated too hard right after being started. This occurs because the piston gets hot first and expands at a faster rate than the barrel, which takes much longer to warm up and expand the correct amount to provide the proper piston to cylinder working clearance.

Most two-stroke engines are air-cooled, but even water-cooled engines rely indirectly on air to stabilise the temperature of the cylinder head and barrel. The cooling arrangement of every internal combustion engine performs the vital function of dissipating heat in order to maintain normal engine operation.

The two-stroke engine is, in fact, a heat engine in that it relies on the conversion of fuel into heat, and then into mechanical energy to produce power at the crankshaft. Only about 23% of the heat is converted into power, another 33% is lost through the exhaust, and the rest is eliminated through the cooling system.

Lately, a lot has been said about applying a ceramic insulating coating to the combustion chamber and piston crown, to reduce to some extent the heat energy which is lost to the cooling system. It was felt that since it was heat energy, produced by the burning of a fuel, which heated the gases in an engine and caused them to expand and force the piston down, then reducing heat conduction to the cooling system should increase cylinder pressure, and result in more power.

In theory, ceramic coatings to thermally insulate the combustion chamber and piston crown sound a logical way to increase power, but in practice it hasn't worked out. In many instances the reverse has occurred, due to the end gases detonating as a result of increased pressure and temperature within the combustion chamber. I think many tuners realise that a liquid-cooled engine operating at a coolant temperature of 75°C will make significantly more power than if operated at 95°C, even though in the latter case considerably less combustion heat energy is lost to the cooling system. Why is this? Well, charge density will be superior with a cool engine and the combustion process will be more controlled, reducing the incidence of detonation.

Ceramic coatings are, I feel, only beneficial in low-speed engines and engines operated mainly at small throttle openings. Low-speed engines lose much more heat energy to the cooling system than high-speed engines, because each combustion cycle is longer. In the case of engines operated at light throttle openings the combustion process is often retarded, due to excessive dilution of the fuel charge by residual exhaust gas. With a ceramic coating applied to the combustion chamber and piston crown, combustion will be faster and more complete, due to the increase in combustion temperature.

The only other situation in which ceramic coatings may be beneficial is for coating the piston crown only in engines used for desert racing or those burning exotic fuel such as nitro and nitrous oxide. Such engines seem particularly prone to piston burning and, under these circumstances, ceramic coatings appear to offer a degree of protection.

One company which applies ceramic coatings is Heany Industries in America. Using a plasma-spray system, a ceramic coating 0.012-0.014in. thick is applied. The plasma coating process, called Heanium coating, utilises an electric arc device, into which argon gas is injected to generate a plasma stream of high temperature gas (up to 171

30,000°F). Powdered materials introduced into this plasma stream turn into a molten spray as they are propelled towards the surface to be coated.

As the Heanium coating is 0.012-0.014in. thick, a piston which has had the crown coated will cause an increase in the compression ratio and a decrease in the piston to head (squish) clearance. To overcome both of these problems a thicker head gasket will have to be used.

Heanium coating may also be applied to the exhaust port and the inlet port of motors with relatively straight ports. This will not do much to improve power, except that inlet charge density may increase a little, but cylinder distortion and overheating will be reduced. Cylinder distortion is not such a problem with liquid-cooled barrels, so I feel that you would be wasting your money coating the ports of these engines. Air-cooled barrels definitely will benefit from Heanium coating in the exhaust and inlet ports. Coating the exhaust tract will reduce the amount of heat which the finning on the exhaust side of the barrel has to dissipate. Hence that side of the motor will be cooler and, as a result, the cylinder bore will distort less. Conversely, coating the inlet port will increase the temperature of this side of the barrel because the insulating barrier will prevent the fuel charge from cooling the metal surround the inlet tract. The end result will be a lower temperature differential between the exhaust and inlet sides of the cylinder, and less distortion.

Besides reducing the heat load on the cooling system by using Heanium-coated ports, air-cooled engines can have the heat radiating area of their cooling fins increased. It has been found that blasting the head, barrel and crankcase with aluminium oxide increases the surface area about five times. If these parts are then sprayed with Kal-Guard coating and oven baked to keep the aluminium oxide on the metal surfaces, engine operating temperatures will be reduced by 10-13%. Of course, the cooling fin area can also be enlarged by more direct means. Both DG and Webco produce a range of replacement cylinder heads for Japanese engines. These heads have a bigger fin area to improve cooling and reduce any tendency for the engine to detonate or seize pistons.

It is essential to ensure that your cooling system is working at 100% capacity. Heat radiation from the cooling fins is retarded by the presence of oil and mud, so make sure they are clean. Fins and crankcases painted flat black radiate heat considerably better than shiny silver surfaces. Anything that is obstructing air flow onto the head and barrel should, if possible, be relocated elsewhere. On road bikes, check to see that the horn is not blocking air flow to the head. Also investigate to see if the exhaust can be better located, as the header pipe always seems to be in the way. Every move you make to encourage air flow over the engine will help performance and reliability.

Water or liquid-cooling is now looked on as the answer to two-stroke cooling difficulties. However, liquid-cooling is not without problems peculiar to itself. The two major deterrents to proper heat transfer from the combustion chamber and cylinder to the liquid cooling medium are deposits and air in the cooling system.

Metallic oxides twelve thousandths of an inch thick formed in the water passages will cut heat transfer by up to 40%. Therefore, in order to maintain optimum heat transfer, the cooling passages should be cleaned in a special bath that won't attack aluminium. Additionally, the system should contain an inhibitor that will keep coolant passage surfaces clean and free of deposits.

There are two basic types of inhibitors: chromates and non-chromates. Sodium chromate and potassium dichromate are two of the best and most commonly used water-cooling system inhibitors. Both are toxic, so handle them with care.

Non-chromate inhibitors (borates, nitrates, nitrites) provide anti-corrosion protection in either water or water and permanent anti-freeze systems. Chromates must not be used with anti-freeze.

If you decide to use a coolant other than water, ethylene glycol is to be recommended. Methyl alcohol-based anti-freeze should not be used because of its very low boiling point and its damaging effect on radiator hoses and water pump seals.

When ethylene glycol anti-freeze is used in concentrations above 30%, additional inhibitor protection against corrosion is not required. I do not recommend the use of cooling solutions composed of more than two-thirds ethylene glycol and one-third water, as heat transfer is adversely affected.

Anti-freeze containing cooling system sealer additives should not be used, as the sealer may plug the radiator core tubes and possibly even coolant passages in the engine. Stop leak or sealer of any description is not to be recommended, except in an emergency to get you home or to finish a race. Then, as soon as possible, it should be cleaned out by a cooling system specialist, using a high pressure air and water flusher.

Petroleum-derived products such as soluble oil, often used as a water pump lubricant and corrosion inhibitor, should never be used. A 2% concentration of soluble oil can raise the cylinder head deck temperature by up to 10%, due to reduced heat transfer efficiency of the coolant. One popular radiator stop leak contains a high proportion of soluble oil, which is an additional reason for staying clear of radiator sealers. Soluble oil turns water milky when it is added.

The presence of air bubbles in the coolant reduces the heat transfer capacity of the coolant by acting as an insulator. Water pump efficiency is also reduced. Air can be sucked into the system through a leaking hose and gas bubbles can form due to localised boiling around the combustion chamber. In the first case, air can be kept out of the cooling system by ensuring that there are no air or water leaks, and by keeping the coolant at the proper level.

Gas bubbles or steam pockets are prevented by pressurising the system to the degree necessary to prevent the water boiling. By pressurising the radiator to 14psi the boiling point of water is raised from 100°C to about 125°C. Normally, the water around the combustion chamber should not reach this temperature, but this gives a safety factor to permit normal operation at higher altitudes. Periodically the radiator pressure cap should be inspected for deterioration of the seal and the 'blow-off' pressure should be tested.

As the actual heat exchange between the cooling medium and air takes place at the radiator, it is important that it is free of bugs or any other debris that would restrict air flow and hence reduce cooling efficiency. The radiator should be painted matt black to provide the best radiating surface, and also to minimise the effects of external corrosion.

It is a mistake to run the cooling system without some form of restrictor or thermostat, as the engine could be over-cooled. If too much heat is transferred to the coolant, power will be lost. Therefore, do not let the engine run cooler than about 75-80°C. Below about 70°C, cylinder wear increases to a level as serious as operating the engine at too high a temperature.

Chapter 9

Power Measurement and Gearing

I AM CONSTANTLY surprised that so few two-stroke tuners ever spend any time testing and developing their engines on a dynamometer. Now don't get me wrong, engine dynos are definitely not the 'be all and end all' of engine tuning. There are clearly definable limits to their usefulness, due to the static nature of the load applied to the engine. On the dyno you can't, for instance, check an engine's rideability, how smoothly it comes onto the power, or its throttle response: these factors can only be determined on the race circuit.

With dyno testing, you are in a good position to see precisely what influence a change in the spark advance will have on the power output. You can determine how much power increase, if any, a larger carburettor will give at maximum rpm and ascertain what the hp loss is at lower speeds. Without the benefits of a dyno work-out, you can only tune according to instinct and/or past experience, and then rely on your lap times or 'feel' through the seat of the pants to indicate if a particular modification is successful or not. This takes a lot of time and is often inconclusive as, unfortunately, most of us can't feel a 5% difference in power.

There are two basic types of dynamometers: the rolling road and the engine dyno. The rolling road is not very popular for motorcycle engine tuning, as its worth is rather limited. With this type of dyno, the bike is tied down with the rear wheel on a pair of rollers, which are connected to some sort of loading device (the brake). The engine is run and, according to the twisting force applied through the rollers to the brake, the torque and horsepower figures are calculated.

The main problem with the rolling road is that it can never be made sensitive enough for engine development work. Because of tyre slip and friction on the rollers, the twisting force being transmitted to the brake is in a state of constant fluctuation. Therefore, to keep the readout needle fairly steady, it must be heavily damped, otherwise it would be bouncing back and forth so rapidly the operator wouldn't be able to read it. As a result of the damping, the dyno becomes unresponsive to small changes in power output, so it would be a waste of time checking the effect of a change in spark advance or main jet size.

The engine dyno, on the other hand, is quite sensitive and will give a clear indication of precisely how much advance or what size main jet the engine prefers for best power. With this type of dyno, the engine is coupled with the brake via a chain, driven from the countershaft sprocket. Therefore there is no slip (unless the clutch is slipping) and the frictional losses in the primary drive, gearbox and secondary drive remain fairly steady.

As I mentioned earlier, you can't check an engine's rideability on the dyno. Usually the areas where you will get caught out are with carburation and expansion chamber testing. For example, you may check three or four different brands and sizes of carburettors and find they give a seemingly identical performance on the dyno. But at the race circuit there will generally be one setup which is superior to the rest, allowing improved lap times, or maybe just a better 'feel' when coming onto the power as you exit a turn.

There are several types of engine dynos in use and, while all do a good job in enabling us to see which way our development work is going, you should not take a lot of notice of the power figures. Variations of up to 10% from one dyno to another are not uncommon. The reason for this is that tuning companies do not have the money to spend on the latest, most accurate dynos. Instead, in many cases, they make do with older, or maybe even new but less sophisticated, types. Also dyno manufacturers use various methods of calibration, which tend to give a different power reading from one brand of dyno to another.

This in itself is not such a bad thing, providing all the tuning is done on the same dyno. Otherwise you might try out some new trick part and find it gives you 7% more power on a dyno over the other side of town, when in truth you had lost power. It was just that this dyno is reading higher than the one on which the engine was originally tested (TABLE 9.1).

TABLE 9.1   Dyno comparison test of Yamaha YZ250

| rpm | Dyno A | | Dyno B | |
	hp	Torque (lb/ft)	hp	Torque (lb/ft)
4000	8.6	11.3	8.8	11.5
4500	9.5	11.1	10.0	11.7
5000	11.1	11.7	11.6	12.2
5500	15.4	14.7	17.7	16.9
6000	21.1	18.5	23.0	20.1
6500	24.9	20.1	27.1	21.9
7000	26.4	19.8	30.0	22.5
7500	25.6	17.9	30.3	21.2
8000	25.1	16.5	29.1	19.1
8500	19.9	12.3	22.3	13.8

Note: This motor was not altered in any way between the two tests. The hp and torque figures have been corrected to compensate for changes in air density.

Something you are sure to have noticed is the variation between the manufacturer's claimed horsepower and the engine's power at the countershaft sprocket. For example, Yamaha quote the RD400 (the European model) as producing 44hp at 7500rpm, whereas you will usually be able to roundup only about 36 of those horses during dyno testing. Where have the others strayed off to? First, somewhere up around 12 to 15% will have been used in overcoming friction in the primary drive and gearbox, and also in the secondary chain driving from the countershaft to the dyno. (Manufacturers take their power figures at the crankshaft, not the countershaft). That accounts for 6 of the strays, and the other 2 are unaccounted for as the result of differences in the test procedures and dyno calibration.

Unfortunately, few people realise how little the horsepower figures actually tell about engine performance, or how well an engine has been modified. The true measure of engine performance is the torque and brake mean effective pressure figures. These indicate much more to us and show where we are heading with our modifications.

Torque is the ability of an engine to do work, measured in pounds/feet. This is a measure of the work the engine will do, regardless of whether it is 80cc or 450cc. If an engine is producing torque of 20 lbs/ft it means that a crankshaft with a 1 ft lever attached has a twisting force capable of lifting a load of 20 lbs. If a lever 2 ft long was attached to the crankshaft, the same motor would lift 40 lbs, or 60 lbs if its lever was 3 ft long. This is why we have a gearbox, to multiply the twisting force (torque) of the crankshaft. If this engine with 20 lbs/ft torque was operating in a bike with an overall low gear ratio of 30:1, we would have a twisting force of 600 lbs/ft, at the rear wheel $(20 \times 30 = 600)$.

Power is the rate at which work is done,

$$\text{Power} = \frac{\text{work (or torque)}}{\text{time}}$$

In the Imperial system, power is measured in lbs/ft per minute. However, these units are small, so the unit we know as horsepower (hp) is the one used today. One horsepower equals 33,000 lbs/ft per minute. This was worked out as a result of experiments done by James Watt, using strong dray horses.

It is obvious, realising power is the rate at which work is done, that two motors both producing 20 lbs/ft torque could have differing power outputs. In fact, if one motor lifted its 20 lbs load twice as quickly as the other, then it must be twice as powerful, or have double the horsepower. Engine speed is measured in revolutions per minute, so this is the time unit we use in calculating horsepower, therefore:

$$\text{hp} = \frac{\text{torque} \times \text{rpm}}{5252}$$

Earlier, I mentioned that high horsepower figures can be misleading. We can end up with a nice big power output because the motor will turn a lot of rpm, but in actual fact the motor will do no more work than it did previously, because the torque output has remained unchanged, or may even have dropped. For this reason we have a measure called brake mean effective pressure (BMEP). This gives a true indication of how effectively the engine is operating regardless of its capacity or its operating rpm. It is, in fact, a measure of the average cylinder pressures generated during both engine strokes. We calculate the BMEP using the formulae:

$$BMEP = \frac{hp \times 6500}{L \times rpm}$$

or

$$\frac{torque \times 6500}{L \times 5252}$$

$$L = \text{engine capacity in litres}$$

The highest BMEP will occur at the point of maximum torque, which also happens to be where peak volumetric efficiency occurs.

A stock engine, intended for use in a sports or touring bike, will have a BMEP of 80-90psi, depending on the cylinder size. With an increase in cylinder displacement the engine does not breathe as well, hence the BMEP falls. Typically a road bike with 125cc cylinders will be working at a BMEP of 90psi, while a single cylinder 250's pressure will be closer to 80psi.

Enduro machines with a displacement of 175 to 400cc, and 350 to 450cc motocross bikes, generally operate in the 90-98psi bracket. There are exceptions though: bikes with the Rotax rotary valve engine will usually show a BMEP of 120 or 110psi depending on whether the engine is a 175 or 250cc, as the rotary valve permits much improved breathing without any loss of tractability.

125 and 250cc motocross engines are a rather mixed bag. The Honda CR125R and CR250R both perform very creditably with BMEPs of 117 and 115psi respectively, and the 250 can be tuned to work at a pressure of 122psi without making the bike hard to manage on a motocross circuit. The Suzuki RM125 has a 123psi BMEP which is excellent. The rest are only working at around 100 to 105psi for 250 and 125cc displacements, which indicates the respective manufacturers still have quite a way to go in engine development and/or expansion chamber design.

The 125 and 250 production road racers, such as the Honda MT125 and Yamaha TZ250, generally run at a BMEP of 123-127psi, leaving little room for improvement as a BMEP of around 125-130psi can be considered about the maximum for a conventional piston-ported engine.

The exceptional rotary valve Rotax and Morbidelli 125 production racer engines operate at 137 and 142psi respectively, and the works Morbidelli is approaching 150psi BMEPs.

To give you an indication of how important the BMEP is, and to show how it gives a more meaningful expression of an engine's true performance level and its potential for future development, I have included some dyno figures for the Yamaha YZ125E and Suzuki RM125C (TABLE 9.2 and FIGURE 9.1). As you can see, both engines put out about 22hp, but just look at the differences in the mid-range power and the width of the power band. The Yamaha makes maximum power at 11,000rpm and then the motor proceeds promptly to drop dead, whereas the Suzuki, because it is working 177

TABLE 9.2 **Dyno test of stock Suzuki RM125 C and Yamaha YZ125 E**

rpm	Suzuki RM125		Yamaha YZ125	
	hp	Torque (lb/ft)	hp	Torque (lb/ft)
6500	7.8	6.3	7.4	6.0
7000	10.0	7.5	7.3	5.5
7500	13.1	9.2	8.7	6.1
8000	16.1	10.6	12.5	8.2
8500	19.4	12.0	15.4	9.5
9000	21.1	12.3	17.5	10.2
9500	21.7	12.0	17.9	9.9
10000	21.5	11.3	19.2	10.1
10500	20.6	10.3	20.4	10.2
11000	15.1	7.2	21.8	10.4
11500	9.9	4.5	11.6	5.3

Note: Maximum BMEP for RM 125 = 123psi
Maximum BMEP for YR 125 = 104.5psi
Both engines were tested on the same dyno and the figures have been corrected to compensate for differences in air density.

much better (as evidenced by the high BMEP pressures), holds within a few percent of its peak hp over a 2000rpm range (from 8500-10,500rpm) and it is still making good power at 11,000rpm and down at 8000rpm.

An engine like this is easy to tune for much higher power outputs, without knocking the mid-range about too much. With just some porting and carburation changes it can be made to produce significantly more top end power, as indicated in TABLE 9.3. Maximum power has not been lifted much, but at 10,500 and 11,000rpm there is a 2hp and 3.1hp increase. Note also that the BMEP has been maintained at 123psi. If it had slumped to 120psi this would be a sure indication that our modifications had actually upset the proper functioning of the engine.

TABLE 9.3 **Dyno test of modified Suzuki RM125C**

rpm	hp	Torque (lb/ft)
7000	8.3	6.2
7500	11.6	8.1
8000	15.7	10.3
8500	18.8	11.6
9000	20.4	11.9
9500	22.3	12.3 BMEP 123psi
10000	22.5	11.8
10500	22.6	11.3
11,000	18.2	8.7
11500	11.3	5.2

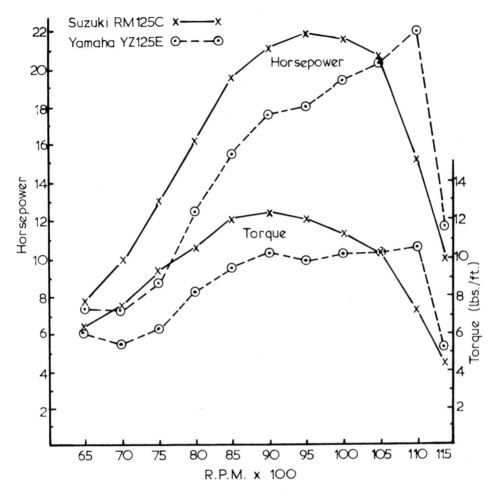

Fig. 9.1   Yamaha & Suzuki power curves.

When a motor is run on the engine dyno, a record is made of its output each 500rpm over its operating range. These output figures must then be converted to tell us what the hp and torque is, as most dynos do not give a direct reading in lbs./ft. At the time these calculations are being made, a 'correction factor' is also introduced to keep the output figures standard. If this was not done we would have no way of accurately comparing the engine's power level on another occasion, when the atmospheric conditions are sure to be different.

Throughout the dyno session a check is made of the barometer reading and at frequent intervals wet and dry bulb air temperature readings are taken, as these factors influence the air density. It stands to reason, the cooler the air and the higher the air pressure, then the more oxygen and fuel you can cram into the engine, which in turn gives more power. Conversely, if the temperature is high and the barometric pressure low, the performance will fall. To compensate for this during the test session, and to give a true comparison with earlier and possibly subsequent tests, a correction factor is added to the conversion formula.

The conversion formula to calculate the torque on one particular type of dyno is this:-

$$Torque = \frac{W \times 26.26 \times C/F}{2}$$

where W = readout indicated by the dyno needle
C/F = correction factor

For example, if the dyno indicated the twisting force (W) to be 2.18, and the barometric pressure was 30.06ins., with a wet and dry bulb temperature of 48°F and 68°F respectively, the engine would be producing the following torque:-

$$Torque = \frac{2.18 \times 26.26 \times 1.016}{2}$$

$$= 29.08 \text{ lbs/ft.}$$

The correction factor, in this example 1.016, is found from tables or graphs which are readily available.

When the dyno session is over, don't go home and just file the dyno sheet away. The next thing you must do is work out your gear change points for maximum acceleration. In TABLE 9.4 I have listed the dyno test of a Honda MT125 R-3 road racer. The standard engine makes fairly good power, but the power band is pathetic. No 125 can work very effectively with a 1500rpm (9000-10,500rpm) power range regardless of how close the gear ratios are. The modified engine has a better power spread of 2000rpm (9000-11,000rpm), but it would still be hard work keeping the engine on the power around a tight road circuit.

TABLE 9.4 Dyno test of Honda MT125 R-3

rpm	Standard		Modified	
	hp	*Torque (lb/ft)*	*hp*	*Torque (lb/ft)*
8500	16.67	10.3	14.16	8.75
9000	18.2	10.62	17.03	9.94
9500	19.9	11.0	19.54	10.8
10000	21.95	11.53	22.37	11.75
10500	24.39	12.2	25.01	12.51
10750	13.0	6.35	21.25	10.38
11000	10.05	4.8	18.64	8.9
11250			14.07	6.57
11500			8.58	3.92

TABLE 9.5 indicates the overall gear ratios of the MT125 with the standard 17 tooth to 32 tooth final drive.

TABLE 9.5   Honda MT125 R-3 gearing
Using 17 to 32 final drive (1.882)

1st	12.42
2nd	10.15
3rd	8.785
4th	7.82
5th	6.99
6th	6.46

Using the formula:

$$\text{Road speed} = \frac{\text{rpm} \times \text{tyre circumference}}{\text{gear ratio} \times 1050}$$

we can work out the bike's speed in various gears, and prepare a table similar to TABLE 9.6. You will note that this chart also has a column headed 'Torque'. There, figures are tabulated from multiplying the engine torque by the gear ratio.

TABLE 9.6   Stock Honda MT125 R-3 — rear wheel torque and road speed

rpm	1st gear 12.42		2nd gear 10.15		3rd gear 8.785	
	Torque	*Speed*	*Torque*	*Speed*	*Torque*	*Speed*
8500	128	46	105	56	90	65
9000	132	48	108	59	93	68
9500	137	51	112	62	97	72
10000	143	54	117	66	101	76
10500	152	56	124	69	107	80
10750	79	57	64	71	56	82
11000	60	59	49	72	42	83

rpm	4th gear 7.82		5th gear 6.99		6th gear 6.46	
	Torque	*Speed*	*Torque*	*Speed*	*Torque*	*Speed*
8500	81	72	72	81	67	88
9000	83	78	74	86	69	93
9500	86	81	77	91	71	98
10000	90	85	81	95	74	103
10500	95	90	85	100	79	108
10750	50	92	44	103	41	111
11000	38	94	34	105	31	114

As you look over this table remember the higher the twisting force (torque) exerted on the rear wheel the faster the bike will accelerate. Some riders change up a gear when the engine reaches maximum hp revs., while others wind the engine way past this point. Most riders run the standard MT125 past 11,000rpm, but is there any benefit in doing this? Well you can see there isn't, the engine drops dead just after 10,500rpm.

At 10,500rpm in low gear, the torque is 152 lbs/ft If you run the engine to 11 grand, the torque falls off to 60 lbs/ft. However, if you change up to 2nd at 10,500, the torque drops to 105 lbs/ft, so there will be a significant improvement in acceleration. Checking right through the table you will see that this particular engine will pull best if the change-up speed is 10,500rpm. By way of comparison, the modified MT125 should be changed up at 11,000rpm (TABLE 9.7). You will note that the gearing of the modified engine is too tall for a 110mph top speed, for which the standard bike is geared. It should have a 16 tooth countershaft sprocket.

TABLE 9.7   Modified Honda MT125 R-3 rear wheel torque and road speed

rpm	1st gear 12.42		2nd gear 10.15		3rd gear 8.785	
	Torque	*Speed*	*Torque*	*Speed*	*Torque*	*Speed*
8500	109	46	89	56	77	65
9000	123	48	101	59	87	68
9500	134	51	110	62	95	72
10000	146	54	119	66	103	76
10500	155	56	127	69	110	80
10750	129	57	105	71	91	82
11000	111	59	90	72	78	83
11250	82	60	67	74	58	85
11500	49	62	40	76	34	87

rpm	4th gear 7.82		5th gear 6.99		6th gear 6.46	
	Torque	*Speed*	*Torque*	*Speed*	*Torque*	*Speed*
8500	68	72	61	81	57	88
9000	78	78	69	86	64	93
9500	84	81	75	91	70	98
10000	92	85	82	95	76	103
10500	98	90	87	100	81	108
10750	81	92	73	103	67	111
11000	70	94	62	105	57	114
11250	51	96	46	107	42	116
11500	31	98	27	110	25	119

Ideally, there should be little or no loss of torque in the change from one gear to the next. With its 2000rpm power band, the modified engine comes very close, but the standard motor is some way off the mark, particularly in the lower three gears. As the

Honda already has very close gears, the problem can be overcome only by modifying the engine to spread the power band or by adding extra gears, this latter being quite impractical.

Engine tune must always be kept compatible with the available gearbox ratios, otherwise the engine will dip out of the power band, and possibly 'load up', because of the gaps between gears. This fact must be kept in mind when you set about modifying any two-stroke engine. Motocross engines are the most forgiving as they already have very close gears (almost as close as a road racer), but street bikes and enduro bikes, because of their widely-spaced cogs, demand a wide power range.

To illustrate the type of problem that you are going to be up against when a two-stroke with wide spaced gear ratios is modified for competition, we will take a look at the Yamaha MX175, which is a dual purpose trail/play bike. In standard tune the MX175 performs very well, and the engine can easily be modified to produce good power (TABLE 9.8) for enduro racing or high speed fire trail riding.

TABLE 9.8 Dyno test of Yamaha MX175

rpm	Standard		Modified	
	hp	Torque (lb/ft)	hp	Torque (lb/ft)
4000	6.6	8.7	6.2	8.1
4500	7.9	9.2	7.2	8.4
5000	9.4	9.9	8.7	9.1
5500	10.8	10.3	9.8	9.4
6000	12.5	10.9	9.8	8.6
6500	13.9	11.2	12.0	9.7
7000	14.0	10.5	14.9	11.2
7500	13.7	9.6	18.4	12.9
8000	12.6	8.3	19.5	12.8
8500	10.4	6.4	20.1	12.4
9000			20.0	11.7
9500			19.5	10.8
10000			11.0	5.8

TABLE 9.9 Yamaha MX175 gearing (14/49 sprockets)

1st   39.53
2nd 25.00
3rd 17.57
4th   13.45
5th   10.81
6th   9.04

Even though the modified engine is in a relatively mild state of tune and the power band is quite wide (7000 to 9500rpm) the gearbox ratios are totally inadequate for enduro racing. Just take a look at TABLE 9.10 and notice the 'holes' between first and second, second and third, and third and fourth. Using a change up speed of 9,500rpm, which is probably 500rpm higher than most riders would use, we drop from 427 lbs/ft torque at the rear wheel down to 215 lbs/ft torque on the change from first to second. As the engine makes best power above 7000rpm, we would want to keep above that engine speed if possible; however, the gear spacing is so wide we fall down to 6000rpm, 1000rpm out of the power band.

TABLE 9.10   Modified Yamaha MX175 rear wheel torque and road speed

rpm	1st gear 39.53 Torque	Speed	2nd gear 25.00 Torque	Speed	3rd gear 17.57 Torque	Speed
4000	320	7	203	12	142	17
4500	332	8	210	14	148	19
5000	360	9	228	15	160	22
5500	372	10	235	17	165	24
6000	340	11	215	18	151	26
6500	383	12	243	20	170	28
7000	443	13	280	21	197	30
7500	510	14	323	23	227	32
8000	506	15	320	24	225	35
8500	490	16	310	26	218	37
9000	463	17	293	27	206	39
9500	427	18	270	29	190	41
10000	229	19	145	30	102	43

rpm	4th gear 13.45 Torque	Speed	5th gear 10.81 Torque	Speed	6th gear 9.04 Torque	Speed
4000	109	23	88	28	73	34
4500	113	25	91	32	76	38
5000	122	28	98	35	82	42
5500	126	31	102	39	85	46
6000	116	34	93	42	78	50
6500	130	37	105	46	88	55
7000	151	40	121	49	101	59
7500	174	43	139	53	117	63
8000	172	45	138	56	116	67
8500	167	48	134	60	112	72
9000	157	51	126	63	106	75
9500	145	54	117	67	98	80
10000	78	57	63	70	52	84

On the change from second to third, the torque slumps from 270 lbs/ft down to approximately 190 lbs/ft. Then, between third and fourth, there is a fall of about 30 lbs/ft, but this is not so serious as the engine is getting into the power band here, and pulling quite well.

By way of comparison now check TABLE 9.11 and note the suitability of the gearbox cogs when mated with the stock engine, which has a power range running from 5500rpm to 8500rpm. Changing up at 8000rpm there is an 80 lbs/ft torque gap between first and second gears, a 27 lbs/ft difference between second and third, and there isn't any fall in torque in the change from third to fourth. Also, you will notice that the engine only drops out of the power band on the change from first to second, and this could be avoided by running to 8500rpm in low gear before changing up.

TABLE 9.11   Standard Yamaha MX175 rear wheel torque and road speed

rpm	1st gear 39.53 Torque	Speed	2nd gear 25.00 Torque	Speed	3rd gear 17.57 Torque	Speed
4000	344	7	218	12	153	17
4500	364	8	230	14	162	19
5000	391	9	248	15	174	22
5500	407	10	258	17	181	24
6000	431	11	273	18	192	26
6500	443	12	280	20	197	28
7000	415	13	263	21	184	30
7500	379	14	240	23	169	32
8000	328	15	208	24	146	35
8500	253	16	160	26	112	37

rpm	4th gear 13.45 Torque	Speed	5th gear 10.81 Torque	Speed	6th gear 9.04 Torque	Speed
4000	117	23	94	28	79	34
4500	124	25	99	32	83	38
5000	133	28	107	35	89	42
5500	139	31	111	39	93	46
6000	147	34	118	42	99	50
6500	151	37	121	46	101	55
7000	141	40	114	49	95	59
7500	129	43	104	53	87	63
8000	112	45	90	56	75	67
8500	86	48	69	60	58	72

Of course, all of these calculations will be wasted if your tachometer is inaccurate. Therefore, it must be checked and recalibrated. Only then can you be sure that you are getting the best performance from the engine, changing up at the right rpm and keeping within the power band. Unfortunately, many believe that the tacho reading is infallible 185 and beyond question. However, I have not found this to be so; mechanical units are typically 400-700rpm fast and electronic digital readout tachos can be all over the place, depending on the ambient temperature and the quality of the unit.

Final tuning on the race track is also necessary, even after a full tuning session on the dyno. This is because the load applied on the dyno may have been just a flash loading, i.e., just long enough to get a power reading. Such a brief run at full load may not allow sufficient heat build-up in the piston crown, combustion chamber or crankcase, to cause detonation. Under normal racing conditions, where full load may be applied for a much longer period, detonation might occur due to the mixture being a fraction lean, and in some instances the ignition advance may be a little early. At times it will be found necessary to run even more advance on the race circuit than on the dyno, to get better throttle response and acceleration, when the jetting must be considerably richer to cool the piston.

Throughout the testing you should make one change at a time. This is the only way that you are going to find out to what the engine is responding. With just one variable introduced for each test it is often difficult to know just what step to take next, so you will appreciate that the introduction of two or three changes will make it virtually impossible to know where you are heading with your tuning.

At the start, race track tuning can be extremely frustrating, because you seem to keep going up so many dead end streets. However, if you stick with it, and go about your tuning in a systematic way, you are sure to have the engine responding better and making more power than before you started. The thing you must do is make just one change at a time, keep accurate notes of any changes, and make sure that you have got a good stop watch operator who can be relied upon to time each lap accurately.

Appendix I

Introduction

This section of the book should enable you to understand clearly the practical application of two-stroke principles expounded throughout the previous nine chapters. Each working example that I have chosen has its own story to tell. Some engines demand a great deal of modification before they are able to produce acceptable performances; others, such as the big 400cc motocross and enduro engines, require only a clean up of the ports; for some (eg. go-kart engines) the best thing one can do is to 'blueprint' the motor.

Unfortunately, the engines used as examples will not be the current models by the time you read this book. But the principles of modifying any of them will apply to two-strokes generally, for many years to come.

Usually, the modification of each engine is divided into two rider categories: namely 'average' and 'expert'. We have to face the fact that most of us fall into the average class. This means that we require an engine which gives a nice smooth delivery of power over a wide rev range. On the other hand, an expert can tolerate a much narrower power band. He has the ability to control a quick rush of power and he seldom misses a gear change. Obviously if you are not one of the handful of riders to whom the latter description applies, then forget about the hotter 'expert' modifications as they will prove to be a hindrance to you.

A Motocross Modifications

1 Yamaha YZ80F

In standard tune, the YZ80F is a very quick, but difficult to ride, bike. The engine produces excellent power (TABLE A.1) and it pulls cleanly over a wide rev range. However, the power comes on too suddenly, making control of the bike's rear end exceedingly difficult. The only way to make the bike easier to ride is by smoothing power delivery to the rear tyre.

187

TABLE A.1 Yamaha YZ80F power output

rpm	Standard		Modified	
	hp	*Torque (lb/ft)*	*hp*	*Torque (lb/ft)*
8000	8.7	5.7	7.8	5.1
8500	9.9	6.15	10.4	6.4
9000	11.1	6.5	10.8	6.3
9500	12.1	6.7	11.9	6.6
10000	12.9	6.75	12.3	6.45
10500	13.3	6.65	14.2	7.1
11000	14.2	6.8	14.6	6.95
11500	7.7	3.5	13.8	6.3
12000			11.1	4.85

This goal is realised in two ways: raising the transfer ports and modifying the expansion chamber.

The transfer duration as delivered from the factory is far too short when matched with a relatively wild 197° exhaust open period. The simplest way to increase transfer duration is to raise the barrel 1.0mm using a 0.7mm aluminium spacer plate and an additional base gasket. This will give a transfer event of 129° as compared with the standard duration of 121°. The boost port should be raised an extra 1.5mm to give a duration of 138°.

Raising the barrel will also lengthen the exhaust timing, in this instance to almost 203° duration. In many engines this would be far too wild, but this unit will be running to almost 12,000rpm so a long exhaust event is required.

The factory expansion chamber is an unusual design which works none too well. The header pipe tapers at a fairly steep 1.65° and then diverges into a 2.9° and 5.4° diffuser. The 'belly' section, which appears to diverge and then converge abruptly, is in reality a silencer, so do not be fooled by its odd shape. The baffle cone converges at a fairly conventional 9.75°, but it is very badly deformed to clear the bike's frame (FIGURE A.1).

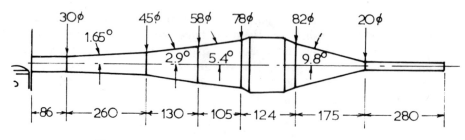

Fig. A.1 Yamaha YZ80F expansion chamber.

The expansion chamber could be replaced completely, but in this instance I believe it is much easier and just as effective to modify the factory chamber. As you will notice in FIGURE A.2, this basically involves cutting a section out of the centre of the

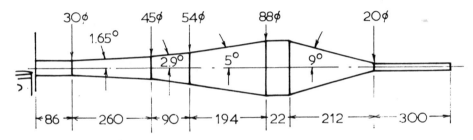

Fig. A . 2   Modified Yamaha YZ80F expansion chamber.

chamber and welding in a new baffle cone and secondary diffuser. The standard header pipe and stinger is retained, but as the new centre section is shorter than standard, a 20mm length of pipe will have to be welded in to lengthen the stinger to reach the baffle cone.

The long secondary diffuser with a taper of 5° serves to improve mid-range and top end power. Normally 5° would be too steep for a motocross engine of this size but working in conjunction with the 90mm section of diffuser tapering at 2.9°, which was retained, the resulting two stage diffuser works very well.

The baffle cone taper is reduced to 9° in the interests of widening and smoothing the power band. It reduces top end power a little but this is a price that must sometimes be paid. If the chamber is correctly formed it will not be necessary to notch the diffuser to clear the frame tubes.

Because the tuned length of the chamber has been reduced so that it now works at 11,000rpm rather than 10,200rpm, the belly section is just 22mm long. You will note that this section no longer does any silencing. Yet if the standard silencer attached on the end of the stinger is retained, and the new cones are made of 1mm sheet steel, you will find that the modified chamber provides much quieter running than standard.

After smoothing power delivery, we can now think about raising the YZ80F's power level. This basically involves getting more air into the engine, particularly above 10,500rpm.

The first thing we must do is rebore the standard 26mm Mikuni carburettor to 27.3mm. Really the carb should be bigger, but this is the maximum to which the carburettor can be bored. The jetting will not have to be altered, except that on very fast tracks a 195 main jet may be required instead of the standard 190. Usually, I have found it beneficial to lower the needle to the centre clip position as the engine tends to run a little rich on the factory 4th groove setting.

The reed valve assembly doesn't flow exceptionally well. It can be replaced by a Nogucchi reed block, which will flow about 25% more air. As this assembly is physically bigger than the standard reed block, the inlet port must be enlarged for it to fit.

Alternatively, the standard block can be modified as indicated in FIGURE A.3. First, the reed block openings must be carefully widened to remove the lip Yamaha leaves in manufacture. Then the openings can be increased in length to further increase flow area. If phenolic reed petals are available, these should be fitted.

To improve air flow into the cylinder, the inlet port must be enlarged, but care is needed here as excessive widening will allow the lower back wall of the cylinder to 189

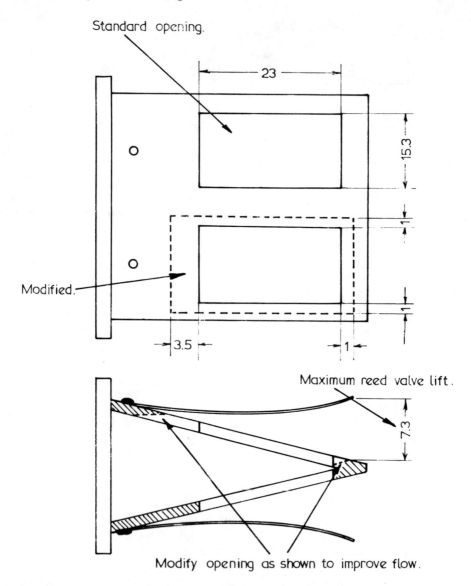

Standard opening.

Modified.

Maximum reed valve lift.

Modify opening as shown to improve flow.

Fig. A .3 Yamaha YZ8OF reed block modification.

break away. What you must do is ovalise the sides of the port and smooth the side walls into the opening in the cylinder sleeve. The port width can be increased from 30mm to 32mm at the top (FIGURE A.4).

If the piston is due for replacement, fit a later G model piston as it is much stronger than the F piston and it lets more air into the crankcase. As shown in FIGURE A.5, the skirt is 2.5mm shorter and the port windows are opened up to 13mm by 20mm. There is also another advantage in using the G piston. It has circlip extractor slots, which means that circlips without tails can be used. The F model is a real problem in this respect. Tail-type wire circlips always spell trouble and the YZ80F is no

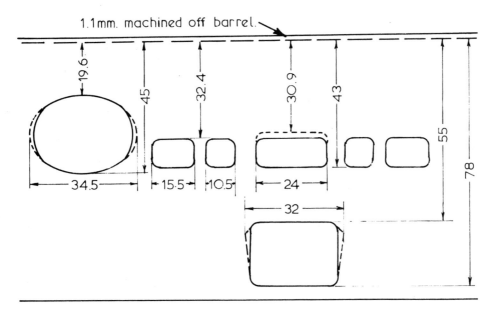

Fig. A . 4   Porting modifications.

F model.   G model.

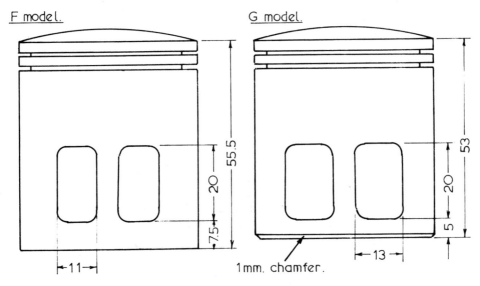

1mm. chamfer.

Fig. A . 5   Comparison of F & G model pistons.

exception. The constant rubbing of the gudgeon pin against the circlip wears through the tail, allowing it to drop into the cylinder, scoring the bore and possibly seizing the motor.

The piston modification to improve flow from the crankcase into the transfer ports is very simple and doesn't cause any trouble. Enlarging the cut-away below the 191 piston boss exposes a larger area for fuel/air mixture to flow through into the transfers (FIGURE A.6).

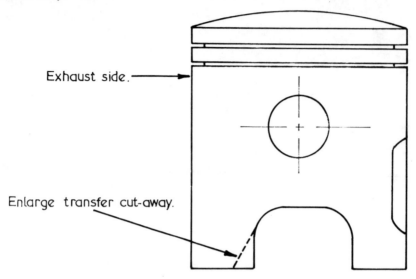

Exhaust side.

Enlarge transfer cut-away.

Fig. A . 6   Piston modification to improve flow into transfer ports.

To improve flow from the crankcase further, the base gaskets must be trimmed back with a sharp knife if their edges lap over into the transfer passages. Then match the passages in the barrel to the pattern provided by the trimmed base gaskets. In YZ80s, the divider between adjoining transfer passages is very disruptive to flow, so it must be thinned down and made more streamlined.

Exhaust flow is enhanced by widening the port 1.0mm to 34.5mm. This is the maximum practical width. The shape of the port must not be changed, just smooth out the 'dingle berries' but leave the basic 'D' shape of the port as it is. Many tuners have been caught out grinding the YZ80F exhaust port to a conventional round shape. The results are always disappointing: peak power increases slightly, but the mid-range falls flat on its face.

If 97 octane fuel is being used, the compression ratio can be pushed up to 15.5:1. To achieve this, the top of the barrel will have to be machined approximately 1.1mm. This will restore what was lost from raising the barrel, and give a little extra compression on top.

In this state of tune you will need a Champion N-59G plug gapped at 0.020in. The ignition timing should remain at 0.8mm before TDC as for the standard engine.

An engine like this, running in excess of 10,000rpm, does not need two rings, so leave off the second ring. This will reduce cylinder wear, particularly above the exhaust port, and frictional losses will be lessened.

A YZ80F modified in this manner will produce a good spread of power far in excess of the standard unit (TABLE A.1). If a 28mm Mikuni bored to 29mm is fitted, the performance is even better. Peak power will not improve, but the engine will produce more power at 12,000rpm.

On most motocross tracks, a 12 tooth countershaft sprocket will provide the correct gearing. This is a considerable reduction on the 14 tooth sprocket fitted by the factory. Riders under eight stone will be able to start in second gear, without bogging the motor. Heavier juniors will have to use low gear, except for down-hill starts or where traction is poor.

2   Suzuki RM125C

As delivered from the factory, Suzuki RM125 engines have always been real little gems. They produce a wide spread of easily managed power as well as excellent peak hp. Few other 125s can stay with them on any motocross track.

With careful porting modifications, the RM125 can be coaxed to deliver even more top end power without affecting the mid-range, but leave the expansion chamber alone as it cannot be improved upon. Any changes in the pipe to make it work better at the top-end seem to kill the power band, so leave well alone.

Many tuners claim that the 32mm Mikuni fitted as standard is too small, but I disagree. A 34mm Mikuni (or a 32 bored to 34mm) will not increase peak hp, but it will allow the engine to run to 11,500rpm with ease. With a 32mm carburettor the engine runs out of breath just past 11,000rpm. When tested on the dyno, an engine with a 34mm Mikuni doesn't appear to lose low end power (i.e., at 9000rpm) when compared with a 32mm unit, but out in the real world of motocross racing throttle response does not appear to be quite as good.

The exception is when the RM is modified for expert riders. In this instance the 32mm carburettor just cannot flow enough air to keep up with the demands of an engine with radical, almost road race, porting. At 11,000 and 11,500rpm a 34 or 35mm carburettor is necessary to allow this wild porting to work. In the hands of an expert rider the resulting increase in power seems to compensate for what has been lost in the mid-range.

Because it has a crankcase reed valve, the RM still relies on the piston skirt to open and close the inlet port. For this reason Suzuki have kept the inlet duration to a fairly tame 155°, about equivalent to a pre-reed valve enduro motor like the Bultaco Matador. Lowering the inlet port 3.0mm increases the inlet event to 167°. The increase in duration gives the air more time to get into the motor, and grinding the floor of the port 3.0mm lower gives it a bigger, less restrictive hole to flow through. Cutting 3.0mm off the piston skirt would also increase inlet duration to 167°, but the inlet port would remain a small restrictive tract. Before you leave the inlet port, increase its width by 3.0mm to 40mm and then match up the inlet manifold with the port and the carburettor bore (FIGURE A.7).

When working on the inlet port, you will notice that the reed valve doesn't match very well. What you have to do is remove the stainless steel petal and then grind the port and/or reed block to give air flowing into the crankcase via the reed valve a clear, unrestricted passage. Replace the stainless steel petal with two phenolic petals. I recommend that two petals be fitted, as this improves crankcase filling at high rpm by eliminating petal flutter. Be sure to Loctite the screws retaining the reed stop and petals. You don't want those screws falling out and dropping into the motor.

The RM125 transfer ports are a good size and shape, but unfortunately they are very rough. Without altering their shape all the 'dingle berries' must be ground out of the ports, and when they have been smoothed they should be matched to the crankcase transfer passages and base gasket.

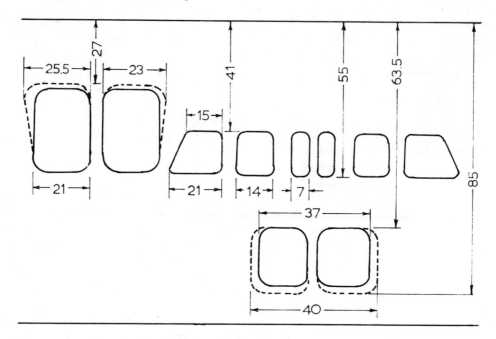

Fig. A . 7   Suzuki RM125C porting modifications.

Probably the worst aspect of the RM engine is its exhaust port. It exits at a very bad angle, restricting gas flow quite severely. Fortunately, there is enough metal in the barrel around the exhaust port to permit one half of the port to be ground much wider, to handle the bulk of exhaust gas exiting the cylinder. Standard, each half of the port is 21mm wide. To increase gas flow the left exhaust window (viewed from the front of the bike) should be ground to increase its width, at the top, to 23mm. It can be made wider, but this half of the port exits at such a terrible angle you will be wasting your time. The right window is the one on which to concentrate your efforts. It can be ground 25.5mm wide. Take care not to go any further than this, otherwise the piston will not be able to seal the crankcase from the exhaust port.

Do not increase the exhaust port width at the bottom. The port is already too close to the transfers at this point, and making the port wider here would just allow more fuel/air mixture to spill out into the exhaust, particularly below 9000rpm.

Quite a few RM125 exhaust ports require lowering by 0.5-0.75mm, so that they don't stand proud of the piston crown at TDC. While you are attending to this, also grind the 'bump' out of the exhaust port floor (FIGURE A.8).

The standard exhaust duration is about 192°. Raising the port 1.0mm increases this to 197° and lifts peak hp nicely.

When you have finished modifying the exhaust port, fit the exhaust header flange and mate it to the port. Generally, the match is not good, so you will have to grind the flange evenly all the way around inside to increase its internal diameter, and don't forget to trim the gasket to suit. The flange should be attached using Allen head screws with a drop of Loctite on them.

If 97 octane fuel is used, the compression ratio can be brought up to 14.7:1. This can be achieved by machining the head approximately 0.2mm or, if you are very

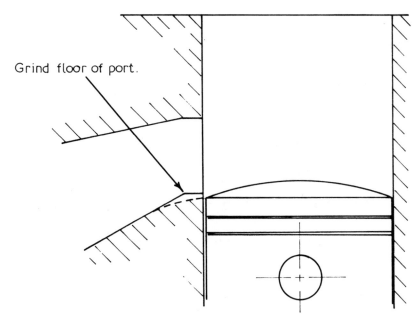

Grind floor of port.

Fig. A .8 Exhaust port modification.

careful, the head gasket may be thinned with a sheet of wet and dry paper on a piece of plate glass.

In this state of tune the engine will require a Champion N-59G plug gapped at 0.020in. (On very fast tracks an N-57G may be required). Leave the ignition timing at 2.8mm before TDC.

To reduce frictional losses, use just the top compression ring. The second ring really only helps below about 8000rpm, so there is no point in fitting it as it reduces power and increases bore wear.

You should not have to alter the carburettor jetting in any way. On most tracks the 240 main will be about right, but on slower circuits a 230 may give a slightly superior throttle response.

Expert riders will be able to handle more power and a narrower power band. The main changes to achieve this goal involve increased exhaust and inlet opening periods. Raising the exhaust port an additional 0.5mm lifts duration to about 199°, which is the practical maximum for motocross, although you can go another 0.5mm higher for TT racing.

The inlet port can be lowered an extra 1.5mm, giving 173° inlet duration. It can be lowered a further 1.5mm for TT racing. This achieves an inlet event of 180° duration.

The 32mm Mikuni will have to be bored to 34mm or be replaced with a 34mm carburettor. It will not require any jetting changes except for a 250 main jet.

The expansion chamber also has to be altered to work in tune with the 'hot' expert porting. You will have to cut 50mm out of the belly section of the chamber to reduce the overall tuned length.

Finally, replace the reed valve assembly with a DG reed block. The DG reed has twice the flow area of the standard Suzuki valve. It won't do anything to pick up mid-range power, but peak hp is improved due to increased air flow into the motor. 195

3 Honda CR250R

The Honda CR250R works very nicely in stock trim, but it can be modified to produce better mid-range and top-end hp. All it needs is a new expansion chamber and some work on the transfer ports.

The standard expansion chamber is quite unusual in many respects. The parallel wall header pipe is rather old hat by today's standards. After that there is a 4.5° diffuser, followed by a strange three-stage baffle. For half its length it tapers at 2.5° and then closes in at 7.5° and finally 9°.

The chamber we want is illustrated in FIGURE A.9. The header pipe with a taper of 1.22° picks up power right through the range, while the slightly shallower diffuser and baffle cones improve mid-range power.

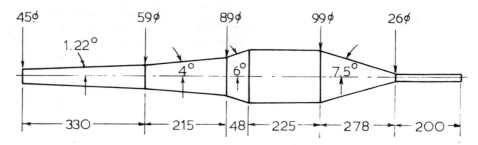

Fig. A.9 Special Honda CR250R expansion chamber.

Basically, the Honda barrel is very good, but I don't like its transfer ports. The duration of 124° is a trifle short, so the first modification is to raise them 1.0mm to increase duration to 129°.

The main problem with the transfers is that they discharge the fuel/air mixture into the cylinder at the wrong angle. The main transfer ports (i.e., those flanking the exhaust port) are pitched upwards at 15°, while the secondary ports are tilted at 30°. What must be done is grind the ports to the shape shown in FIGURE A.10. This modification reduces flow turbulence and minimises mixture dilution with exhaust gas, by directing mixture flow across the piston crown, and towards the back of the cylinder. The bottom of the transfers are opened up 2.0mm to smooth and hasten flow.

To increase top-end power the exhaust port is moved up 1.0mm, increasing duration by 4° to 184°.

With these modifications the CR250 produces power figures indicated in TABLE A.2. You will note that mid-range power has increased by a minimum of 1hp and peak power is up 2.6hp.

4 Yamaha YZ465H

Unlimited class motocrossers produce more power than the majority of riders can handle. The 465 Yamaha is no exception: it pushes out close on 42hp, so attempts to extract more power are merely an academic exercise. However, on some very fast tracks the 465 is at a slight power disadvantage to the big 490 Maico, so if you think you can handle more power, this is the way to get it. Switch to Avgas 100/130 and bump the compression ratio up to 12.5:1. Then raise the exhaust port 0.7mm and the back boost port 1.0mm.

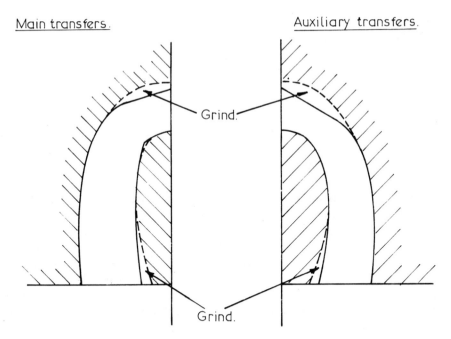

Main transfers.   Auxiliary transfers.

Grind.

Grind.

Fig. A .10 Transfer port modification.

TABLE A.2   Honda CR250R power output

rpm	Standard		Modified	
	hp	*Torque (lb/ft)*	*hp*	*Torque (lb/ft)*
4000	10.0	13.1	10.6	13.95
4500	11.1	13.0	12.2	14.23
5000	13.1	13.8	14.4	15.1
5500	19.0	18.13	20.5	19.6
6000	25.2	22.1	26.5	23.2
6500	28.2	22.75	30.7	24.8
7000	29.7	22.3	31.3	23.5
7500	29.8	20.9	32.4	22.7
8000	27.7	18.2	29.4	19.3
8500	23.1	14.27	25.2	15.6

If your 465 is a dual purpose play/motocross bike, you may prefer to soften the power delivery a little. There are a couple of ways you can go about this. By far the easiest method is to fit two base gaskets under the barrel. This lowers the compression ratio and raises the transfers, de-tuning the engine. Alternatively, you can machine the combustion chamber to lower the compression ratio to 11:1 and then raise the boost port 1.0mm. If the engine runs rich in the mid-range, fit a White Bros. reed block spacer.

B Enduro modifications

1 Yamaha IT175F

The IT175F has a very responsive engine. It produces good power and maintains a wide power range. This makes it suitable for most enduro riders with some previous experience of enduro machines. However, beginner riders starting out on an IT175 may find it just a little peaky in low speed situations, which call for a delicate application of power. All competition bikes have a tendency to lurch forward as the throttle is twisted open. When the course is easy this is not a problem for a beginner, but in tighter sections this tendency may intimidate a rider because of front wheel lift-off and/or rear-end sliding which usually results.

For beginners, I would suggest that you tame the engine in two ways. First, replace the standard 34mm Mikuni with a 32mm unit. If you have a mate with a YZ125 you may be able to do a swap. The 32mm carburettor will require jetting the same as the 34mm carburettor. Since you are a beginner you will most likely have to fit a smaller 340 main jet.

The other change required is to raise the boost port in the back of the cylinder 1.0mm. This smooths the power curve without reducing maximum hp.

Most riders will want to leave the engine in the same tune it leaves the factory. However, if a little more top-end power is desired, this can be easily accommodated. A simple clean-up of the ports to remove 'dingle berries', and matching the transfer port openings to the crankcase, will increase maximum power by 1hp and improve power at peak revs by almost 2hp.

Expert riders can pick up a little more power by boring the carburettor to 35mm (leave the jetting standard) and raising the exhaust port 1.0mm. If Avgas 100/130 fuel is used, the compression ratio should be increased to 14:1 to swell mid-range power (TABLE B.1). Really, the IT175 could do with a new expansion chamber in this degree of tune. However, I don't feel that it is worth the trouble and expense. If you are good enough to use the sort of power that a new pipe will release, then you should be on a Can-Am or SWM. These bikes are expensive but by the time you have bolted new suspension units onto your IT to transmit all of this new found power to the ground, you will be in front financially with one of these exotic machines.

2 Suzuki PE175N

The Suzuki PE175 is a very nice bike, particularly for beginners. However, as the rider's ability improves, he will soon notice that the PE cannot match other 175 enduro machines in sheer power.

The first modification that I would recommend for all riders is to remove the two restrictors out of the exhaust. These were originally fitted to make the bike street legal, but as such a low noise level isn't required in competition, these must go. The restrictor fitted behind the exhaust flange is easy to remove. Just unscrew the three Phillips head screws which hold the flange in place, and take out the restrictor. The other restrictor, situated inside the expansion chamber, is much more difficult to get at. It is located in the baffle cone just before the stinger. You will have to cut the chamber open, then pull it out and reweld the pipe. With the restrictors out of the way the engine will gain 1hp from 7000rpm to 10,000rpm.

To give the PE a smooth power band, Suzuki have kept the inlet port area and duration very conservative. This problem can be overcome in two ways. By lowering

TABLE B.1   Yamaha IT175F power output

	Standard		Expert modified	
rpm	*hp*	*Torque (lb/ft)*	*hp*	*Torque (lb/ft)*
4000	6.3	8.3	4.9	6.5
4500	7.4	8.7	5.8	6.8
5000	8.7	9.1	6.3	6.6
5500	10.0	9.6	7.5	7.2
6000	9.8	8.6	8.7	7.65
6500	12.0	9.7	10.4	8.4
7000	15.1	11.3	13.3	10.0
7500	18.2	12.73	15.4	10.8
8000	19.6	12.9	18.0	11.8
8500	20.5	12.7	20.1	12.4
9000	20.3	11.85	21.6	12.6
9500	19.9	11.0	22.6	12.5
10000	11.6	6.1	19.6	10.3
10500			9.2	4.6

the inlet port 3.0mm, port area is increased and duration is extended 12°. Inlet area is also enlarged considerably if the standard two-petal reed is replaced by a six-petal DG reed assembly. Just by itself the DG reed will lift power through the whole range and make the PE much more competitive.

PE175s all seem to suffer from very ragged ports, so these must be aligned and smoothed to pick up top-end power. While you are about it, raise the exhaust port 0.75mm to extend the exhaust duration from 184° to 186°.

To increase mid-range torque, the compression ratio can be bumped up a little, depending on the fuel being used. With 97 octane premium petrol, the PE will run very well at 13.5:1 compression. On 100 Avgas this can safely be increased to 14:1. Be sure to use a Champion N-57G gapped at 0.020in.

3   Kawasaki KDX175

The KDX175 is one very nice engine with power characteristics well suited to the most inexperienced rider. It pulls smoothly right through the power range and produces a good peak of around 20hp. The stock suspension can easily cope with a more potent engine.

The very first modification required is to replace the factory reed petals with the patented Eyvind Boyensen reeds. The Boyensen reed petals are actually a dual assembly with a thin 0.01in. reed riding on top of a thicker 0.027in. reed. The thin one opens readily under a low pressure drop and the thick reed takes over at higher rpm. This gives the benefits of good low speed air flow as well as the absence of petal flutter at high speed. An added benefit is that the four ribs can be trimmed out of the KDX reed cage, due to the design of the thick petals. Consequently the reed assembly will flow more air and exercise more control over both high rpm and low rpm flow.

This Kawasaki is geared for too much speed, like most enduro bikes, topping almost 80mph. As this is an ideal beginner's machine, I would suggest that the 52 tooth rear sprocket be swapped for a 58 tooth sprocket. Top speed will be reduced to 72mph, but you will find it much easier to climb first gear hills.

Because the KDX175 handles so well, expert riders will be able to use considerably more power. Basically, the ports must be cleaned up and aligned and the exhaust and boost ports should be raised 1.2mm and 0.8mm respectively. Bore the carburettor to 35mm (retain stock jetting) and raise the compression ratio to 14:1 for use on Avgas 100/130 fuel (TABLE B.2).

TABLE B.2   Kawasaki KDX175 power output

rpm	Standard		Expert modified	
	hp	*Torque (lb/ft)*	*hp*	*Torque (lb/ft)*
3000	3.3	5.7	2.7	4.8
3500	4.3	6.5	3.5	5.3
4000	6.0	7.9	4.9	6.4
4500	6.9	8.0	5.8	6.8
5000	7.8	8.2	7.2	7.6
5500	8.5	8.1	8.4	8.0
6000	10.4	9.1	9.5	8.3
6500	11.8	9.5	11.9	9.6
7000	13.3	10.0	13.6	10.2
7500	16.0	11.2	16.4	11.5
8000	17.2	11.3	18.0	11.8
8500	18.1	11.2	18.8	11.6
9000	18.2	10.6	19.5	11.4
9500	19.7	10.9	21.4	11.8
10000	13.9	7.3	16.8	8.8

4   Suzuki PE250T

This model PE Suzuki works very well as it comes from the factory. The ports require a good clean-up and aligning with the crankcase. This will lift power by approximately 1hp in the upper rev range from 5500 to 8500rpm. Unfortunately, due to poorer fuel atomisation at lower rpm when the air speed is slow, bottom end power is reduced a little.

To increase power right through the rpm range, the standard reed should be replaced by a high flow unit. The six-petal DG reed assembly and the R & R Hi-Volume reed both flow significantly more air than the factory reed valve. After fitting either assembly, be sure to match the reed cage to the inlet passage in the cylinder.

Expert riders can pick-up more power by raising the exhaust port 0.75mm. To help restore low rpm torque, the compression ratio will have to be increased to 13.7:1. When the compression is raised to this extent, it is necessary to use 100/130 Avgas to avoid engine overheating and detonation.

5   Can-Am 250 Qualifier III

Along with the 250 SWM, which shares a similar engine, the Can-Am 250 is the most powerful enduro machine in this class. As well as having good peak power, the rotary valve Rotax engine also has an excellent spread of power. The first step to obtain more power is to remove the foam filter cover from around the stock K & N air filter. Then carefully match the barrel to the crankcase passages and clean up and align the entire inlet tract. Next check the rotary valve timing. It should open 137° before TDC and close 75° after TDC. After this, measure the compression ratio. Preferably it should be about 13:1, if it is less than 12.5:1 machine the head to bring the compression ratio up to 13:1. Fit a Champion N-59G plug gapped at 0.5mm and set the timing at 1.2mm before TDC.

If you are an expert rider, the engine can be modified for even more power. Running Avgas 100/130 the compression ratio can be bumped up to 13.8:1. Set the timing at 1.2mm and use a Champion N-59G plug gapped at 0.5mm. For more high rpm power modify the rotary valve disc to close at 80° after TDC (leave the opening at 137° before TDC). Then raise the exhaust port to increase the open period to 184°.

6   Can-Am 350 Qualifier III

The Rotax engine fitted to this bike is considered by many to be a misfit. In actuality it is only 277cc, so it tends to be written off as an open class bike, However, I do not agree. In tight or muddy going the little 350 Qualifier is an outright contender and for a beginner it makes an excellent dual purpose play/enduro bike, due to the engine's smooth power delivery characteristics. Basically, the engine can be treated in exactly the same way as the 250, the only exception being that the timing should be set at 1.4mm before TDC.

Expert riders should rework the engine as follows. Switch to Avgas 100/130 and increase the compression ratio to 13.5:1. Leave the ignition timing at 1.4mm before TDC. Raise the exhaust port to give 184° duration and modify the rotary valve disc to close at 82° after TDC. Fit a Mikuni 34mm carburettor bored to 35.3mm, 310 main jet, P-6 needle jet, 6DH-7 needle 3rd groove, 3.0mm slide cutaway and 60 idle jet (TABLE B.3).

TABLE B.3   Can-Am 350 Qualifier III power output

rpm	Standard		Expert modified	
	hp	*Torque (lb/ft)*	*hp*	*Torque (lb/ft)*
2500	5.3	11.2	4.6	9.7
3000	6.6	11.6	6.0	10.5
3500	9.7	14.5	8.4	12.6
4000	11.1	14.6	10.7	14.0
4500	13.8	16.1	11.8	13.8
5000	17.1	18.0	16.1	16.9
5500	22.5	21.5	21.2	20.3
6000	25.0	21.9	25.4	22.2
6500	27.6	22.3	28.0	22.6
7000	30.4	22.8	32.0	24.0
7500	30.3	21.2	32.7	22.9
8000	31.4	20.6	32.3	21.2
8500	24.4	15.1	28.2	17.4

One problem with the 350 Qualifier is the large gap between first and second gears, which even this engine's wide spread of power will not cover. Therefore, I would suggest that novice and play riders fit a 14 tooth countershaft sprocket in place of the stock 15 tooth sprocket if they do much riding in the lower gears.

If you have a 250 Can-Am, it can be uprated to 350 specifications very simply, and as a bonus you will have the added benefit of a 6 speed transmission as opposed to the 350's five speed unit. All that is required is a 350 barrel and piston. Then the 250 head and cases will require machining to fit the 4mm larger barrel. The only other parts you will require are a 350 head and base gasket and a 2.76 needle jet to replace the stock 250's 2.73 jet.

7   Suzuki PE400T

This is one of those engines which are better left alone. It works well in standard form, so spend your money on a pair of Ohilins shocks. If you want to do some work on the engine, clean up and match all the ports. Then fit a high flow reed valve assembly to increase power right through the range.

Expert riders who can handle a narrower power band and a sudden rush of power, can raise the exhaust port 0.8mm and bore the carburettor out to 37mm. Then raise the compression ratio to 12.3:1. It will be necessary to run Avgas 100/130 to avoid engine overheating or detonation.

C   Road race modifications

1   Yamaha KT100S Kart

This engine is very popular in the beginner karting classes and, as such, most ruling bodies restrict the engine to stock tune. However, within the definition of stock tune, there is a considerable amount of modification which can be done. Basically, we have to read the rules carefully and then modify the engine to take advantage of factory tolerances.

The first thing we must do is raise the compression ratio so that the engine pulls harder out of tight corners. Some engines have a compression ratio as low as 9.8:1, although about 10.2:1 is average. What we want is a compression ratio of 11.5:1. Higher than this the con rod tends to self-destruct.

The specifications state that the head gasket thickness should be 0.7 to 0.9mm. Obviously, we want the thin gasket; if yours is thicker, carefully dress it, using wet and dry paper on a sheet of glass. According to the rules the base gasket should be from 0.25mm to 0.5mm thick. All the factory gaskets I've measured seem to be 0.4mm thick, so it will be necessary to buy some good quality 0.25mm gasket material and cut a gasket to suit. FIGURE C.1 illustrates the cylinder head requirements to which we must work. As you can see, the minimum depth of the squish band must be 1.20mm. If the squish band is deeper than this, have the head machined down. Now reassemble the engine and very carefully measure the combustion chamber volume with the piston at TDC. Hopefully, the volume will be about 9.5cc (or about 11.8cc if you measure to the top of the spark plug hole). Engines with a combustion chamber volume greater than 9.7cc will need additional measuring and machining.

The next move is to measure the distance from the head gasket recess in the barrel to the top of the exhaust port. The minimum allowable dimension is 26.3mm. Most cylinders are very close to this standard (I've even seen a few under this figure) but occasionally you will find a cylinder which measures out at 26.5mm. If you have such a cylinder, have the recess cut 0.2mm deeper. Some people question this move, reasoning that it would be preferable to raise the exhaust port and gain performance in this manner. Let me assure you that the KT100S is one engine which does not need more

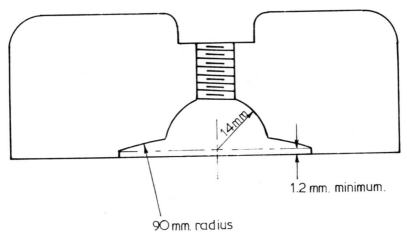

90 mm. radius

14 mm

1.2 mm. minimum.

Fig. C . 1   Yamaha KT1OOS combustion chamber detail.

exhaust duration, in fact the engine would work better with about 5° less duration on short, tight, sprint tracks.

Barrels which are already down to the minimum exhaust port to gasket recess dimension, should be measured to determine if the base of the barrel can be machined to reduce its length. The minimum distance allowable is 80.4mm, measured from the cylinder base to the head gasket recess. If you cannot do any good here, the next move is to check the crankcase deck height (FIGURE C.2). You will note that the minimum dimension permissible is 21.2mm. Finally, if the tolerances have not allowed you to raise the compression ratio up to 11.5:1 by this point, and you are really desperate to get the maximum performance out of your engine, you will have to split the crankcases and measure the crankwheel diameters. The minimum diameter according to the specifications is 86.6mm. As most crankwheels measure close to 87.0mm you can have the wheels turned down, thus reducing the crankcase deck height and opening the way legally to mill material from the crankcase deck.

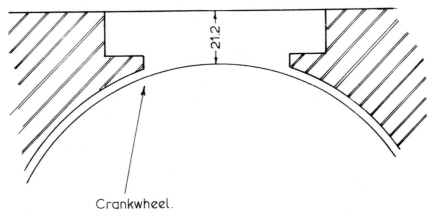

21.2

Crankwheel.

Fig. C . 2   Minimum crankcase deck height.

If the rules allow the ports to be cleaned up and aligned, you should take advantage of this provision. First, match the transfer ports to the crankcase and, at the same time, narrow down the bridge separating the transfer openings in the bottom of the barrel. Then fit a piston in the cylinder and check that both halves of the exhaust port are at the same height; as supplied, many barrels have uneven port heights. If the ports are not opening together, the lower side will have to be raised, being very careful to keep the height within legal limits.

The final work required on the barrel is the modification of the inlet port. Do not lower the inlet floor even if it is above the legal limit, as this will only lose bottom end power. Instead, widen the port out to the legal limit of 34.8mm and square off the floor of the port. To minimise piston scuffing, a radius of at least 4mm will have to be left in the bottom corners of the port. If the regulations do not specify what height the inlet port should be (most do not), then it should be raised to the same level as the piston skirt with the crank at TDC. However, before raising the inlet roof, be very careful to check that this modification will not expose the piston ring and allow it to snag in the inlet port when the piston moves to BDC.

When working the inlet port, you will notice that the phenolic spacer and the aluminium carburettor mounting plate do not line up very well with the inlet port or the carburettor. The regulations specify a maximum hole size of 26.4mm and 26.3mm respectively, for the spacer and the mounting plate, so if opening the holes out to the maximum does not rectify the misalignment, the mounting holes will have to be elongated to correct the problem.

The Walbro carburettor fitted to this engine should be measured to ensure that the venturi and throttle bore are 24.13mm and 25.65mm respectively. Be sure to check the fuel filter, located behind the pump diaphragm, regularly as it is prone to blockage. This will severely limit high speed fuel flow and could cause engine seizure.

On high speed circuits use a Champion N-59G gapped at 0.020in. Slower tracks usually require the use of an N-2G plug.

The expansion chamber required for this engine is illustrated in FIGURE C.3. The header tapers at 1.25°, followed by a two-stage diffuser with 3° and 5.5° tapers. The baffle cone has a very shallow 9° taper.

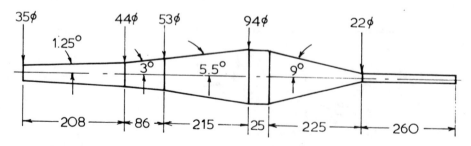

Fig. C.3 Special Yamaha KT100S expansion chamber.

2 DAP T72 100cc International Kart

Few International kart engines require modification to any extent, but all have to be carefully 'blueprinted' to give a winning edge. As it comes from the factory, the T72 will perform very well and win races, but both power and reliability are improved when it is rebuilt to precise specifications. In fact most of the improved performance that you can gain from your T72 will come from correct assembly.

Before you strip the engine down, there are a few clearance checks which must be made. The first thing we wish to know is the crankshaft end-play. To determine this, lightly clamp the engine in a vice (between soft jaws) and attach a dial indicator to either the engine or the vice so that the plunger directly contacts the end of the crankshaft. Then, with the crank pushed as far as possible to one side of the engine, zero the indicator. Next, push the crank towards the dial indicator, noting the dial reading.

Having done that, remove the head and barrel. Before removing the piston, check the little end clearance — the clearance between the piston and the face of the con-rod little end. Then measure the big end bearing cage side clearance. To do this, insert a feeler blade between the crank wheel and big end thrust washer, and repeat until you find a feeler that is a nice slide fit in the gap.

Finally, split the crankcase and remove the crank assembly to check crankshaft run-out. (See Chapter 7).

The first thing we must correct is big end side clearance and crank end-float. When using C3 fit main bearings, the end-float we want is 0.2mm. If the engine has, say, 0.25mm end-play and 0.5mm big end clearance, we can press the crank wheels a further 0.05mm apart to reduce end-play (0.25-0.2=0.05mm). This will, of course, increase big end clearance to 0.55mm (0.5+0.05=0.55mm), but this improves lubrication and bearing cooling.

On the other hand, where the crank end-float is too tight, the fix may be more difficult. For example, if end-float is 0.15mm and big end clearance is 0.55mm we can increase the end-float by pressing the crank wheels together 0.05mm (0.15+0.05=0.2mm). Big end side clearance is reduced to 0.5mm when this is done (0.55-0.05=0.5mm), which is the minimum acceptable side clearance. If, however, the big end clearance is already marginal (i.e. 0.5mm), too little crank end float cannot be corrected in this way, otherwise the big end will overheat due to a lack of lubrication. What has to be done is to machine the main bearing housing deeper to increase end-float.

The crankshaft run-out should ideally be zero as any run-out decreases bearing life and performance, and increases vibration. A run-out figure over 0.025mm is unacceptable.

The cylinder bore must be checked to ensure that it is round, parallel and square to the barrel base (see Chapter 7). If the barrel does not meet these requirements then the bore and/or base will require machining. The piston to bore clearance required is 0.0028-0.003in. Correct ring gap is 0.2mm-0.25mm.

The ideal little end clearance is 0.2-0.25mm. If it is tighter than this, the bearing will overheat. The cure is to lap the standard thrust washers on 180 grit paper to increase clearance to the ideal figure.

With all of the above taken care of, the motor may be re-assembled. Then measure the squish clearance (see Chapter 2) and machine the head, if necessary, to achieve the desired figure of 0.7mm. Be sure to keep the compression ratio below 13:1. Also measure the clearance between the rotary valve and the valve cover. If it is less than 0.25mm, the cover face will have to be machined to increase valve clearance, otherwise 205 performance will drop due to excess drag occurring because of the cover and valve scuffing together. More than 0.3mm clearance increases leakage past the valve when it is closed, which also reduces power, especially at lower speeds. To decrease valve clearance, the mating face of the cover will have to be machined.

While you are working with the rotary valve cover, check that the inlet opening aligns with the inlet tract in the crankcase. Any mis-match here will knock top-end power, so grind the cover inlet until perfect alignment is achieved.

Generally speaking, the port specifications should be left alone. The ports should be cleaned up but retain stock timing, as the factory knows what it is doing. Fiddling with the ports and/or valve timing usually results in sluggish performance out of tight turns.

For circuits with relatively fast corners it is advantageous to have a spare rotary valve and barrel modified to lift maximum hp. The valve should be modified to open at 50° after BDC and close 75° after TDC. The exhaust port should be raised to increase exhaust port duration from 170° to 177° and the TT port and transfer ports should be moved up to give open periods of 134° and 128° respectively.

Assuming that the head and barrel have been sandblasted (to increase fin surface area) and painted matt black, the ignition timing should be set at 2.5mm before TDC on Avgas 100/130 petrol. On a few very slow circuits you may have to retard the timing back to 2.2mm to avoid engine knock when pulling out of slow corners under full load. If you are right on the maximum weight limit, this is not usually a problem, but overweight drivers can put a tremendous overload on an engine when hauling out of tight, uphill turns.

Most International drivers are happy with the Vevey expansion chamber and factory header connected by a length of convolute tube (FIGURE C.4). However, I believe the Vevey pipe leaves much to be desired, and the parallel wall header can certainly be improved. I'm not at all in favour of the convolute interconnecting tube either. It usually leaks and its life expectancy is always short. One thing in its favour is that the tuned length of the exhaust can easily be altered by using convolute tube of varying lengths.

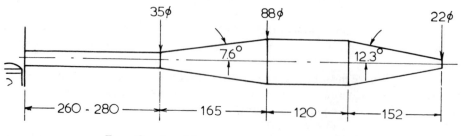

Fig. C.4   Vevey expansion chamber.

I have found a pipe of an entirely different design to give much better performance right through the power range (FIGURE C.5). This chamber is designed to make a slip-joint connection with the factory header pipe, which has been shortened by 100mm. You will note that the new pipe has a header taper of 1.5°, diffuser tapers of 4° and 8° and a baffle taper of 11.5°. The cone tapers are much shallower than the 7.6° diffuser and 12.3° baffle tapers of the Vevey pipe. Also, the Vevey has a perforated baffle which reduces its effectiveness in returning a good pulse and, as it doesn't have a stinger to create back pressure, the pipe does not have the ability to ram very much escaped fuel/air mixture back into the cylinder.

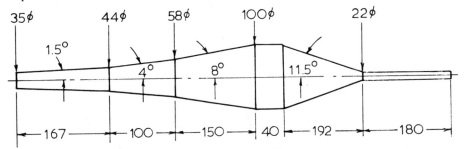

Fig. C.5 Special rotary valve kart expansion chamber.

The pipe illustrated will work on most circuits, but on slower tracks the 'belly' length will have to be increased and on faster circuits it may need to be shortened slightly. If you prefer, you may wish to construct this chamber with a slip-joint type belly section, so that the tuned length can be changed quickly to suit the circuit (FIGURE C.6). When this is done, be sure to use two good quality hose clamps and three light springs to prevent the chamber from falling apart. Also, to stop any leakage, seal the joint with Silastic. Exhaust jointing compounds may be used, but I have found Silastic to be superior.

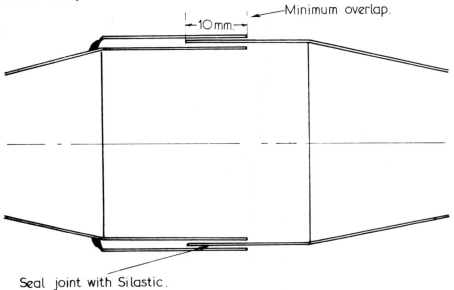

Fig. C.6 Slip-joint type belly section.

3 Suzuki RM125B

The Suzuki RM125B motocross engine makes an excellent road race power plant. In the right frame it can hold its own against the Honda and Yamaha production 207 racers. It is quite an inexpensive engine, as used units in reasonable condition can often be purchased from motorcycle wreckers. This engine, like that of the later model Suzukis (which are also just as suitable for modification), is very reliable. Piston and ring wear is always incredibly small and the cylinder will stay true and show little sign of wear, even after hundreds of miles of racing. The only problem is the big end bearing which Suzuki use. It has a copper-plated cage which does not like engine speeds much in excess of 11,500rpm. Therefore, engines in a very high state of tune must use a better big end bearing. Lesser engines will also keep their bottom end intact if a silver-plated steel cage big end is used.

I haven't been able to find a bearing to suit the Suzuki's crankpin and con-rod, so I use a bearing, thrust washers, crankpin and con rod from a Honda CR125M. This change-over is reasonably straight forward, but it does involve some very precise machine work. Both rods are 100mm centre to centre and share the same size little end. However, the crankpin at 20mm diameter is 1.0mm larger than that of the Suzuki. Also, the big end bearing is 0.6mm wider. To fit the Honda parts, the crankpin holes must be bored 1.0mm over-size, with a 0.05mm interference fit and a fine machine finish. Additionally, the big end recess in each crank wheel must be machined 0.3mm deeper to accommodate the wider bearing.

As may be expected, the major change to bring the RM125 up to road race specifications involves the porting. The transfer ports and the reed valve port should be treated in exactly the same manner as the RM125C which was discussed earlier. The inlet port should also be reworked along the same lines, but in this instance it should be lowered 9.5mm. Care is required when lowering the port to this degree, otherwise the back of the cylinder could be severely weakened, allowing the bottom of it to break away. What you must do is leave a generous radius in the lower outside corners of the

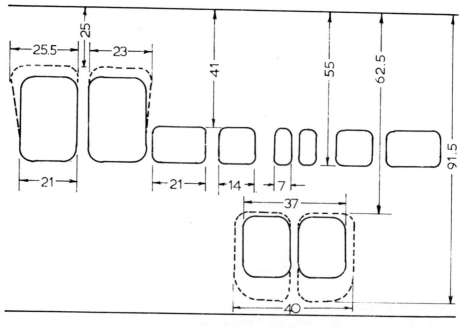

Fig. C . 7 Suzuki RM125B road race porting.

port. This leaves more metal around the port and also makes the action of the piston skirt against the lower lip of the port much more gentle (FIGURE C.7). Next, raise the inlet roof 1.0mm if you intend using only one compression ring.

The exhaust port is not good in the RM125B. It requires a drastic rework to encourage the type of hp we are after for a road racer. Novice riders should not raise the exhaust windows more than 2.0mm. This increases the exhaust open period to 201°. Expert riders can increase the duration to 203° by raising the ports 2.5mm. Go-karts, by virtue of the fact that they can operate on a razor-thin power band because of their fantastic cornering traction, can operate at up to 205° duration, using the port layout shown in FIGURE C.7.

After grinding the exhaust windows to the correct height, the exhaust outlet (i.e., the flange mating fact) must be raised and moved to the right to assist gas flow out of the cylinder (FIGURE C.8). If you break through the wall of the port doing this (it

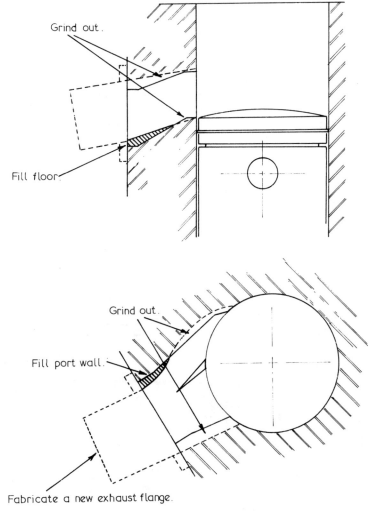

Fig. C.8 Exhaust port modification.

often happens), don't worry as the hole can be filled in when the floor of the port is being welded up to give the port its new shape. As you will notice in the illustration, the port diameter is increased to 38mm (from 37mm). It has been raised 4mm and moved 3mm to the right. After welding (use only argon arc) check the barrel for distortion.

To encourage better air flow into the engine a bigger carburettor is required. Either the standard 32mm Mikuni can be bored to 35mm, or a 36mm carburettor taken out to 37mm may be used. Basically, the jetting will remain standard, with two exceptions. A 35 pilot jet and a 260 or 270 main jet will be needed.

The reed valve assembly should be replaced by a six petal DG unit. It will flow considerably more air at high rpm than the standard reed block.

Expert riders and go-karters can also use a little more inlet port open duration, to further improve high speed cylinder filling. With a full length piston skirt, the port duration is 195° when the barrel is ported as shown in FIGURE C.7. Trimming 1.0mm off the inlet side of the piston skirt increases this figure to a little over 199°. This is the maximum which I recommend for motorcycles and most go-karts. Some kart engines seem to respond favourably to an inlet open period of 204°, achieved by cutting 2.0mm off the piston.

There are two expansion chambers that I have found to work well with the RM 125 in road race tune (FIGURE C.9). The chamber which suits the majority of riders and kart drivers on tighter circuits, is tuned to work at 11,500rpm and allow the engine to pull strongly to 12,000rpm. It uses fairly shallow tapers of 1.45° for the header, 4.5°, 7° and 9° for the diffuser and 11.5° for the baffle. The high speed kart pipe peaks the engine at approximately 11,800rpm and raises maximum engine speed to almost 12,500rpm.

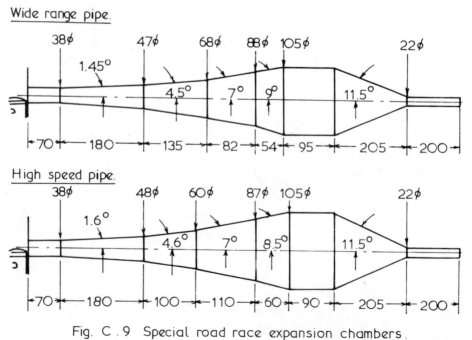

Fig. C.9 Special road race expansion chambers.

An engine burning Avgas 100/130 may have the compression ratio raised slightly to 14.5:1 by using a thinner 0.35mm head gasket. The spark advance should be left at 2.8mm before TDC. Use a Champion N-57G plug gapped at 0.5mm. On very fast circuits with a long main straight an N-55G may be necessary.

4 Rotax 124 LC Kart

This little engine is one of the most advanced two-strokes available. It will win races in the form in which it is delivered from the factory, but for the ultimate in performance and reliability it should be blueprinted and all the ports must be smoothed and aligned. By giving careful attention to aligning the inlet passages in the primary case, the rotary valve cover and the crankcase, you will pick up at least 1hp between 10,000rpm and 12,000rpm. Many engines have a 2 to 3mm misalignment between the valve cover and left side crankcase opening, which disrupts air flow and causes the inlet port to close 3° or 4° early. Obviously this lip in the crankcase has to be eliminated, either by filing or grinding (TABLE C.1).

TABLE C.1   Rotax 124LC power output

| | Test 1 | | Test 2 | | Test 3 | |
| | | Torque | | Torque | | Torque |
rpm	hp	(lb/ft)	hp	(lb/ft)	hp	(lb/ft)
8000	11.0	7.2	11.7	7.7	9.7	6.4
8500	13.8	8.5	13.4	8.3	14.4	8.9
9000	18.3	10.7	18.5	10.8	17.1	10.0
9500	20.4	11.3	21.0	11.6	20.1	11.1
10000	22.5	11.8	23.4	12.3	24.2	12.7
10500	24.0	12.0	24.6	12.4	25.2	12.6
11000	26.2	12.5	27.0	12.9	27.6	13.2
11500	26.7	12.2	27.8	12.7	29.8	13.6
12000	28.1	12.3	29.5	12.9	30.6	13.4
12500	21.2	8.9	24.0	10.1	25.7	10.8

Test 1 — *Standard engine with factory VSK103 expansion chamber.*

Test 2 — *As above but with engine blueprinted and inlet port matched and modified as detailed in FIGURE C 10.*

Test 3 — *Fully modified engine with high compression ratio, bored carburettor and special expansion chamber as detailed in FIGURE C 12.*

You will also note that the machined left side of the crankcase inlet port does not match the cast right side and floor of the port (FIGURE C.10). What must be done is fill the floor of the port on the right side, using Devcon F epoxy, to bring it up level with the machined section. Then fill the right wall of the port to align with the port in the valve cover as there is about a 16mm misalignment here. This misalignment comes about due to the factory using crankcases designed for Can Am and SWM bikes with a rear-mounted, rather than a side-mounted, carburettor.

While you are working on the crankcase you will notice a series of numbers cast 211

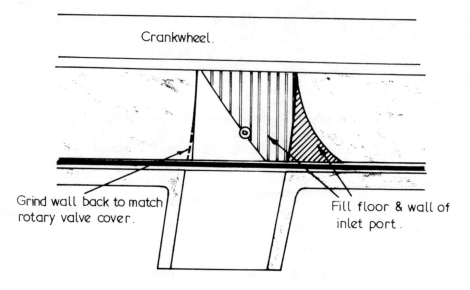

Crankwheel.

Grind wall back to match rotary valve cover.

Fill floor & wall of inlet port.

Fig. C.10   Match inlet port to rotary valve cover.

into the transfer slots. Grind these out; they are only small but they do disrupt high rpm air flow. Also match the crankcase to the barrel and base gasket, and vice versa.

Initially, fit a 50 pilot jet and a 390 main jet in the carburettor to begin testing. Also fit a 3.0 or 3.3 needle and seat as the standard item just will not flow enough fuel to keep the fuel bowl full at high rpm. Although the standard 34mm Mikuni will allow the engine to run well and produce good power at 12,000rpm, a carburettor bored to 35.3mm will lift the hp output above 11,500rpm.

Set the ignition timing at 1.0mm before TDC and use a Champion N-57G plug gapped at 0.020in. If 100/130 Avgas is used, increase the compression ratio to 15.8:1 and fit a Champion N-57G plug. Leave the timing at 1.0mm. On very fast circuits a N-55G plug will be required.

Late model engines employ a different Motoplat ignition unit which automatically retards the spark at higher engine speeds. The timing with this ignition should be set at 3.76mm before TDC. Then check, using a strobe light, that the timing marks align at 5000rpm.

Engines manufactured before mid-1980 can beneficially be converted to the later ignition by replacing the rotor, stator and coil. When this is done, the engine works better below 10,700rpm and above 11,700rpm. With fixed timing the engine really only has optimum ignition advance over a narrow rpm range.

One area for concern with this motor, and this applies to all liquid cooled two-strokes, is that water flow must be regulated by a thermostat or a restrictor to maintain the water temperature at 75° to 82°C. If the water temperature is less than 70°C, the carburettor will be impossible to tune and the engine will not pull very well. On the other hand, if the coolant temperature is higher than 85°C the engine will not be making best hp either.

Looking at FIGURE C.11, you will note that the thermostat is located in the return hose between the cylinder head and the radiator. To stabilise head and cylinder

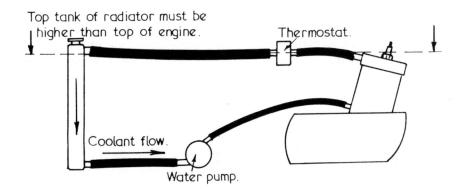

Fig. C . 11 Cooling system arrangement.

temperatures when the thermostat is closed, it is necessary to drill a 4mm by-pass hole in the body of the thermostat to allow limited coolant circulation.

Before leaving the cooling system, check the coolant passage in the barrel below the exhaust port. This small, but critical, passage must not be obstructed by any casting slag. If coolant flow through here is restricted, the side of the cylinder opposite the water inlet will overheat and distort.

Rotax supply two diagrams for suitable expansion chambers. One, the VSK095 pipe, is now considered by the factory to be more suitable for the air-cooled kart engine, while the wide range VSK103 pipe is preferred for the liquid-cooled model. Personally, I like a chamber a little different to both of these designs (FIGURE C.12). This expansion chamber will give more power above 11,500rpm than either pipe and extends the useable power band to almost 12,500rpm. On very high speed circuits the belly section should be reduced to 80mm long.

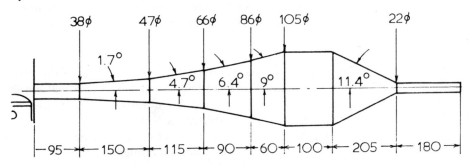

Fig. C . 12 Special Rotax 124 LC kart expansion chamber.

The silencer detailed in the drawings supplied by Rotax is very quiet but, unfortunately, quite restrictive. An entirely different muffler should be fabricated following the details outlined in Chapter 4. If you are already using a silencer built to the Rotax specifications, I would suggest that you cut the rear section of your exhaust open and reduce the length of the perforated, fibreglass-filled section from 250mm to 150mm. This modification will increase power and reduce the piston crown temperature.

Although the standard engine makes good power, it can be modified to work 213 better at high rpm. You will note that the fifth transfer port, the boost port, is almost closed off from the crankcase when the piston descends to BDC. To increase mixture flow through this port at high rpm, modify the piston skirt as shown in FIGURE C 13. This modification weakens the piston but, on the positive side, little end lubrication and cooling is very much improved. If a caged little end bearing is being used, this is a very important consideration in an engine of this size, running at 12,000 to 12,500rpm.

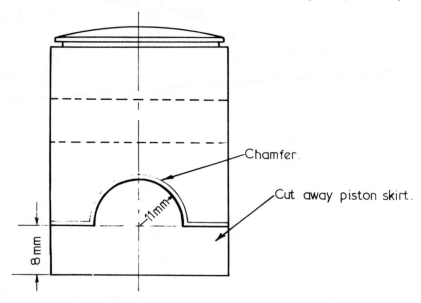

Fig. C . 13 Boost port feed cut-away.

For even more top end power increase the exhaust duration to 204° by raising the port 0.6mm and set the inlet timing at 126°/90° by modifying the rotary valve disc.

5 Yamaha TZ250 E

The Yamaha TZ250 is quite a good mass-produced engine. Straight out of the crate some TZs will run well but most demand a lot of work before they will run fast and reliably. The basic design of the engine is good, but unfortunately Yamaha won't spend the time assembling them to the correct tolerances. Therefore, the first thing you must do is to blueprint the engine. Don't ever think about modifying the ports or changing the carburettors until the basic motor has been brought up to specification.

After stripping the motor, check the crankshaft to determine what work it requires. Generally, even brand new cranks need a full rebuild, so completely dismantle it and crack test and measure everything.

Beginning with the rods, measure their length. Ideally, they should both be the same length, but up to 0.1mm difference is acceptable. Then check that they are not bent and that the big end and little end bores have been machined parallel. To determine this you will have to make a pair of dummy pins about 100mm long to fit the little end and big end. Measuring between both ends of the dummy pins will determine if the rods are bent or have holes out of parallel. Next check that the rods have big ends and little ends machined in the same plane (i.e., not twisted). To do this, set up the big end of the rod on a pair of parallel V-blocks, with a dummy pin fitted. Then, with a dial gauge, measure to see that both ends of the dummy pin fitted in the little end are the same distance from the surface plate. Finally, see that both rods are balanced (i.e., have little ends and big ends each of the same weight).

Next, measure and weigh the crankpins. They must be of the same diameter and weight. A heavy pin can be lightened by grinding on a sanding belt to bring it down to the same weight as the light pin, but to find pins of the same diameter may take a good deal of searching through dealers' parts bins.

After this, you have to find big end bearings which give acceptable little end side shake. Many bearings have so much radial clearance between the crankpin and rod that the little end of the rod can move up to 1.5mm from side to side. Try and find bearings which allow no more than 1.0mm side shake.

The crank wheels must all be checked for concentricity and be machined to the same diameter. Variation in size and eccentricity in the wheels will cause crankshaft vibration. This robs the engine of power, cuts bearing life and in TZs will also damage the crankcase.

After it has been determined that all crankshaft components meet specification, the crank may be assembled and trued. Hold run-out to a maximum of 0.001in.

TZ pistons and cylinders are numbered by Yamaha to make assembly in the factory quicker, but don't ever rely on this method when building your engine. The piston to bore clearance you want is 0.0017in. (±0.0001in.) or 0.043mm. Obviously the Yamaha system doesn't work too well, as most new TZs seem to have 0.0025 to 0.003in. clearance, which is the maximum service limit.

When you have selected a pair of pistons which give the correct clearance, be sure to have them crack tested and balanced. Then measure their skirt length and compression height. Any variation in these measurements (assuming both rods are the same length) will alter the port timing and compression ratio in each cylinder. Usually the difference isn't great, yet I have seen pistons up to 0.5mm longer or shorter, so it is a good idea to check as any difference over 0.1mm is not acceptable.

Without altering the port timing, smooth and match all ports. Trim the base gasket to match the case transfer slots and grind the bottom of the transfer ports in the barrel to match the gasket. Then very patiently deburr the edges of all the ports where they open into the bore. To the naked eye the port windows appear smooth enough, but actually they are very sharp and ragged. If left undressed they very quickly destroy the piston ring and prevent it from bedding in. Dress the port openings using a fine-grained Arkansas stone, or a 180 grit carborundum stone, the shape and size of a cigarette.

When barrel preparation has been completed, the engine may be assembled and the squish clearance determined. If the clearance is more than 1.0mm, the head will have to be machined to close up the clearance. Then cut the combustion chambers to lower the compression ratio back down to 15.5:1.

To allow more air into the motor at high rpm, bore the stock 34mm Mikunis to 35.3mm diameter. Leave the jetting standard.

Yamaha recommend that the timing is set at 2.0mm before TDC. I have found that most engines will not tolerate more than 1.8 to 1.85mm advance on regular racing fuel. Burning Avgas 100/130, the timing may be advanced to 2.1 to 2.2mm without sending the motor into detonation.

Use Champion N-57G plugs gapped at 0.5mm. If the combustion chamber has been modified to close-up the squish band, take care to fit thicker plug washers to prevent the plug seating too deeply into the combustion chamber.

Expert riders can go a little further than merely blueprinting their motors. The exhaust ports may be raised 1.0mm to increase duration to 202° and the inlet side of the piston skirt can have 1.0mm cut off to add 4° to the inlet event.

In this tune you will probably need N-55G plugs on fast circuits. Also, you may have to fit a larger 159 Q-4 needle jet and drop the needle one groove to richen the mid-range a little.

The standard expansion chamber works fairly well right through the TZ's power range. For improved acceleration the standard pipe can be modified as illustrated in FIGURE C.14. Peak power will not be improved, but the bike will pull much better. Basically, the header is shortened by 69mm and the diffuser section is cut out of the stock chamber and replaced by a new section with tapers of 3.9° and 7.2°. The tuned length is reduced by 24mm to raise peak power rpm. You will note the stinger is extended by 50mm to an overall length of 200mm.

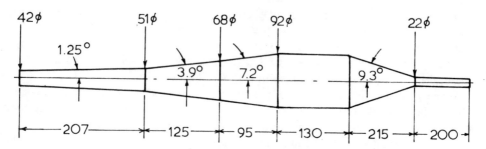

Fig. C. 14 Modified Yamaha TZ250 D/E expansion chamber.

6 Yamaha TZ750E

This engine is in exactly the same form as the TZ250. It is a good motor, but for it to work well and be reliable, it must be carefully assembled following the procedure outlined for the 250.

Basically the 750 two-wheel class is a 'dead' category, so we will look at what can be done to make the TZ perform well in the unlimited sidecar class. To be competitive here, the engine must have exceptional mid-range power otherwise it will not accelerate strongly out of tight corners. Other than cleaning up the ports, about the only change required in the porting is to raise the boost port 1.0mm. This will help smooth the power curve right down to 5500rpm, and increase peak power at the same time.

The major change should be to the expansion chamber. On an outfit, there isn't such a problem finding room for four fat pipes, so we can discard the slender two wheeler chambers and fabricate a much better exhaust (FIGURE C.15). You will note that the new pipes have a shorter header and a three-stage diffuser with tapers of 1.3°, and 3.6°, 6.3° and 8.2° respectively. Also, a two-stage baffle is utilised. The first section converges at a very shallow 4.8° and finally necks down at 12°. The belly is now

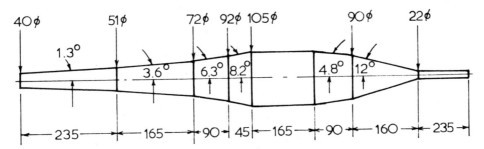

Fig. C.15 Special Yamaha TZ750E outfit expansion chamber.

25mm larger with a diameter of 105mm and the stinger has grown from 200m to 235mm.

As you can see, this is a rather complex pipe comprising six cones in all. The shallow diffuser and baffle sections help increase power in the 6000 to 8000rpm range, while the steeper stages restore the power which these shallow sections would otherwise have chopped off peak hp.

7 Yamaha TZ750E — 500cc conversion

The TZ750 can be converted for 500 class racing quite easily. All that is required is to lift off the 750 heads, barrels and pistons and replace them with TZ250 parts. (Note: for 650 class racing, use a 750 barrel on one half of the motor and a 250 barrel for the other side).

That is the easy part of the conversion. Unfortunately, the stock 750 pipes will not work very well, so you will have to fabricate a set to the dimensions shown in FIGURE C.16. These pipes will suit the majority of engines being run up to about 11,000rpm. FIGURE C.17 shows the pipe design required for outfits to extend the power band and pump up mid-range hp. Preferably, the sidecar chambers should be fabricated with a slip joint belly section so that the tuned length can be changed to suit the circuit. On slower circuits the mid-section length may have to be increased up to 40mm, to help the engine pull out of tight, uphill corners.

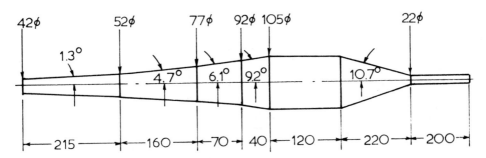

Fig. C.16 Special 500 conversion expansion chamber.

Quite often, when a 750 is converted for 500 class sidecar use, you run into trouble actually getting the engine to fire up and to pull strongly out of slow corners. This 217

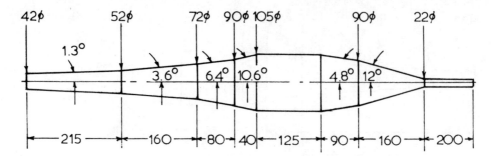

Fig. C. 17 Special 500 conversion outfit expansion chamber.

occurs due to excessive spit-back in the inlet tract. To overcome the problem, the inlet open period has to be reduced by filling the floor of the inlet port with Devcon F epoxy. If you have a lightweight outfit, and you can give it a good strong push at the start of a race, try cutting the inlet duration down to 180° if you are having trouble with starting etc. If the outfit is very heavy, the inlet open period may have to drop down to 173°. To make starting easier when the engine is cold, use a medical syringe to squirt 1.0cc of petrol down each spark plug hole. The engine should fire the moment the clutch is engaged.

Appendix II

Table of useful equivalents

1 inch = 25.4mm   1mm = 0.03937 in.

1 horsepower = 0.7457 kilowatt   1 kilowatt = 1.341 horsepower

1 pound foot torque = 1.3558 Newton metre

1 pound inch torque = 0.11298 Newton metre

1 Newton metre = 0.7376 pound foot

1 psi = 6.89476 kilopascals

    or 33.9 millibars

    or 2.0345 inches of mercury

    or 27.67 inches of water

$$°F = \left(\frac{9}{5} \times °C\right) + 32$$

$$°C = \frac{5}{9} \times (°F - 32)$$

1 gallon (Imperial) = 160 fluid oz   1 fluid oz (Imperial) = 28.4125cc

             or 4.546 litre

1 gallon (US) = 128 fluid oz   1 fluid oz (US) = 29.5703cc

             or 3.785 litre

Appendix III

Speciality Suppliers

Bombardier — Rotax GMBH
P.O.Box 5
A-4623 Gunskirchen, Austria

Two-stroke engines for bikes, karts and snowmobiles

DG Performance Products
1170 Van Horne
Anaheim, California 92806, USA

Expansion chambers, cylinder heads, reed valves, cylinder porting

Heany Industries
Fairview Drive
Scottsville, New York 14546, USA

Ceramic coating for pistons, combustion chambers etc.

Honda Motor Co.
27-8, 6-Chome,
Jinguumae, Shibuya-Ku
Tokyo 150, Japan

Two-stroke engines for bikes and karts

Kal-Gard
16616 Schoenborn St.
Sepulveda, California 91343, USA

Gun Kote engine paint

J.T.Racing
303 W.35th St.
National City, California 92050, USA

Boyensen reed petals

K & N Engineering
P.O.Box 1329
Iowa Ave.
Riverside, California 92502, USA

Air filter elements and filter oil

Limantour Corp. 4539 Hamilton Blvd. Allentown, Pennsylvania 1803, USA	Boyensen reed petals
Mugen USA 6878 Santa Fe Ave. East Hesperia, California 91744, USA	Air and water-cooled heads and cylinders for Honda motocross engines
PK Racing Products 525 N. Azusa Ave. La Puente, California 91744, USA	Reed petals, expansion chambers, cylinder porting
Protopipe Exhaust Systems 100 Cristich Lane Campbell, California 95008, USA	Expansion chambers
R & R Racing 208 W. First Danville, Illinois 61832, USA	Reed valves for RM and PE Suzukis
Suzuki Motor Co. P.O.Box 116 Hamamatsu, Japan	Two-stroke engines for bikes
Yamaha Motor Co. 2500 Shingai Iwata Shi-Shizuoka-Ken, Japan.	Two-stroke engines for bikes, karts and snowmobiles

Index

C